LES ORTEILS
N'ONT PAS DE NOM

ISBN 978-2-211-22182-5
Première édition dans la collection *lutin poche* : avril 2015
© 2010, l'école des loisirs, Paris
Loi numéro 49 956 du 16 juillet 1949 sur les publications
destinées à la jeunesse : mars 2010
Dépôt légal : avril 2015
Imprimé en France par Clerc SAS à Saint-Amand-Montrond

JEAN LEROY - MATTHIEU MAUDET

LES ORTEILS
N'ONT PAS DE NOM

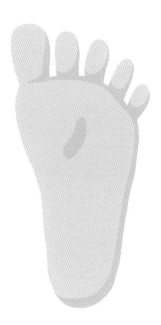

lutin poche de l'école des loisirs
11, rue de Sèvres, Paris 6ᵉ

LES DOiGTS DE LA MAiN
ONT TOUS UN NOM.

Le majeur

L'annulaire

L'index

L'auriculaire

Le pouce

LES DOIGTS DE PIED,

EUX, N'EN ONT PAS.

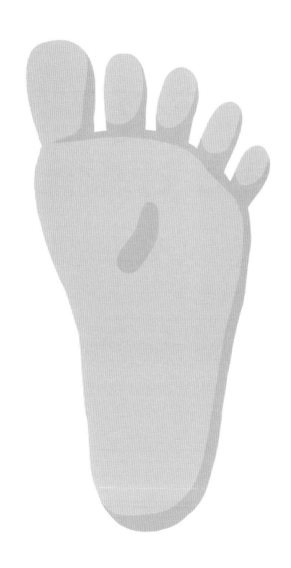

CE QUI LES REND

TRÈS MALHEUREUX...

QUELS NOMS POURRAIT-ON

BIEN LEUR TROUVER ?

HUM... NON,
TROP ALPHABÉTIQUE !
IL FAUDRAIT
UNE AUTRE IDÉE...

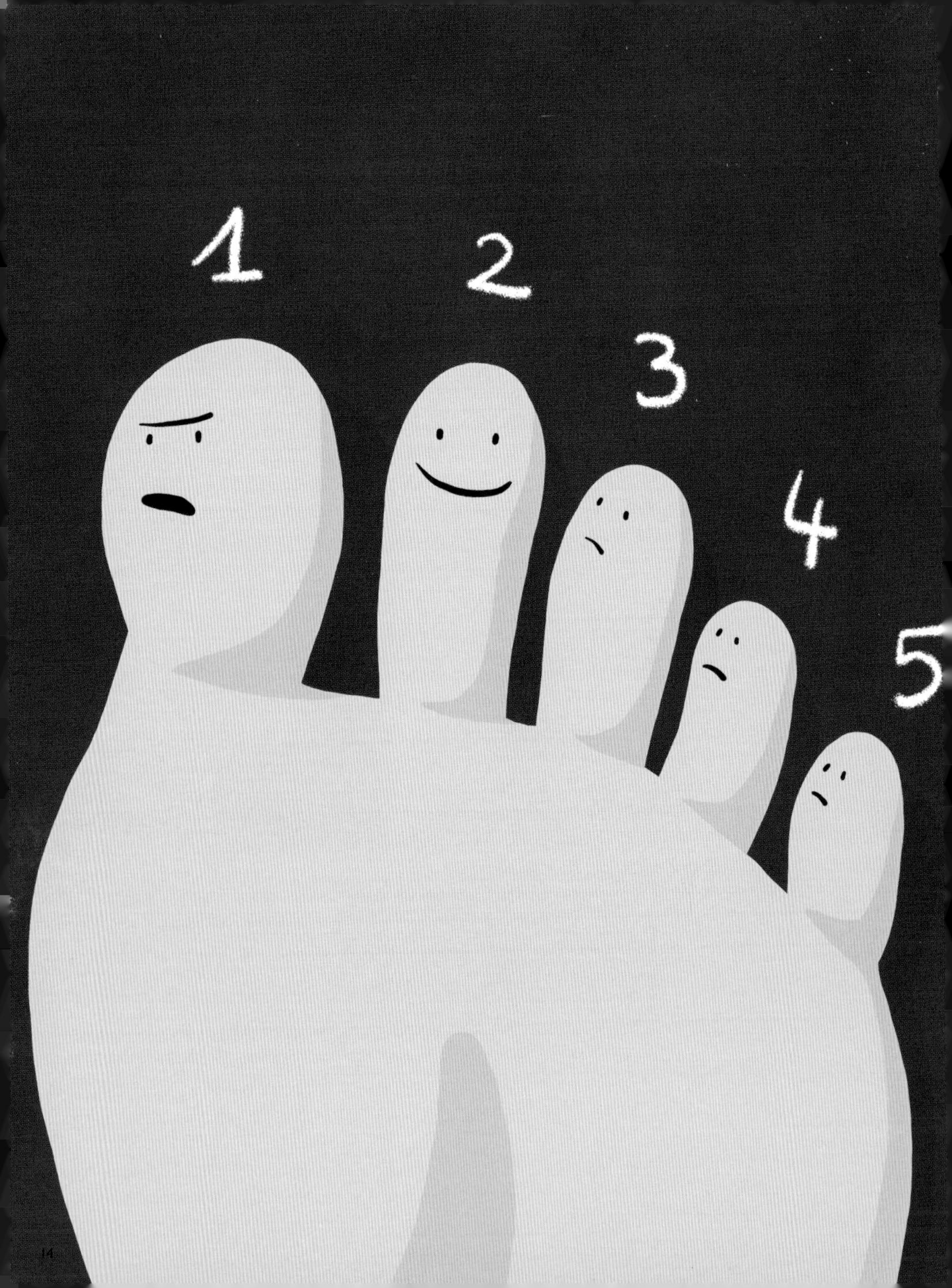
1
2
3
4
5

HUM... NON,

TROP MATHÉMATIQUE !

IL FAUDRAIT

UNE AUTRE IDÉE...

HUM... NON,

TROP MUSICAL !

IL FAUDRAIT

UNE AUTRE IDÉE...

Rouge

Vert

Jaune

Bleu

Orang

HUM... NON,

TROP COLORÉ !

IL FAUDRAIT

UNE AUTRE IDÉE...

Pomme

Orange

Poire

Banane

Fraise

HUM... NON, TROP TARTE!

BON, EH BIEN...

TANT PIS !

PAS DE NOMS

POUR AUJOURD'HUI...

UNE AUTRE FOIS, PEUT - ÊTRE ?

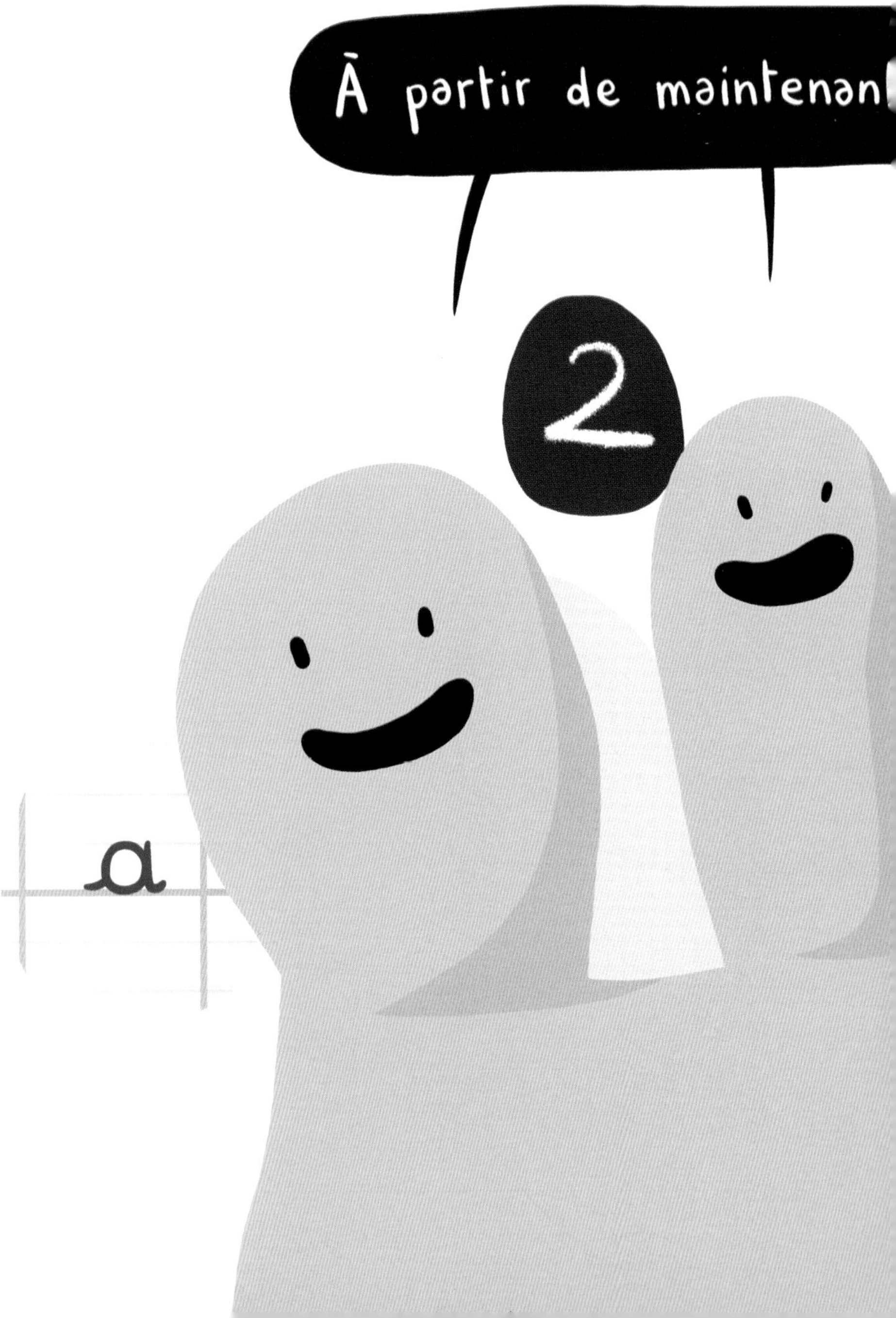
À partir de maintenan
2
a

SLOUCH WITCH

HELEN HARPER

For couch potatoes everywhere.

MAGICAL HIERARCHY

Hallowed Order of Magical Enlightenment Hierarchy

First Level

- Neophyte
- Zelator
- Theoricus
- Practicus
- Philosophus

Second Level

- Adeptus Minor
- Adeptus Major
- Adeptus Exemptus

Third Level

- Magister Templi

- Magus
- Ipsissimus

CHAPTER ONE

THE MAN DIDN'T LOOK LIKE MUCH AT FIRST GLANCE. TALLER THAN me but weedy, with an oddly bulbous head perched on top of a white, scrawny neck. He was smartly dressed, with a suit and tie, but I should have known better than to assume that clothes maketh the man. I'd had some ridiculously wealthy people in the back of my cab in the past and the most affluent of them looked as if he'd been sleeping rough for three months. Maybe that was why he had such a healthy bank account – because he didn't waste time on things like shaving or brushing his hair or, um, washing.

Anyway, this man, the one holding a thin arm up to flag me down, looked like a strong gust of wind would blow him over. Judging from his pale skin, he didn't get outside much. Perhaps he had a fear of strong breezes. Whatever, I figured that one more customer would be good enough to see me through until the end of the week. I hoped, however, that he wasn't travelling far. I'd kicked people out before for requesting destinations that were going to take hours to reach. Not the done thing, but I have a life too. I've got better things to do than spend *all* of it driving people around and having the same conversations over and over again about their holidays or the weather or the latest goings on in *Enchantment* over on Channel 5. Not that I dislike my job – far from it – but I don't live to work. I'm not deranged.

I pulled up at the kerb and he got into the back, sitting directly behind me. 'Cutteslowe,' he grunted. Then he glanced at me and did a double take. I get that a lot; for some reason, people always seem to find it surprising that a woman drives a taxi. I have no idea why. It's not as if it takes a special skill set that I don't have because of my gender. Having some dangly bits wouldn't make holding a steering wheel and finding my way around a small city like Oxford any easier. No, my breasts do not impair my ability to drive. And yes, I can park. I've heard all the jokes. They're never funny. Men can be witches and women can be taxi drivers. Big bloody deal.

'Absolutely, sir,' I murmured, flashing a smile in the mirror. I didn't receive so much as a crack of a grin back. It suited me; the quiet ones are less work.

I pulled out, making the driver in the battered BMW coming up behind me gesture in my direction with an angry scowl. Now, now. He had plenty of room to slow down. I reckon that anyone who gets irritated by something like that needs to sort their life out. If you're getting stressed out by having to brake slightly, what happens to your equilibrium when your pipes burst or your kid gets suspended from school or your mum is diagnosed with cancer? It simply isn't worth the effort to sweat the small stuff.

My passenger didn't notice. He was fiddling with his jacket and his left eyebrow was twitching furiously, as if someone had attached it to an invisible piece of string and was yanking at it from above. I could have calmed him down, I suppose, but it probably wouldn't have made any difference in the end. Instead I turned up the radio and got a hustle on. The faster we made it to Cutteslowe and I dropped this guy off, the faster I could get home and put my feet up.

We were just pulling off the main road towards the little

suburb when I felt it. I hadn't even noticed him lean forward – I'd been too preoccupied with the bus right in front of me – but when the cold metal pressed against the back of my neck, I knew exactly what was going on.

'I want all your money,' he hissed. 'Now.'

A gun. Great. Why did I always end up with the psychotic idiots? I licked my lips. 'Do you want me to get the money or do you want me to avoid ploughing into the back of the bus?' I asked. 'Because I'm not sure I can do both.'

There was a momentary pause. 'Pull over here. And don't think I won't pull the trigger just because you're a girl.'

I considered a smart response but in the end I shrugged and did as he asked. I turned off the engine but otherwise didn't move.

'Give me your fucking money.' Perhaps he thought I was hard of hearing and it was important to repeat his request with added emphasis to make sure I didn't misunderstand his intention.

I pursed my lips. 'I don't have much. None of us ever carry much. You know, in case someone puts a gun to the back of our head and demands it all.'

'Listen, bitch…'

'All I'm saying,' I continued blithely, 'is that perhaps you should weigh this up a little more. Risk versus reward. I'm not sure you've really thought this through and I'd like to give you another opportunity to do that.' I softened my voice to show him that I was in earnest. 'Everyone deserves a second chance.'

Unfortunately, my lanky gentleman wasn't listening. He pushed the muzzle of the gun deeper into my flesh. Okay, that hurt. And I was starting to get irritated.

'I'll give you one last chance,' he told me, 'before I splatter your brains all across your windshield.'

I wanted to tell him that my brains were located where you'd expect and that if he pulled the trigger right now it would be my windpipe that would see the damage; my brains would remain intact. Somehow I didn't think this was the time for an anatomy lesson.

'Okay,' I said soothingly. 'I have a cashbox in the glove box. I need to lean across.'

'Don't try anything funny.'

Maybe it was his tone of voice but more likely it was his choice of words. In any case, when I stretched out to open the glove box with my left hand and sketched out a rune onto my thigh with my right hand, I knew exactly what I was doing. And, yes, I thought it was pretty funny.

'What the…?' he spluttered. 'What the fuck?' He yanked what had been a lethal weapon away from my neck and stared at what was now a banana. Clichéd, sure, but it made me smile.

'I wouldn't recommend trying to eat it,' I said sunnily. It might look like a banana and feel like a banana but magic could only go so far. Unfortunately.

His eyes swung from the banana to me and then back again. I didn't think it was possible but he seemed even paler than before. 'You're a witch.'

Duh. 'Yes, I am,' I replied pleasantly.

'What is a witch doing driving a cab?'

That was a long, long story that I certainly wasn't getting into with this guy. 'I did give you the chance to change your mind,' I told him.

His eyes shifted as he calculated the odds. I reckoned it was about fifty–fifty whether he lunged for me or made a run for it. Fortunately for both of us, he chose the latter. He grabbed the door handle and tugged furiously but, of course, it didn't open. Central locking. I was feeling generous, though, because I activated the button to open the door and he fell out. He scrambled to his feet, almost tripping over them in his haste to get away. Then he veered down the road, narrowly avoiding getting run over by a double-decker bus.

I watched him for a moment or two as he sped away towards

the pavement and his supposed freedom. The smart thing to do would be to let him go; less hassle on all accounts. But there was a niggling voice in the back of my head that told me he'd be free to try this again – and on someone with fewer defensive abilities than me. I couldn't do it. I rolled my eyes. Some days I wish I didn't have a conscience.

I counted to three under my breath then raised my hand and drew out another rune. There was a loud crack and a heavy tree branch crashed down onto the head of my would-be assailant. He collapsed instantly.

'Stay here,' I murmured to the taxi. I shoved my hands in my pockets and, whistling, wandered over towards the idiot who'd ruined my day.

A passing car stopped and a dark-haired woman leapt out and ran towards him. I supposed from this angle he did look like a victim of an arboreal attack instead of someone who'd received his just desserts.

I reached her as she began tugging at the branch that was pinning him down. 'I wouldn't do that,' I remarked.

She stared up at me. 'This man is trapped! He needs our help.' She yanked at the branch again, although all she succeeded in doing was to get several small twigs caught in her designer jacket. There was a ripping sound as the expensive fabric gave way. I winced.

'We might do him more damage. It's always safer to wait for the professionals,' I advised. 'And believe me, this guy is not worth the effort.'

She shook her head in dismay. 'One minute you're walking along the street, minding your own business and munching on a banana, and the next a tree is lying on top of you.'

I nibbled my bottom lip. 'I wouldn't really say tree. Most of the tree is still standing.' I eyed the banana, which was still in his hand. Hmm. I glanced at the woman. 'Do you have a phone? You should call the police.'

5

Cheeks flushed from her exertions, she swung her head towards me and gaped. 'Police? This man needs an ambulance!'

'He was running down the street with a gun in his hand,' I pointed out.

'Gun? But…' She faltered as she looked down. Reversal runes are complicated for most witches, especially when you only have a second or two to spare and you are technically only a First Level Neophyte. But I'm not most witches.

The brunette's mouth dropped open and she took a step backwards. 'I swear that was a banana.'

I offered a reassuring smile. 'Shock will do that to you. Your brain panicked when it saw the gun and didn't want to register the truth. It's fairly common during stressful situations.'

She passed a hand over her eyes. 'I'm normally very calm under pressure. But it's been a long day.'

I certainly agreed with her on that point. I thought mournfully of my sofa and the time it would take to give a statement to the police. Arse.

It was very dark by the time I made it back to my block of flats and the sting of cold was definitely in the air. My timing sucked. If things had gone to plan, I could have grabbed my usual parking place beside the door. Instead it seemed that all my neighbours were already back from work and had nabbed the best spots. I scowled and trudged to my front door. I needed a long, hot bath with candles and chocolate and wine. Lots of wine.

'Ivy!'

The chirpy call from the other side of the street made my heart sink but I pasted a smile on my face and turned towards Eve. 'Hey, you just back from work?'

She jogged over, her shiny ponytail swinging, and beamed at

me revealing perfect white teeth. 'I clocked off at six so I took advantage of the early finish to go for a run.'

I looked her Lycra-clad body up and down. 'Good for you,' I murmured. Not that I thought six at night was an early finish, given that she was up and out the door by five thirty most mornings. The reason I knew that was because last month I'd binge-watched several episodes of *Enchantment* and only crawled to my pillow when the sun was rising and she was leaving for work.

'You should come with me some time. It's a really invigorating way to end the day.'

I resisted the urge to point out that she is tall, fit and lithe whilst I tend more to short and plump, with breasts that have the potential to take out one of my eyes, even when I'm wearing the most advanced sports bra on the market. I like Eve, but she isn't the kind of person who takes *'hell no'* as an answer. It was far safer not to give any response and hope that she'd quickly move on to another topic.

'How is work these days?' I asked.

Fortunately, my mention of her favourite subject made her eyes brighten and all thoughts of forcing me to join her fitness regime fled. 'It's good. Really good. I've got all the basic runes down pat and I'm pretty confident with Myomancy. My supervisor reckons I'll be ready to take the Second Order exams next month. There's even a chance that I'll be moved to Arcane Branch.'

I watched as she bounced from toe to toe at the thought. Eve lived, breathed and probably dreamed the Order. Or rather The Hallowed Order of Magical Enlightenment to give it its official title. Most people don't bother to use its full title, probably because it sounds less like the all-encompassing, all-powerful magical organisation for almost every witch in the United Kingdom and more like a happy clappy hippy enclave.

'Are you sure you'll like Arcane Branch?' I asked. 'Aren't those guys a bit too much strait-laced geeks and sombre Simons?'

'Ivy!' She punched my arm playfully but with such unintended force that I flinched. 'Arcane Branch is where it's at! Of course, they're serious – their job is the most important in the country. Without them, there'd be chaos on the streets.' She raised her eyebrows in admonishment. 'They deserve our utmost respect.'

Yeah, yeah. I didn't want to rain on Eve's parade. 'You're right,' I lied. 'They're wonderful.'

She nodded with the fervent zeal of a true believer. 'I hope I'm good enough to meet their criteria and join them.'

I shook my head. 'Are you kidding? If they don't want you, it's because they're worried that you'll show them all up.' I wasn't lying; Eve might be a little too enthusiastic about the Order for my liking but I couldn't deny her dedication or her ability. 'They'd be lucky to have you.'

She smiled. 'Thanks, Ivy.' She paused. 'Anyway, how was your day?'

I dismissed her question easily. 'Same old, same old.' I grinned at her. 'You know me. And, before you say anything, don't worry. I've not forgotten that you're away tomorrow.'

'You're sure it's alright? I'd take him with me but…'

'You don't want to advertise that you're a witch.'

Eve grimaced. 'Not in this case. It's going to require a delicate touch. I'll only be gone for four or five nights.'

'I'm more than happy to look after your familiar, Eve. Honestly.' Cats I could manage, especially when they weren't my own furry little bastard.

'I'll owe you big time.'

I only just stopped myself from suggesting that she cleaned my flat as payment. We entered the main door and Eve headed straight for the stairs, casting a glance over her shoulder in my direction when she realised I wasn't following.

'I've sprained my ankle,' I told her. 'Old sports injury. I'm going to take the lift.'

She frowned. 'That's sounds painful. Let me know if you want any bandages. I know a great physiotherapist, too.'

I waved her off. 'I'll be fine. But thanks.' I nodded towards the stairs. 'You go on.'

'If you're sure…'

Good grief. I had to come up with some better excuses. I was actually starting to feel guilty. 'I am.'

'Well, take care.' Eve smiled brightly and started to sprint up the first flight. 'See you later, Ivy!'

I punched the lift button and slumped against the wall. It was hard work watching Eve.

As soon as I got inside the door, I dumped my bag and lurched for the sofa, flopping down face-first. Bliss.

From somewhere above me, there was an irritated hiss. 'Food.'

I strained my head upwards. 'Hi, Brutus.'

His yellow eyes stared down at me, unblinking. 'Food, bitch.'

I sighed. 'I've told you time and time again. If you call me that, I'm not going to feed you.'

'Food.'

'Give me a minute.'

'Food.'

'I'd like the chance to get a cup of tea first.'

'Food.'

'Piss off.'

'Food.'

I muttered a curse, got up and hobbled to the small but perfectly formed galley kitchen. The remnants of this morning's breakfast lay on the counter. I swept all the dishes into the sink and turned on the tap while Brutus kept up his nagging. 'Food. Food. Foooooooooood.'

I sighed, found a clean bowl and opened a tin, gagging slightly at the familiar scent of processed tuna. I scooped some out with a spoon and presented it to him. Brutus stepped up and sniffed delicately. I turned away to close off the tap.

'Food.'

I gritted my teeth. 'I just gave you food.'

He pawed at the bowl and looked utterly disgusted with tonight's offering. I gazed at him in exasperation. 'You liked this one last week.' His head turned away. He wouldn't even look at it. 'Brutus…'

A low growl reverberated from deep within his throat. I crossed my arms. He wasn't giving an inch. 'Foo…'

'Fine,' I snapped, interrupting him. Sometimes the path of least resistance is the best. I opened the cupboard, selected a different flavour and presented it to him. I received the tiniest purr in response. Rolling my eyes, I got rid of the first lot of food and gave him the second. Then I stomped to the phone to order myself a pizza.

CHAPTER TWO

It would be nice to think that the rest of my week improved but things only went from bad to worse. It's fair to say that if I'd appreciated how bad life was about to get, I would never ever have emerged from my duvet on Friday.

Even with Brutus perched on my chest repeating his mantra for breakfast, I was tempted to pull the cover over my head. It was so snug and warm. Unless I got up and threw him out of the window, however, it was clear I wouldn't get any peace and quiet. I could have done that but it wouldn't have been worth the hassle afterwards. Not that Brutus would have hurt himself; he's only used up two of his nine lives so far, which I reckon is pretty good for a cat of his age and temperament. But given that the time I accidentally stepped on his tail caused seven full days of feline hatred, where I was afraid to open any of the doors in my own damned flat, I dreaded to think what I'd receive in return for giving him flying lessons.

'I'm getting up,' I told him. 'In two minutes.'

'Food.'

'Quit it.'

I tried to relax once more; it wasn't hard. I was drifting back into the wonderful land of snuggly slumber when a paw, with claws outstretched just enough to rake my skin, scraped along my cheek. I opened one eye. I suspected that Brutus had waited the exact two minutes that I'd promised.

'Food.'

'Yeah, yeah.'

Sighing, I stuck one foot out from under the duvet. It was freezing. I yanked it back and moaned. Brutus went for my face again but I dodged his attentions by smothering my head into the soft pillow.

I could do this. On the count of three.

One.

Two.

Three.

I didn't move. Gritting my teeth, I steeled myself and tried again. This time I sprang upwards and darted for my dressing gown hanging on the bedroom door. I wrapped it round me and ran, wondering why I lived in a flat which had beautifully polished parquet floors that were bloody freezing under my feet rather than inch-thick pile carpet. Where the arse were my slippers?

Hopping from foot to foot, I nipped into the kitchen and flipped on the kettle before opening the cupboard that housed the small boiler. I peered at it. It was still there; it hadn't blown up in the middle of the night. So why, in the name of all that was icy and unpleasant, wasn't it working?

I thumped it a couple of times. There was an odd gurgle but, other than that, nothing seemed to be happening. I wrinkled my nose and tried to think. I knew various runes for starting fires but I'd never had occasion to use them and somehow I didn't think setting my own home alight would be wise.

I grabbed a bowl for Brutus and poured out some dry cat food that I knew he liked, then made myself a mug of tea. I warmed my frozen fingers round it while I considered my options. The trouble with magic is that it involves ancient skills and knowledge which have very little to do with technology. When it comes to the mystical arts and twenty-first century advances, it's always best to work on the premise that never the twain shall meet. If they do, you can expect explosions and violent death and the very real possibility that you'll be engulfed in a hailstorm made up of shards of glass and hornet stings.

I pondered my options. As I'd told that good Samaritan yesterday, some things are best left to the professionals. I glanced outside. Eve would have already left for her trip up north, which meant I could vamoose over to her place, check on her cat, call a plumber and wait in the warmth. Sounded like a damn good plan to me. I nodded wisely to myself; go me.

Brutus butted his head against my shin and I crouched down to scratch behind his ears. 'It's cold here,' I told him, rather unnecessarily. 'I'm going to Eve's to feed Harold and wait for help to arrive. Right now, a Saint Bernard with emergency rum rations would be particularly appreciated. You're welcome to come with me if you want.'

He flung a disdainful look in my direction. He'd never said anything but I had the distinct impression that he considered Harold – or rather Harold Fitzwilliam Duxworthy the Third, to give Eve's familiar his true title (witches enjoy long titles and lines of heritage) – was beneath him. He abandoned my bid to stroke him in favour of turning round and presenting me with his arse, before sauntering off to find a morning sunbeam. I checked the clock. Okay: afternoon sunbeam. But only just. Still, I felt guilty for grousing at Brutus when he'd clearly been very patient before waking me up.

'I'm sorry!' I called out. 'I hadn't realised the time.'

There wasn't an answer. I shrugged. Without wasting any more time or body heat, I grabbed Eve's keys and shoved my feet into a pair of wellies, which I'd bought last year as part of a misguided and impulsive plan to go foraging for herbs. The boots had lain unattended in the same corner ever since.

Hugging my dressing gown closer, I nipped out into the shared corridor. Fortunately, no one else was around; the last thing I wanted was the good-looking guy at number twenty-three to see me wandering around with a shabby dressing gown and bed hair, even if it might have given me an effective opening to encourage him round to inspect my own bed. I darted to Eve's place, quickly unlocked the door and hopped inside.

This wasn't the first time I'd been round to her flat. I'd looked after Harold on a few other occasions when she'd been away for work and had once ventured there for a party she put on to impress her boss. Alas, I inadvertently mistook him for one of the local binmen who serve this building and always have a cheery smile and a kind word. When I asked him how the rubbish business was going, he assumed I belonged to one of the many witch-hating chapters and looked ready to throttle me. I apologised profusely but the situation was only compounded when Eve appeared to smooth things over and introduced me. Of course, he recognised my name. It might have been years since I had anything to do with the Order but apparently I was still mud as far as the upper echelons of the Second and Third Levels were concerned. Whatever.

Every time I was in Eve's flat, I was struck by how *clean* everything was. I'd have known if she paid someone to do her dusting for her. It was possible she'd mastered a complicated series of runes that enabled her to use magic to keep the place spick and span but I suspected that she used nothing more than elbow grease. The poor woman needed to get out more.

'Harold,' I called. 'Harold! It's Ivy from down the hall.'

The cat didn't answer. Perhaps I was being too familiar with the familiar. I tried again. 'Harold Fitzwilliam Duxworthy the Third? Are you there?'

There was a faint meow from the living room. My brow

furrowed slightly. I followed the noise, pushing open the door in time to see a small brown shape dart at full speed across the coffee table. A heartbeat later Harold flew after it, knocking over several black candles and what had to be a year's supply of enchanted bee pollen across Eve's spotless floor. I sucked in a pained breath; I knew how much that stuff cost. Then I sneezed three times in quick succession and grimaced.

'Sneeze on Friday, sneeze for woe,' I muttered to myself. That didn't bode well.

Leaving the pollen for now, I edged round the table to try and find Harold and discover what he'd been chasing. He was squeezed into the gap between the wall and the sofa, staring fixedly with huge pupils at something underneath it. I grabbed him and received a yowl and a vicious scratch for my efforts. I tossed him into the kitchen and locked the door then hunkered down on all fours and peered under the sofa. From the gloom in the corner, I could make out a tiny twitching nose and quivering whiskers. A mouse.

I pulled back. Huh. Although Eve had said she was doing well at Myomancy, it seemed likely that the little creature was scampering around and causing havoc not because her flat had a nest of rodents but because she was using him to hone her skills. I tapped my mouth thoughtfully. It was a long time since I'd practised the art of reading rodent behaviour; I wondered whether I could still do it.

I let myself relax, emptying my mind as I'd once been taught, and focused on the mouse. For a long moment it remained frozen but, when I crooked my little finger, it skittered towards me. I let out a silent breath. I still had it.

I reached underneath the sofa and turned over my palm. The mouse wasted no time; it tentatively advanced, its small paws tickling my skin. I gave it a moment to get comfortable and then slowly drew it out. Standing up, I held it aloft and looked into its shiny eyes. 'So, Mister,' I began. The mouse twitched. 'Sorry. I mean Miss.' It relaxed again.

'What do you have to tell me?' I enquired, pushing out a tendril of magic towards it. 'I could do with some good fortune coming my way.'

The mouse quivered, its long tail falling over my thumb. As if startled by its own actions, it spun round, lunged for my thumb and sank in its teeth. I yelped and dropped it. From the kitchen, I could hear Harold hissing and scratching at the closed door. The little rodent darted back for the safety of the sofa whilst I stared at the beads of blood rising up from my skin. This was not good, not good at all.

Before I could seek out the mouse once more, there was a sharp knock on the door. I cursed. Eve was never around at this hour – who on earth could be calling on her? I shuffled over and opened it, gazing at the two figures waiting there.

Given that the nearest one was wearing a red, hooded cloak, it didn't take a genius to work out who they were. Order geeks – and Order geeks here on official business. Honestly; didn't they check their own work schedules before they came out all this way?

My gaze swung to the other figure and I registered close-cropped dark hair and a clean, square jaw. There was a long scar running from his ear almost to his nose but it didn't detract from his appearance; if anything, it gave him a deliciously dangerous air. Two piercing blue eyes watched me expressionlessly. Less of a geek and more of a walking advertisement for virile masculinity. Hello.

'Eve Harrington,' Red Cloak intoned. 'We are pleased to inform you that you have received provisional Second Order status.'

My mouth dropped open; Eve had told me yesterday that she'd not even taken the exams yet. She really was a rising star in the Order. Before I could tell him that she wasn't in, Red Cloak grabbed my arm and began to mutter.

'Hey!' I protested. Unfortunately, it was too late. Far, far too late.

'You are now bound to Raphael Winter for the next 588 days as you complete your transition to the Second Order of The Hallowed Order of Magical Enlightenment. He will act as your mentor and guide while you both work for our glorious and esteemed institution.' For a brief moment, his eyes twinkled and his voice softened. 'Congratulations. You're very lucky to have him as your partner. I'm sure you'll do great things together.'

My arm tingled painfully as the binding pierced my flesh and tied itself to my soul. I stared at the Order official in horror. What the bejesus had he done? 'You … you…' My jaw worked but the words wouldn't come out.

The other man stepped forward and I realised that what I'd thought was a lack of emotion was actually an air of sneering disappointment. 'Perhaps, Miss Harrington, you should put on some more appropriate attire for such a decorous occasion.'

Decorous occasion? He might look like a sex symbol but he was clearly a pompous idiot. A pompous, foolish idiot. A pompous, foolish, moronic idiot who couldn't see the truth when it was staring him in the damn face. Yeah, I'd been right the first time. Another Order geek.

'You plonkers.' Both men frowned slightly. 'You absolute plonkers.' I shook my head. 'Do you have any idea what you've done? I'm not Eve Harrington! Do I look like a six-foot brunette?' I waved at my plump blonde form. 'I'm Eve's neighbour. I just popped in to check on her cat. She's not here – she's gone up north on sodding Order business!' I scratched furiously at my arm. 'Get this damn thing off me!'

The red-cloaked man paled, his eyes rounding as he stared at me. 'You're joking, right?'

I put my hands on my hips and glared. 'Do I look like I'm joking?'

'But you have to be a witch,' he blustered. 'The binding spell wouldn't have taken if you weren't.'

'Of course I'm a damned witch,' I snapped. 'But I'm not First Level. I'm not even a Neophyte. I'm not in your stupid Order!'

Both of them looked shocked. Bully for them. 'You're a witch but you're not in the Order?'

'Are you guys for real? It's not compulsory, you know.'

Red Cloak blinked rapidly. 'Yeah, but anyone with any kind of power…'

'Oh, piss off.' He wasn't even being accurate: there is a whole group of witches who have plenty of power who avoid the Order like the plague. They've created their own special snowflake coven and plot nonsensically to bring the Order down. I'm not one of them – but that doesn't mean they don't exist. Not to mention that half the non-witch population also possesses some magic skills, even if most of those skills are weak and barely noticeable. 'Just because the majority of witches sign up doesn't mean we all do.' I took a deep breath and tried to stay calm. 'Now get this bloody binding off of me.'

They exchanged glances. 'Perhaps we should go inside.'

If it meant getting these idiots out of my life, I'd strip naked and do the can-can. I gestured them in. 'Then get a move on.'

Red Cloak shuffled towards the living room; Sexy-But-Annoying Geek strode in like he owned the place. He gazed round at the strewn bee pollen and raised a dark eyebrow. 'In the middle of something, were you?'

'As it happens,' I answered through gritted teeth, 'yes, I was.' I crossed my arms. 'How could you be so stupid? Don't you check before you go around willy-nilly placing magical soul-bindings on people?'

His gaze turned icy. 'This is Eve Harrington's residence. She lives alone. You answered the door wearing…' he looked me up and down and I could swear his lip curled '...*that*. Common sense would dictate—'

I stepped up to him. 'Don't you dare. Don't you dare bring up common sense when it's patently clear that neither of you have any. Didn't you check whether she was away?'

A muscle jerked in his cheek. 'We were unaware of that.'

'Unaware?' I mocked. 'Some great Order you are! You don't even know where your own people are when you're the ones who sent them away!'

'I'm sure this can all be sorted out.' He glanced at Red Cloak. 'Biggins? Remove her binding and we can let this … person leave.'

I rolled my eyes. He couldn't have sounded more disdainful if he went for a bath in the Sea of Disparagement and washed his hair in Sneer. 'Yeah, Biggins,' I added, matching his tone. 'Remove the binding.'

Biggins coughed. His cheeks flushed red and I started to get a very bad feeling deep in the pit of my stomach. 'Well, Adeptus Winter,' he demurred, 'the thing is…'

'What?'

Biggins scratched his neck. 'Everyone knew you weren't very keen to take on a trainee.'

'So?' Winter glowered in a perfect personification of his name.

'Ipsissimus Smythe didn't want you to change your mind when you got, uh…' Biggins was growing redder and redder. Despite the ridiculousness of this situation, I was fascinated.

'When I got what?'

'Bored or, er, irritated.'

'What exactly does that mean?' Winter snapped.

I sighed. 'It's obvious, isn't it? Because you're some kind of bully who doesn't play well with others, he's made the binding unbreakable.'

Winter's blue eyes narrowed. 'I am not a bully, I just have high standards.' He drew himself up. 'And no binding is unbreakable.'

He wasn't as smart as he thought he was. I hate herblore but that doesn't mean I don't know a fair bit about it. 'Actually,' I told him, 'if you use essence of lavender and combine it with a sprinkling of red clover in your pre-ritual preparations, and then you use the right combination of runes, you can create an unbreakable binding.' I glanced at Biggins. 'Right?'

He seemed relieved that I'd provided the answer. 'Right.'

I hate it when I know stuff like this.

'I knew I should have gone for that Tarquin fellow,' Winter muttered. I stiffened immediately and he glanced towards me. 'I selected Ms Harrington because she is at the top of her game. I require a trainee who is astute, hard working and prepared to go above and beyond the call of duty. My work is not frivolous and not to be taken lightly.'

Ooooh. Big words. I ignored him and addressed Biggins. 'What are the precise terms of the binding?' I asked.

He swallowed. 'It's for 588 days.'

'Yes,' I said impatiently. 'I got that part. It's an important magical number. What else?'

'You have to remain within five miles of each other.'

I winced. Well, that would make driving a taxi complicated. Perhaps I could petition the Order for compensation, though, and take the next two years off. 'Anything else?' I demanded.

Biggins cleared his throat. 'All assignments have to be completed in tandem. You have to be together and work together when you are investigating.'

I closed my eyes; this was even worse than I thought. I inhaled deeply. 'It's simple then. Winter, you take a sabbatical until the binding is removed. We both stay in Oxford to avoid anything untoward happening.' I nodded to myself. 'Job done.'

Winter glared at me. 'First of all, you will address me as Adeptus Exemptus Winter.'

I raised my eyebrows. He was at the very top of the Second Level. I wondered whether he ran his own Department; it was certainly possible. He seemed rather young to have such power but what did I know?

'Secondly,' he continued, 'I am not taking a sabbatical. You obviously know something about how the Order works and it appears you have a working knowledge of magic. We will work together and,' his lip curled in distaste, 'somehow get through this.'

'Nope. Not happening.'

'Now, listen—'

I pulled myself up. 'No, *Adeptus Exemptus Winter*, you listen. I have a life. I don't want to be in the Order. You can't make me work with you. Plus,' I added, pulling out my trump card, 'you can bet your life-savings that the Order doesn't want me.'

Biggins undid his cloak as if it were starting to constrict him. 'What did you say your name was?' he asked.

I smiled. 'Ivy Wilde.'

He flinched. 'Oh.'

My smile grew. 'Oh indeed.'

CHAPTER THREE

B<small>IGGINS SKITTERED OFF TO MAKE HIS REPORT TO THE</small> O<small>RDER AND</small>
to find out if there was a way to undo the binding spell; boy, I'd
like to have been a fly on *that* wall. Meanwhile I put down some
food for Harold and took Winter to my own flat. As I opened the
door and realised that it was colder inside than it was out in the
draughty corridor, I remembered that I still hadn't called a
damned plumber. That sucked – but at least it was a problem I
had a chance of fixing.

Winter's gaze swept across my living room. No prizes for
guessing what he was thinking. There might be an absence of bee
pollen but this wasn't the gleaming place that Eve's was. I picked
up my bra from the back of the sofa and absently twirled it on
one finger. He stared at me. Screw him. I wasn't going to apologise for *my* clothes lying around *my* home.

'So,' he said, averting his eyes from my offending underwear,
'I'm going to assume that you're not in the Order because you
couldn't pass beyond Neophyte. You have the intelligence but not
the magic.'

'Guess again.'

He pointed at my thumb. 'You've recently been bitten by a

rodent of some kind,' he said smugly. 'That means you've not even mastered Myomancy.'

I held up the offending digit. 'This is proof that I'm a Myomancy expert,' I told him serenely. 'It's a bad omen. And look, here you are: the living embodiment of bad luck.'

'A bite isn't an omen.'

'It is if you're as adept as I am.'

He snorted. 'Yeah, right. What can you actually do?'

I might have told him if the tone of his voice hadn't been so incredulous but I didn't need to prove myself to him. He needed me a hell of a lot more than I needed him. 'What can *you* do?' I returned.

'I'm an Adeptus Exemptus. I should have thought my capabilities were obvious.'

The fact that I didn't answer was answer enough.

Winter half-shrugged as if my silence was evidence that I was useless and changed the subject. 'Why are you wearing wellington boots? Are you expecting a flood?'

'I'm wearing them to guard against the pathetic tears of Order geeks like you.'

Anger flared in his eyes. 'Let's get one thing straight, Ms Wilde. I'm in charge here. Until we get this mess straightened out, you will follow my lead and do as I say. You will stop the insults and watch that smart mouth of yours. You will not test my patience.'

'Was that one thing?' I asked, cocking my head. 'Or about five things? Do they not teach arithmetic at the Order these days?'

It was probably fortunate for both of us that Brutus chose that moment to saunter in and flop at my opponent's feet. 'At least you have a familiar,' Winter grunted, avoiding my eyes in an apparent bid to reduce the antagonism between us.

'This is Brutus,' I told him.

My cat rolled onto his back and gazed upwards. 'Pet,' he demanded.

Winter leapt about three feet backwards. 'Your familiar just spoke.'

'Yeah.'

'Pet,' Brutus hissed again.

'He wants you to stroke him,' I said. Winter stared at me. He really did have the most intense blue eyes. I shrugged. 'I've had him for a long time. Back when I was younger and more enthusiastic, I had the brilliant idea that I could develop and market a way for people to talk to their pets and have them talk back. After a lot of trial and error, I came up with the right series of runes and, hey presto. Brutus can talk.'

'It worked?' Winter gazed from me to the cat. He seemed to still think I was throwing my voice *à la* street magician.

'In a manner of speaking. Yes, he can talk but he only has a vocabulary of about twenty words and most of them aren't very nice. I abandoned the plan to make millions from the spell when I realised that people would finally realise their cats are selfish little bastards who only care about themselves. There would have been mass feline abandonment if they heard what their pets really have to say. It seemed prudent to keep the magic to myself.'

Winter blinked. 'I see.'

'Pet,' Brutus repeated. 'Bitch.'

'Don't be offended,' I said. 'He calls everyone that.' I winked at Brutus and turned on my heel. Clothes would probably be a good option right about now.

I TOOK my time getting ready. Winter could wait. Plus, my hair was pointing in all directions, sticking up like I'd been electrocuted; smoothing it down into something more manageable wasn't easy.

I debated whether to wear my one and only suit, then figured that the Order probably wouldn't give a flying shit what I was wearing. I'd still be me underneath the clothes. Instead I sniffed the crotch of yesterday's jeans, decided they smelled okay and pulled them on, along with a faded white T-shirt emblazoned with the words 'Monkey Magic' from that old television show. Ha! Let them make of that what they would. I completed the ensemble with my neon-green bomber jacket. At least my nemesis wouldn't lose me in a crowd.

When I strolled out, Winter was perched on one end of the sofa while Brutus was on the other with his hackles raised. They appeared to be having some kind of standoff. 'I don't think your familiar likes me,' Winter commented.

I bit back a retort about my cat's good taste in favour of keeping the peace. I could be restrained if the situation called for it. 'Brutus,' I said, 'go and check out Mrs Burridge for me.'

Brutus gave me a look that suggested his plans for the day involved curling up in a corner and snoozing; spying on the old lady upstairs, who insisted on dabbling in runes and herbs even though she didn't have a whisper of power inside her, was a waste of his time. Fortunately, on this occasion he elected not to show me up. He got up, stretched and wandered off.

I put my hands on my hips and eyed Winter. 'Well?' I asked. 'Are we going? I've got things to do, so the faster we get this sorted out the better.' I neglected to tell him that those things included lying on the sofa, eating a family-size bag of salt-and-vinegar crisps followed by copious amounts of chocolate, and occasionally reaching for the remote control.

He raised an eyebrow. 'Is that what you're wearing?'

I gave him a twirl. 'Why yes, it is.' Just because he was wearing an immaculate suit that was probably tailored to fit him and him alone, didn't mean the rest of us had to dress like we were meeting the Queen.

He sighed heavily. 'Fine. Let's get a move on.'

I led the way, taking him down the corridor to the lift. I

pressed the button to call it and he stared at me in astonishment. 'The stairs will be faster.'

'I've hurt my ankle. I need to avoid strenuous exercise.'

'You're fine.'

'You don't know that.'

Exasperation filled his eyes. 'I'm an Adeptus Exemptus. You're in perfect physical condition.'

I brightened. 'Do you think so?'

Winter's mouth tightened fractionally. 'What I mean is that you are not in pain and you are suffering from no health defects beyond an incredible lack of fitness. You could also lose some weight.'

Oh, tell me that he did *not* just go there. 'Lose weight?'

Winter belatedly realised the danger he was in. 'If you wish to achieve the sort of peak physical condition required of a Second Level witch, it might be prudent. Our work can involve a lot of running and considerable effort.'

Screw that. 'And what work is that exactly?' I enquired, my tone dripping with ice.

'Arcane Branch, of course.'

I rolled my eyes. Of course. 'Well, it's lucky that I'm neither Second Level nor working with you on anything other than extricating myself from this ridiculous situation,' I said. Then I crossed my arms and made it clear I had nothing more to say to him.

THE ORDER HEADQUARTERS are nestled between Christchurch Cathedral and Merton College. They like to point out on a regular basis that they've been there far longer than the university and that their members possess skills which the typical Oxford student could only dream of. The truth is that the Order simply likes to keep an eye on their academic counterparts and ensure they don't get too uppity. The Order enjoys a venerable status but in this day and age they know it could be whipped away in favour of the latest breakthrough in bioscience or chemical engineering or whatever.

To be honest, I wasn't sure why they worried about it. *Que sera sera*, and all that. With footholds in every major city in the country, not to mention representatives in the House of Lords, I suspect that Order will be standing long after the university has crumbled into decay.

I avoid this part of town as much as I can. Other taxi drivers can reap the benefits of students separating coins from pocket fluff to pay their fares. I'm not going to let the Order keep me out of my town but neither am I going to wave my existence in their faces.

Winter and I strolled down the pavement towards the main doors. Well, I say strolled: I strolled and Winter marched. Still, it did afford me a very enjoyable view of his arse, which was a particularly tight and well-rounded specimen. He might have had a rod jammed up it but that didn't mean I couldn't appreciate the way it was put together. I was considering whether he maintained a regime that involved several hundred squats a day when he turned round and caught me staring. For the briefest moment, I thought he looked amused.

'Do you like what you see?' he growled.

I shrugged. I'd been caught out; there was no point in denying it. 'Yeah,' I said. 'I do.'

'And how would you feel if I afforded you the same attention?'

'Hey, I'm all for equality.' I turned round to give him the same view of me as I'd had of him. All I heard, however, was a loud scoff and him striding away from me. A girl could get a serious complex hanging around him for too long.

I caught up with him, forcing my legs to move faster so I could keep up. The few students milling around were giving way to more and more red-cloaked Order witches. Considering the wide berth they gave us, coupled with the looks cast in his direction, Winter was both admired and respected. I stifled a smile. Wait until they found out who he was supposed to be working with.

No one had recognised me yet because they didn't expect me to be here. It was some years since I'd trodden these stones but I still remembered what this place was like; word would get around quickly enough. That wasn't my ego talking; I was being realistic. There's nothing like several covens of witches for passing around juicy gossip.

'Adeptus!' a voice called from behind us. 'Adeptus Exemptus Winter!'

Winter stopped walking and I smirked. 'Always got time for an adoring fan, then?' I murmured under my breath.

He looked irritated but didn't say anything. 'Practicus Lindman,' he said, greeting the First Level young woman. 'What can I do for you?'

I stilled. Anthea. I'd not seen or spoken to her in over eight years. She appeared considerably more serious than the girl I used to giggle with over fake IDs and attempts to complete complicated runes to encourage acne-free skin and glossy hair. She didn't even have the pink dye any more; instead her hair was a shiny brown and held up in a sombre bun.

'I'm sorry to interrupt,' she said, without glancing at me. 'But last week you were talking about the runes for seismic displacement and I wanted to ask if you could help me.' She held up a piece of paper. I could tell straight away that she'd angled the first two strokes incorrectly. Given the rosy flush across her cheeks, I doubted that she really cared about the runes. This was all about getting the chance to talk to Winter.

His face relaxed and he smiled at her kindly. Huh. Maybe he had a nice side after all. I bet he didn't tell her she needed to lose weight. 'It's quite simple really,' he said. 'Do you have a pen?'

She nodded eagerly and pulled one out. He took it and re-sketched the first rune then pointed to her version. 'Do you see the difference?'

She cocked her head. 'I do! Thank you so much! Would it be too much trouble to ask you…' She looked at me mid-sentence and her voice faltered. 'Ivy?'

I gave her a little wave. 'Hi, Anthea.'

She swallowed and stared. 'What are you doing here?' She flicked a glance at Winter and her meaning was clear: what are you doing here *with him?*

'Just a little misunderstanding,' I said airily. 'How have you been?'

She blinked several times. 'Good. I've been good. I'm Practicus now. It won't be long until I'm ready to think about moving up to Second Level.'

'Fantastic.' It was obvious from my tone of voice that my heart wasn't in it.

She got the hint. 'I should go.'

'Wasn't there something else?' Winter asked.

She threw another nervous look towards me. 'No, it's alright. I can see you're busy.' Before he could respond, she all but sprinted away. I wondered who she'd tell first.

Winter was patently curious. 'There's definitely more to you than meets the eye, Ms Wilde.'

'Call me Ivy, Adeptus Exemptus Winter,' I said. I didn't need to stand on ceremony the way he did.

'Biggins recognised your name too,' he continued, ignoring my pointed comment. 'What's your real story?'

I did my best to look blasé. 'I was here as a Neophyte,' I told him. 'And then I wasn't.'

'Why not?'

I met his eyes. He didn't seem to want to know the salacious details of the story, he was just vaguely curious. I shrugged. He'd find out soon enough without my help. 'I was expelled from the Order.' He stared. 'For cheating.' I paused. 'And assault.'

Winter didn't move a muscle.

'But,' I added, 'I think the official reason was conduct unbecoming to an Order witch.' I grinned and punched his arm. 'So you're really lucky having me as your new partner.'

Winter didn't say anything. With luck, I'd done enough to avoid any further questioning on the matter. One could only hope.

CHAPTER FOUR

THE REMAINDER OF OUR JOURNEY PASSED UNIMPEDED. IF I'D thought I'd feel nostalgic coming back here, I was surprised to find that it didn't bother me at all. I liked my new life; I didn't need the Order around me to feel fulfilled.

We dropped off all our tech items at the front door so they didn't interfere with the magic inside. For Winter that involved a phone, a watch, an earpiece, a confusing cube-like object, a Taser, a charger and various other accoutrements. All I had to leave behind were my battery-operated car keys.

As a highly placed Second Level official, Winter had access to a good portion of the ancient headquarters. The higher up you are allowed to go, the more important a witch you are. He might not have been able to enter the topmost floors, which are reserved for the few Third Level members, but we could roam around most of the building. When we ascended to the seventh floor, far beyond where I'd been permitted to go during my time here, I knew things were getting serious.

'Wait here,' Winter said curtly as we reached a solid-looking oak door. 'I'll announce our arrival.'

I imagined him striding into the room with a bugle and

tooting a high-pitched tune. I stifled a grin and received a frown in response. He entered, leaving me to cool my heels in the corridor. At least up here the chances of anyone I knew hovering around were slim. Bumping into Anthea was bad enough.

I took the opportunity of some alone time to slide down onto the floor and sit cross-legged, leaning my head against the wall. I reckoned I'd already had my allotted fresh air for today. It was time for a rest. I was just getting comfortable when the door opened again and yet another red cloak beckoned me inside.

Sighing at the imposition, I got to my feet and went in. The room was remarkably grand, not that I should have been surprised knowing this lot. There was a long table, polished to within an inch of its life, and several figures seated round it. To my surprise, Ipsissimus Collings, the Order's leader was at the head. Things must be serious if he was involved; the only other time I'd met him in person was the day he'd expelled me. His expression was as grim today as it had been then.

He stood up and gestured me forward. I stood next to the ramrod-straight Winter who was facing the group. Biggins joined us from the side. It was starting to feel like the Spanish Inquisition.

'Ms Wilde, thank you for joining us today.' There wasn't the faintest hint of censure or accusation in the Ipsissimus's tone. That was a good start.

'You're welcome.'

The Ipsissimus knitted his fingers together under his chin and leant forward. 'First of all, I must ask how you know Philosophus Harrington.'

'Eve? She's my neighbour. We share the same building and I look after her familiar from time to time when she's away.'

'Did you seek her out knowing she was part of the Order?'

That stung; it suggested I had designs on tracking the ins and outs of what these plonkers got up to. I wasn't that nefarious. Even if I had the will, I didn't have the energy.

'No.' This time my tone was short.

The Ipsissimus nodded. 'And have you been practising since you left the Order?'

'I didn't leave the Order,' I said pointedly. 'I was booted out.' He didn't speak. I sighed. 'Yes. I have on occasion used magic.'

One of the other seated men spoke up. 'Have your skills progressed at all?'

I clenched my fists then, realising what I was doing, slowly relaxed. 'They have. Would you like a demonstration?' I'd turn him into a frog if that was what it was going to take.

'That won't be necessary,' the Ipsissimus broke in.

Winter coughed. 'She does have clear, well-honed abilities.'

I looked at him, surprised. He was supposed to be doing all he could to get me out of here, not encouraging this lot to keep me around.

'You've seen evidence of this?' a severe-looking woman enquired. 'Actually watched her cast runes? Or use herblore?'

'No,' he admitted.

The people round the table exchanged looks. 'You arrived after Ms Wilde's expulsion,' she said.

'She alluded to what had happened.'

'Did she now? Well, I think we all know what her skills and abilities are really like.'

There was a titter from several others. I bristled. 'I am here, you know.'

The Ipsissimus offered me a benign smile. 'Our apologies. And our apologies that you were dragged into this … situation. There was a mix-up with the paperwork and we didn't realise that Philosophus Harrington was absent on Order business. The error is understandable, if not forgivable.'

On one side of the table I spotted a red-robed man whose heavy-bagged eyes and unkempt hair suggested that he was under considerable stress. He seemed to shrink into himself. No prizes for guessing whose error it had been.

The Ipsissimus continued. 'We have looked into the specifications of the binding which Adeptus Minor Biggins created and there is some opportunity to remove the spell.'

Praise the heavens. I exhaled. 'Good. Get it off.'

'In one hundred days' time, there will be a slight loosening as the magic begins to wear off. At that time, it is possible we can remove it.'

I looked at him. Had I heard that properly? 'One hundred days?' I asked. 'One hundred days' time?'

The Ipsissimus continued to smile. It was tinged with sympathy but all the same it was becoming mightily irritating. 'Yes. I'm afraid there's nothing else we can do.'

'You'd better not be planning any holidays abroad,' I muttered to Winter. I tilted up my chin. 'So it's settled then. Adeptus Exemptus Winter and I stay within five miles of each other and neither of us leaves Oxford. You compensate me for my future lack of earnings and in one hundred days' time, the spell is removed.'

'And you work with him.' The Ipsissimus addressed Winter. 'It's not ideal but as long as she tags along during all investigations and occasionally helps you with your Arcane work, the terms of the binding will be met. Your forbearance is greatly appreciated but we know you will rise to the challenge. You can learn a great deal from training someone so ... complex.'

Complex? My eyebrows shot up. 'Er, excuse me. I'm not working with him. I don't want anything to do with you lot.'

The Ipsissimus took on an expression of great sufferance. 'You will.'

I crossed my arms. 'No. I won't.'

'When you left the Order—'

'When I was expelled.'

A tiny vein bulged in his forehead. 'When you left the Order, we decided that it would be prudent not to take further action against you, Ms Wilde. You assaulted a fellow Neophyte.'

Now it was my time to twitch. 'What's your point?'

'We can still bring charges against you.'

I met his eyes; the good ol' Ipsissimus wasn't bluffing. I shrugged. 'Go ahead. What's the worst that could happen?'

'You end up in prison for up to five years.'

Oh. 'I doubt the Order would want the negative publicity,' I said calmly. 'It wouldn't look good having a young Order member behind bars.'

'That was certainly the case eight years ago. But you're no longer a fresh-faced teenager.' He consulted a sheet of paper in front of him. 'You've been driving taxis.'

'It's an honest profession.'

'Indeed.' The Ipsissimus rubbed his chin. 'You've had several complaints brought against you for refusing to drive customers long distances. You only put in the minimum hours required. In the time since you left the Order, you've essentially achieved nothing. You're hardly a paragon of virtue. I don't think many people would have sympathy for you.'

My bottom lip jutted out. 'I don't think that's fair! I've achieved a great deal since I was expelled.' I leant forward slightly. 'I once won five hundred pounds on a *This Morning* phone-in competition. And not many other people can say they've never missed an episode of *Enchantment*.' I felt Winter shift beside me. He was probably jealous.

'We are not amused, Ms Wilde,' the Ipsissimus said.

'If I work with him,' I said, jabbing a finger in Winter's direction and making him stiffen dramatically, 'I'll end up causing more problems than I solve. A hundred days isn't that long. Give the poor man a holiday. He certainly looks like he needs it.'

'He's a very important member of the Arcane Branch and has a high success rate. We have no desire to lose him for three months because of a mix-up in the paperwork.'

'If I go to prison, you'll still lose him.'

'Perhaps. But we'll also gain considerable satisfaction in return.'

Well, at least the Ipsissimus was honest. I thought about it; maybe prison wouldn't be so bad. I wouldn't have to cook. I could spend my days lounging around in a cell. It could be restful. Somehow I doubted it, though.

'What about Eve?'

'What about her?'

I rolled my eyes. 'This is her dream. It's not her fault she's not here and I've been flung into her place. She'll be gutted if I've taken her spot.'

'We will find her a commensurate position, I assure you.'

They'd better. There had to be some way to get myself out of all this that didn't involve prison scrubs.

'Oh for goodness' sake,' Winter hissed. 'You don't have to do anything. Just follow me around and occasionally comment or file some paperwork.'

The Ipsissimus looked stern. 'We invoked the binding because you don't work well with others, Adeptus Winter. This will be good practice for you for the future.'

'We all know she doesn't have the skills to do anything anyway,' one of the seated Order bigwigs said. He didn't make the slightest attempt to lower his voice. I glared nastily at him. He didn't flinch. That's when I knew I'd fall into line. There was a part of me that was incandescent with rage that they thought I was weak and useless and had no magic of my own. It was only a glowing ember of anger rather than a burning inferno – but it was enough.

'Fine,' I snapped. 'I'll do it.'

The Ipsissimus nodded as if that was what he'd expected all along. 'Excellent. Then we are done here. For obvious reasons, we shall do what we can to keep this … mistake quiet.' He stood up. A heartbeat later, Winter propelled me out of the room as if my presence were contaminating the air and had to be removed.

It took fewer than three steps after the door closed behind us before I began to regret my words. 'Well, that was stupid,' I muttered. Right now, a hundred days felt like a life sentence.

'I'm glad you've realised that,' Winter said. 'You're lucky to be given a second chance with the Order. If you do well, you might even be welcomed back as a Neophyte.'

I resisted the temptation to kick him sharply on the shins. 'That's not what I meant, Adeptus Exemptus Winter. I meant it was stupid that I caved in.'

'You'd rather go to jail?' he enquired.

It didn't matter what I said; he wouldn't understand. He obviously believed that the Order was the best thing since non-stick cauldrons. I elected not to answer. Instead I huffed along, my hands in my pockets and my shoulders slouched. 'I want to go home now,' I said distinctly.

Winter regarded me for a moment. 'Fine. I'll stop off and pick up the basics for you to get started and I'll take you back. I'm sure your sofa is missing you.'

Sarcasm? 'The next three months are going to be *so* much fun, Adeptus Exemptus Winter,' I responded.

His mouth tightened. 'You don't have to keep calling me that.'

I held up my palms. 'Oh no, you said that's how I have to address you so that's what I'll do. I'd hate to go against Order protocol. Maybe I should add in a curtsey at the end of each sentence. What do you think?'

'That's enough,' he growled.

Good. I was getting under his skin. I was going to make him regret this for every minute of the next hundred days. Him and the rest of the damned Order.

I WAITED outside the Supply Office while Winter went in to get what I supposedly needed to trail after him like a forlorn puppy.

A collar and lead, perhaps. Or I'd get lucky and he'd pick up some treats to make sure I sat like a good girl and gave him a paw when he needed it. Whatever. He could carry all that stuff around if he wanted to. I wasn't going to help. Unfortunately, electing to stay in the corridor wasn't a good move. I wasn't left alone to enjoy the temporary peace for long.

The trouble with the Order headquarters – and indeed most bureaucratic buildings – is that they've been designed with total lack of imagination. They might look impressively ancient from the outside and might well be thoughtfully constructed and a testament to the age in which they are built, but inside they're a box. Criss-crossing offices in grid formation; boxes upon boxes upon beige wall-covered boxes. Google this ain't.

It also means there are long corridors so, from my position at the end of one hallway, I could see perfectly to the other end. My view wasn't blocked by the tired-looking photocopier dumped outside, nor was it hampered by the stack of fire-risk cardboard boxes. So when Tarquin Willingham of Posh Street, London, appeared two hundred metres away, I could do nothing but watch his approach. In theory it gave me time to prepare the right words; in practice, it ramped up my dismay. I guess I knew now who Anthea had sought out after I bumped into her in the quad. I shouldn't have been surprised.

Tarquin was dressed more casually than Winter; he wore a suit but it was minus both a jacket and tie. I wondered whether he'd taken them off – the Order's equivalent of rolling up your sleeves. Then I decided I didn't care.

'I'm surprised you're here alone,' I called, as soon as he got close. 'Aren't you afraid I might hurt you again?'

Tarquin tsked. 'I've spent the last eight years living and breathing the Order, Ivy. I think it's fair to say that I've probably got skills now that you can only dream about.'

Somehow I doubted that. 'What do you want, Tarq?'

He ran a hand through his blond hair. The style was artless, giving the impression that he'd merely run a comb through it. I had a feeling that it took him a lot longer to get it the way he wanted it. With Tarquin, appearances were everything.

'It's good to see you again,' he said.

'I'd say the same,' I told him, 'but then I'd be a big, fat liar.'

Something sparked in his eyes and he dropped all pretence of politeness. 'How did you do it?'

I inspected my fingernails. 'Do what?'

'Wheedle your way back in here. What lies did you tell them?'

'You're the liar, not me. Or have you rewritten history in your own head as well as everyone else's?'

'If you're here to cause trouble—'

I cocked my head, amused. 'Then what? What will you do, Tarq? Because I think you've pretty much done everything already.'

'Look,' he hissed. 'I told you I was sorry. I didn't mean to get caught cheating and I didn't mean for you to take the blame.'

'You didn't own up though, did you?'

'Ivy, you know what my father is like. If he found out—'

'Aw, diddums. Life must be so tough for you, Tarquin. Painted as the victim of nasty, plagiarising Ivy Wilde.' My eyes gleamed. 'Tell me, did you ever master that protective spell or do you still steal from others to cover up your own failings?'

'I don't need to steal. I'm highly respected here these days, Ivy. I've come a long way since then. Adeptus Exemptus Winter knows it. He knows that…'

'Adeptus Exemptus Winter knows what?'

We both turned. Winter was standing there, holding a box and gazing at Tarquin with a hard question in his eyes.

Tarquin swallowed. 'You know that Ivy will be able to start afresh. That she's not the same person she was eight years ago and she can wipe the slate clean. It's very good of you to give her a second chance.'

He just couldn't help himself. He was so desperate to avoid his name being tarnished that he'd keep up his web of lies and deceit even though no one cared. Certainly not me. Frankly, he'd done me a favour all those years ago. If I'd not been blamed for his actions, I'd never have experienced how good it was to be truly free. I'd have been an Order zealot like the rest of them.

'Hmm,' Winter said. 'Don't you have errands to run for Adeptus Major Price? I'm sure you're not here just for yourself.'

Relieved to be given the chance to escape, Tarquin nodded vigorously. 'I do, Adeptus. I'd better get a move on. Thank you so much. I take my duties very seriously, as you know.' He didn't look at me as he said this last part but I knew it was a dig. Then he bowed and scurried away, like the weasel he was.

Winter and I watched him go. As soon as he was out of earshot, Winter glanced at me. 'Do you want to tell me what that was really about?'

'Nope.'

'Hmm,' he said again.

To stave off any further questions, I smiled brightly. 'Is that for me?' I pointed at the box in Winter's hands.

'What? Oh, yes.' He handed it to me; I guessed I'd have to carry it after all. 'This is everything you'll need. Take time this evening to go through it carefully. We'll start tomorrow at dawn in the gym.'

'Dawn?'

Winter nodded impatiently.

'Gym?'

He sighed. 'Part of my job is to make sure you have the skills to do this job. When we are not undertaking missions, I will be training and mentoring you. Believe me, there are plenty of other things I'd rather be doing with my time.'

I didn't care a jot about Winter's time; it was the loss of *my* time that bothered me. What happened to following him around for a bit and throwing in a comment every so often? I didn't like the sound of this at all. 'I'm only here for a hundred days. There's no point. If I were Eve, things would be different but I'm not, so I really think…'

'Stop arguing. The Ipsissimus was very clear about his expectations. I'm not about to shirk my responsibilities, regardless of who you are. I have to prove to the Order that bindings like this are unnecessary for me because I'll perform my duties as expected, despite the circumstances. I'll see you tomorrow.' His blue eyes darkened forbiddingly. 'Don't be late.'

'Yes, Adeptus Exemptus Winter. Three bags full.'

He ignored my sarcasm. 'You will conduct yourself as befits a member of the Order, notwithstanding what happened in the past. This is a serious profession and I will not have it undermined by smart-aleck comments or disorderly behaviour. I've worked hard to get to where I am, and my position will not be compromised because you are tagging along everywhere I go. Some people may think the Order is obsolete but they are very much mistaken. What I do – and what the Order does – is vital to the wellbeing of this country. Magic is not to be trifled with. It's a solemn and grave endeavour. You will be polite and well-mannered at all times.' He glanced at my clothes. 'You will dress appropriately and smartly. If you aford me respect, I will give you the same in return and we can survive the next hundred days relatively unscathed.'

Pompous jackass. I clicked my heels together and saluted.

He opened his mouth to say something else apparently thought better of it. Instead he turned and walked off in the same direction as Tarquin without so much as a friendly goodbye. I shrugged.

Rather than get caught eyeing up his arse again, I stared into the box and registered the items with a sinking heart. This was not going to be fun.

CHAPTER FIVE

By the time I got back to my little flat, after checking on Harold and making sure he was fed, watered and happy, I was footsore and very, very grumpy. I dumped Winter's little box of tricks on my kitchen table, where I resolved never to look at it again, and flounced into the living room. It didn't help matters that I couldn't find a plumber willing to come out – unless it was for an exorbitant emergency callout charge – until Monday. I wrapped myself in my duvet, curled up on the sofa and sniffed.

'This is all a dream,' I told myself. 'A terrible nightmare. I'm about to wake up and I'll laugh at myself.' I squeezed my eyes shut and pinched my arm. For good measure, Brutus appeared and offered a secondary nip with his sharp teeth. Neither worked. I opened my eyes and gazed at him. 'Yeah,' I sighed. 'I knew it was too much to ask. You can't blame me for trying though.'

He blinked at me. 'Ears.'

I reached over and gave him the desired scratch. A deep purr throbbed from his throat. 'More.'

I kept going.

'More.'

'I am thy servant,' I told him, without a trace of irony.

His tail whipped suddenly from side to side. 'Stop, bitch.'

I yanked my fingers away in the nick of time. I'd had enough psychological injury already today; I didn't need physical scratches as well. Brutus hopped off the sofa and stalked away, clearly annoyed that I'd stroked him for a second longer than his desired time.

I leant back and pondered my situation. There had to be a way out; maybe the Order hadn't considered every avenue yet. I stared at the ceiling thoughtfully then dug out my phone. It rang for several seconds and I was on the verge of giving up when someone finally answered. 'What?'

'You know,' I said, snuggling deeper into the duvet, 'you're not going to win friends and influence people with that kind of attitude.'

'Good evening. You have reached the esteemed laboratory of I-don't-give-a-shit. How may we not help you?'

I grinned. Iqbal was a man after my own heart. 'Hi, honey.'

'I'm busy, Ivy. We can't all loll around, some of us have work to do.'

'I work.'

'Sitting on your arse all day long and occasionally turning a steering wheel is not work.'

I raised my eyebrows. 'And reading all day is?'

'You try it,' he snarked.

Tomes and treatises on the history of the British Isles? No thanks. 'How is that PhD coming along?' I asked. Iqbal has been studying for it since I first met him. I keep waiting for someone to tell him that he'll lose his funding if he doesn't get a move on and actually write something, but he seems to keep managing to slide by. Although by the last count, his grandmother has died seven times. The university is generous with its compassionate leave.

'I wrote two hundred words today,' he said, with a hint of pride.

'Great!'

'I deleted three hundred and sixty-two.'

'Well,' I demurred, 'editing is important. What's the actual total?'

'Eighteen.'

'Eighteen thousand? That's brilliant.'

There was a pause. 'No. Just eighteen.'

Ah. 'It could be worse.'

'Could it?' His tone was morose. '"The effect of magic on the substantive growth and expansion of the British Empire by Iqbal L. Sharif". That's all I've got. And I'm including my initial in the word count. I'm also thinking that I should delete "substantive".'

'You realise you're my hero, right?'

He snorted. 'What do you want, Ivy? You can't be calling up just to check on my lack of progress.'

I twiddled a loose blonde curl. 'Why not? That's what friends do. I'm being supportive.'

'Get to the point.'

Fair enough. 'I've been subjected to a rather complicated binding spell,' I said, outlining the details for him.

'Wow. The Order really hate you, huh?'

'Actually, the spell on its own is nothing to do with me. As far as I can work out, it's more binding than usual because they didn't trust their own guy not to dump me when he got fed up.'

There was a pause. 'Who's their guy?'

'Adeptus Exemptus Winter.'

Iqbal let out a low whistle. 'Damn, girl.'

'You know him?'

'I know of him. Everyone knows of him. How come you don't?'

'Because I don't pay attention to what the Order does. You know that, Iqbal.'

'I know you said that. I just thought…'

'What? That I say I don't care about them but really I stalk them at every opportunity?'

'Well, yeah.'

I rolled my eyes. 'I'm a pretty uncomplicated person. What you see is what you get.' Secrets take time and energy. Most of the time, at least. There was one glaring exception to that rule but I'd put it behind me long ago. 'Anyway, what I want to know is—'

'—is whether there's a way to break the binding before the first hundred days are up. I can look into it but it's probably an ancient spell and we both know they're the toughest ones to crack. The good news is I've got all the right books lying around here.'

I beamed. 'Brill.'

'Bear in mind,' he cautioned, 'that this sort of spell sounds like it's been drawn right out of the Cyphers. In that scenario…'

'I get it,' I said. The Cypher Manuscripts are the Bible as far as the Order are concerned. The magic written on their pages is stronger than you'll find anywhere else. It is essentially primeval; it is enchantment in its rawest form. Fortunately, however, its power is rarely harnessed. Even Second Level Order members have to petition to be allowed access to even one dusty yellowing Cypher page. And I'd heard there were thousands. There was no way that the Order had gone to those lengths for a binding spell, no matter how much they wanted to keep Winter in line. 'If Cypher magic was used, then all bets are off.'

'Agreed.' Iqbal paused. 'So what do I get in return for helping you?'

Arse. 'Joy in your heart.'

'Not enough, Ivy. I need more.'

I scrunched up my face. 'What do you want?'

Iqbal didn't hesitate. 'Karaoke.'

'You bastard.'

I could virtually hear him grin. 'Minimum of two hours. At least three songs from you, one of which must be a duet with me.'

'There must be something else. My life savings? My first-born? *Anything?*'

'Those are my terms.'

Damn him. 'No rap.' My mouth didn't work that fast.

'Done.'

'And no Sonny and Cher for the duet.'

'Fine.' He sounded smug. That had me worried but what choice did I have?

'Okay. Find the information I need and I'll do karaoke,' I said reluctantly.

'I'm already on it.'

I hesitated then said, 'Before you go, is there anything in particular I should know about Winter?'

Iqbal was silent for a moment. Finally he spoke. 'Watch your step. That man is on a mission to rise to the top of the Order and he'll do almost anything to get there. He was brought up as an army brat in a non-magical family. His father is some military big shot and Raphael was expected to follow in Daddy's footsteps until his magic showed itself. The family no doubt expects him to rise up the Order ranks as quickly as he would have risen in the army. He's not a Department Head like most others of his rank but that's because he knows the fastest way to the top is through Arcane Branch. He's prepared to bide his time. At least, that's what the word on the street is.'

I didn't like the sound of that at all. Ambition always makes me feel rather queasy. 'Thanks, darling,' I said. I hung up.

I'd done everything I could for now. Yawning, I rested my head on the arm of the sofa. One of these days I was going to train Brutus to make me mugs of tea. And do the washing up afterwards.

'Brutus!' I called. 'Come here, you bugger, and show me how to catnap again.'

He padded into the room and jumped onto the coffee table. That was strange – he normally ignored me when I shouted.

'Problem.' His whiskers quivered.

'Problem with what?'

'Problem.'

Honestly, he was more trouble than he was worth sometimes. 'If you're not going to elaborate…'

He lifted his head and stared at a high point on the wall behind me. Either I was being haunted or there was a spider. Brutus hates spiders.

'Problem.'

'You're not going to let it go, are you?' I pulled myself upright. 'There's nothing there, Brutus. Not even a cobweb. And behind the wall there's nothing because that's Eve's flat.' Then I froze. Brutus looked at me as if to suggest that I was incredibly dim-witted but I was finally beginning to understand. 'Is it Harold?' I demanded. Damn it, Eve would be devastated if anything happened to him while she was away.

Brutus started to wash his face. I grimaced and swung to my feet. That was clearly all I was going to get out of him; I'd have to see what was wrong for myself.

I pressed my ear against the wall. There was a dull thud from the other side. Someone was definitely in there; the question was who.

If Eve weren't a witch, with her own specially pre-prepared magical wards (considered vital for anyone in the Order, even though they're nothing more than a drain of energy and useless against non-magical invasions), I'd simply have cast a rune or two to work out who was in her flat. I wouldn't have even had to open my front door. Alas, I knew my magic couldn't penetrate her spells. I'd have to do this the old-fashioned way.

Cursing under my breath, I went into my Spare Room of Doom, so-called because it has become a dumping ground for everything I don't need and now resembles a hell cave filled with mini-mountains of un-ironed clothes, random boxes and good-ness-only-knows-what. Maybe, I thought hopefully, by the time I'd found what I needed, Eve's visitor would have already vanished.

Poking underneath a pile of wrinkled blankets, I found my old canister of pepper spray, purchased for me by a well-meaning friend who'd been concerned that working as a taxi driver was an open invitation to be raped and dismembered, not necessarily in that order. Nah. I tossed it to one side in favour of a slightly smelly navy anorak and battered baseball cap. Then, at the last minute, I spotted an old ID badge from my short-lived, post-Order stint as a receptionist at a large pharmaceutical company. I grabbed it and pinned it to my chest, using a scarf to obscure most of the lettering. Once I was satisfied, I picked up the nearest cardboard box and headed out, whistling.

I ambled down the corridor, pausing when I reached Eve's door. The low murmur of voices reached my ears: there was more than one would-be burglar. That didn't bode well. Shifting the box in my arms, I raised my hand and knocked.

The voices immediately hushed. I knocked again. I couldn't be arsed kicking down the door and attacking, especially when I was outnumbered and the people I hurt could be Eve's long-lost brothers. Although if my ploy didn't work, it would probably come to that.

Fortunately, whoever was inside was smart enough to know that I'd heard them and that pretending not to be there wouldn't work. Unfortunately for them, they weren't as smart as they thought.

The door opened and a dark-haired woman appeared. She was wearing jeans and a smart blouse and looked to be in her early thirties – and she was no one I'd ever seen before. I pasted on a suitably bored expression. 'Eve Harrington?'

'Yes.'

Liar. Suddenly granted silent permission to hurt her, I smiled. 'I've got a delivery for you.'

She glanced at the box and held out her hands for it. 'Thanks.'

I kept hold of it. 'I need you to sign.' I shrugged amiably. 'The company insists. I've lost my pen though – at my last drop-off, the guy kept it. Can you believe it?' I shook my head. 'I didn't realise until I was halfway here. Honestly, you have no idea how many pens I go through in a month.'

Fake Eve stared at me. 'That … sucks,' she said finally.

'Yeah,' I agreed. 'But I can't leave without a signature. Do you have a pen inside?'

Her eyes shifted. I reckoned she was debating between her desire to say no and get rid of me as quickly as possible and her curiosity about what goodies she could nick from Eve's delivery. Fortunately, the latter won. 'Give me a minute.'

I beamed. 'Great.' Without giving her time to close the door on me, I barged past her. Everything inside looked okay. I cast around surreptitiously for Harold but he was nowhere to be seen.

'Wait here,' Fake Eve muttered, obviously annoyed that I'd gained entry.

Before she could turn away, a male voice called out from the living room. 'Who was it?'

'It's just a delivery, darling.' Her voice was strained.

Her partner-in-crime appeared at the open living-room doorway. He was dressed in a similarly casual fashion but he looked like someone who took life far too seriously. Although he was probably only a few years older than me, his face was lined; there was a deep cleft running from his forehead to the top of his nose that suggested he spent his days wandering around and glowering at everyone he met. When he saw me standing there, he definitely wasn't any happier.

Fake Eve pointed at the box I was still holding. 'I need a pen to sign for the delivery.'

He grunted and turned away. 'I think there's one in here. Wait a minute.'

There was a blur of movement and Harold's furry shape leapt out of the room, claws scratching Eve's wooden floor in his haste to escape.

'Your cat,' I began.

'It's fine,' Fake Eve said. 'She always does that. She'll come back when she's hungry.'

I cocked my head. 'She? It looked like a male to me.'

Something flickered in her expression. 'Force of habit. My last cat was a girl.'

Her companion re-emerged, holding a pen. I was now fairly certain that the two of them were alone. Things could have been worse. 'Here. What do you need me to sign?'

'Your arrest warrant,' I said pleasantly.

It took a moment for my words to sink in. Fake Eve reacted first, leaping towards me, but I was already thrusting the box in her direction and she staggered backwards.

The man lunged for me, his panic causing him to throw a punch in my direction rather than attempt a spell. I saw it coming a mile off and sidestepped neatly, just as Fake Eve dropped the box and began to draw out a rune. Recognising it as one designed to break my bones, I launched myself towards the man, knocking him sideways so he crashed into Fake Eve and interrupted her spell. I got lucky: she stumbled, tripped against the low coffee table and fell to the floor with a heavy thump. Her partner just avoided being brought down with her and threw himself at me again.

It occurred to me belatedly that confronting these two had been a mistake. Harold was safe now and I wasn't exactly a kung fu expert. Two against one hardly seemed fair. Fake Eve was already getting up, albeit rather slowly, and I didn't rate my chances. Pretending not to understand Brutus would have been the sensible move but it was far too late now.

The man grabbed hold of me. I writhed, spinning round so that my back was against his. His grip was painfully strong and I didn't have the strength to break free so I raised my foot and smashed it down onto his. He yelped and released me.

I darted away, breathing hard. Think, Ivy, I told myself. Just think.

I reached out blindly, my fingers curling round a glass paperweight holding down a neat stack of Eve's bills. I raised it and threw it hard at the man who was advancing on me yet again. It smacked into the side of his head with a sickening crack. For a brief moment he looked stunned and then he keeled over, falling face down on the floor. Arse. I hoped I'd not killed him.

'You little…' Fake Eve hissed. 'Who the hell are you?'

I'd have answered her if I'd still had the energy to speak. Unfortunately, I was so focused on her face and her words that I hadn't noticed her hand by her side, already finishing another rune. This time I was too late to do anything about it. The only saving grace was that this time she'd opted for a less violent rune. Rather than being left limbless, I was thrown backwards, ending up pinned against the far wall, my feet dangling about a foot above the floor. I could barely blink, let alone do anything to defend myself.

'I'll say it again,' Fake Eve said, with a furious toss of her head. 'Who are you?'

My lips moved but no sound came out. She laughed at me. 'Can't talk, can you?' There was a definite sneer to her voice. That really bugged me.

She might have been a talented witch but she didn't know everything. As she patted me down, looking for some kind of identification in my pockets, she didn't realise that I was still able – just – to move my thumbs. What most witches don't know is that having opposable thumbs isn't only handy for fashioning tools. It can also be very helpful for magic. It is generally believed that performing runes requires at least four fingers and a thumb.

I smiled smugly to myself. The Order don't know everything. I'd been literally twiddling my thumbs one afternoon when I discovered entirely the opposite.

Using swift surreptitious movements to avoid alerting her, I twirled one thumb and sketched out a brief figure of eight with the other. It was hardly elegant and wouldn't win me any prizes in a magic competition but it served my needs very well. Drawing in the magic that Fake Eve had used against me, I pulled the energy together and flung it back at her. As I fell to the floor, finally released from the invisible force that was holding me up, she was slammed back into the window and glued there spread-eagled like a squashed fly. Ha! Take that, witchy woman!

I limped over to the man and bent down to check him. He was still breathing. That was something, at least. I ran my hands over his body, unable to see any broken bones. Pursing my lips, I went into the kitchen to find something to tie them up with. Eventually I came across a long extension cord in one of Eve's drawers. Struggling against the man's weight, I heaved him into a sitting position and wrapped the cord round his wrists. Fake Eve glared at me the entire time but I ignored her. Her turn would come. I fashioned a gag for the man out of a dishcloth and added a few magical flourishes in case he happened to be Houdini and could wriggle his way free. Then I pulled off Eve's curtain ties and stood in front of the woman. Her eyes spat fire.

'Three,' I said, watching her carefully. 'Two. One.' Nothing happened. I'd mistimed it. A second later, the spell wore off and she slumped to the floor. I reached down swiftly before she could react and looped the ties round her wrists and her feet, ensuring that the magic encircling her was even stronger than it was for her partner. Then I dragged her over to him so they were back to back.

By the time I'd found a suitable gag to keep Fake Eve quiet, the man was coming around. He blinked his eyes, patently confused for a few seconds. Then he turned his head and caught sight of me grinning at him. He seemed even more astonished than I was that I'd bested the pair of them.

I eyed the hapless duo. Burglars taking advantage of a temporarily empty property were one thing – but these witches were something else entirely. I hunkered down until I was eye to eye with the man. 'Who are you?' I asked softly.

He struggled against his bonds. 'Mmmph.'

I dismissed his attempt at an answer. 'Don't worry,' I told him airily. 'I'll find out.' I reached inside his jacket and pulled out his wallet. There, for all the world to see, was his Order ID card. 'Matthew Bell End.'

'Mmmph!'

'Oh, I'm sorry. Matthew Bellham.' I grinned. 'Easy mistake to make.' I placed my fingers under his chin and forced him to look at me. 'Now why is the Order breaking into the flat of one of their own?'

He pressed his lips together and looked away.

'Ve haf vays of making you talk,' I said, with what I hoped was a menacing air.

Unfortunately, he called my bluff. 'Go on, then.'

I leant back and examined him. The frown line in his forehead was growing more pronounced by the second. He wasn't scared but he was concerned. I rubbed my chin, stood up and went over to his partner. I patted her down, looking for identification. Clearly, she was a bit smarter than frowny Matt as she didn't carry anything with her name on it. She did, however, have five carefully separated ziplock bags of dried herbs: rosemary, bakuli pods, tansy, sweetpea and something unidentifiable. I opened the bag and took a careful sniff before recoiling. Yeuch. That was pungent.

Yanking down her gag, I asked, 'What are these for?'

'I'm a keen cook.'

'Really.'

'Yeah,' she sneered. 'Really.'

I tossed the bags to the side. Whatever spell she'd been planning, it was obviously dubious. I'd look it up later. I could only surmise that it was designed to harm Eve in some way – and that made me very pissed off. 'Who are you?' I demanded. 'Are you with the Order too?'

'What's it to you?' she snarled, meeting aggression with aggression. 'Who the hell are you anyway?'

This woman was all fire and brimstone. No doubt she was smarting at being taken down by someone half her size. Deciding to try a different approach, I pasted on a wide-mouthed smile. 'I'm Ivy,' I beamed. 'Pleased to meet you.'

She rolled her eyes. 'Let us go. You'll be sorry if you don't.'

I was already sorry. Goodness only knew what I was going to do with this pair. There were spells I could use to encourage verbosity and elicit the truth about why they were here but they took time to prepare and I didn't have the right herbs. I doubted Eve had them hanging around her flat either. Those kind of things were generally only used by Third Level Order geeks because their inherent danger precluded all but the most skilled from not leaving their subjects as drooling vegetables. Civilised society tended to frown upon such actions.

I could call the police and let them deal with the problem but they'd probably pass the couple over to the Order. And until I knew why the Order had sent them in the first place, or whether they were working alone, I wasn't going to trust any witch, from the Ipsissimus to Adeptus Exemptus Winter to the newest Neophyte.

I left them where they were and wandered out of Eve's flat into the corridor. Harold was at the far end, his pupils dilated and his hackles still raised. 'I know,' I soothed. 'But you don't need to worry. The nasty people are all tied up and won't hurt you.'

He didn't even blink.

'I don't know who they are,' I continued. 'But until I do, I don't want them to get away. Eve wouldn't want them to get away.' I raised my eyebrows pointedly. 'They might have hurt her.' Harold just stared at me. 'It would be fabulous if you could stay inside and keep an eye on them. Only for a day or two.' I paused. 'For Eve.'

His nose twitched. For a moment it was touch and go whether he'd turn tail and run or do as I asked. Fortunately, he chose the latter and padded slowly towards me. He slunk back inside, hissed once in the burglars' direction and settled down on a nearby cushion.

I clapped my hands. 'Perfect.' With Harold watching them, I'd have the time to work out what to do with them. Alternatively, someone else might come looking for them and I'd get a better idea of who they were. I grinned. Delegation was a wonderful thing.

CHAPTER SIX

IT WAS THE LOUD THUMPING WHICH EVENTUALLY WOKE ME. I blearily opened my eyes and realised I was still on the sofa. A trail of drool drooped from the corner of my mouth to the cushion next to my head and my neck was aching.

I hauled myself up and rubbed my eyes. It was still dark so there was no earthly reason why anyone would be at my door – unless it was the police wanting to know why I'd tied up two people and was keeping them hostage in my neighbour's flat.

Yawning and squinting, I pulled the duvet round me and went to unfasten the lock. Winter was standing there with a glower on his face. He looked immaculate, without a hair out of place. Irritatingly, he was also wide-awake and raring to go. 'Come on,' he snapped. 'We need to leave.'

I stared at him.

'What's the matter?' he enquired. 'Have you lost the ability to speak?'

'My brain doesn't compute the words that are coming out of your mouth,' I told him, wiping the side of my face to rid myself of the worst of my saliva.

'I'm speaking English,' he said icily.

'You said to meet you at dawn. It's still dark.'

He gazed at me as if I were mad. I was starting to think I might be. Maybe this was a hallucination. I poked him in the chest to double check that he really was there. Bloody hell, his body felt rock hard.

'What are you doing?'

'Just checking,' I mumbled. 'I hoped you were a figment of my imagination.'

'Clearly I am not.'

'Clearly.' I turned on my heel, leaving him where he was, and stumbled into my bedroom. I flopped onto the bed and heaved my duvet over me. I had barely a moment's grace, however.

'Get up,' he ordered from somewhere overhead.

'Go away.'

'It is time to get moving. I didn't say I'd meet you at dawn, I said we were starting in the gym at dawn. If I left you to your own devices, you'd show up several hours late. This way, by the time we get there the sun will be rising and we'll be bang on time.'

Not only was he an early morning freak, it also appeared he was Mister Pedantic. I didn't even bother answering. I needed more sleep. A moment later, I heard his footsteps as he walked away. Excellent. Normal people did not wake up at this hour. Winter needed to realise that I wasn't going to be pushed around. I sighed happily and snuggled further in. Then the duvet was whipped off and something very wet and very cold splashed across my face.

'What the—' I sat up, spluttering. It happened again. Coughing and choking, I leapt out of bed towards him, droplets of water flying everywhere. 'What the hell do you think you're doing?'

'You've got ten minutes,' he said shortly, placing the now empty glass of water on the bedside table. 'Then we are leaving.'

'This is my house!' I howled. 'Who do you think you are?'

'Our work is very serious. We could be given an assignment at any moment, Ms Wilde. We need to be ready.'

I drew myself up, thoroughly pissed off. 'It's not *our* work. It's *your* work. I'm the one saving your skin by helping out, so I think it's time you showed me some respect. You can't barge into my home and chuck cold water all over me just because you're a sado-masochistic bastard with a hard-on for self-flagellation. This is assault!'

A muscle jerked in his jaw. 'I think you're taking things too far. You're hardly in any pain.'

'What about psychological damage?'

'At this rate, I'm the one who's going to be psychologically damaged from our relationship. Besides,' he added with the faintest touch of smugness, 'you're now obviously wide-awake. Change your clothes and let's get a move on.'

It was on the tip of my tongue to tell him to go shove it. If my bed hadn't been soaking wet and my neck hadn't hurt from crashing out on the sofa, I probably would have done but I could hardly go back to sleep now. Instead I counted to ten and crossed my arms. 'You can't treat me like this,' I told him, forcing myself to breathe deeply and calm down. 'I'm not in the Order. I'm not your minion. You know very well I'm doing you a favour by helping you out.'

His expression shuttered. Maybe, just maybe, he was starting to realise the error of his ways. 'Would you have made it to the Order gym by dawn if I weren't here?'

'I might have.'

Winter all but laughed in my face. 'If I wasn't here, you'd sleep for the next three hours. This is the best time to be awake. Your body is at its optimum energy levels. The earlier in the day we train, the faster we can accelerate your progress.'

I held up my hand to stall his pointless excuses. 'Neither of us wants to be in this situation but I understand we have to make the best of it until the binding can be removed. But I'm not an army grunt and you know this will go much better if we can get along. You seem to have decided that everything will fall apart unless you chivvy me along all the time. We've not even started working together yet and I'm already beginning to hate you. If you want to drag me around kicking and screaming everywhere you go, you're going about it the right way. If you want my cooperation and help then you're going to have to change. Maybe I would have made it to the gym by dawn, maybe I wouldn't. But you decided I was going to fail before I even had the chance to try.'

For a moment I wasn't sure if he was going to magic up another glass of water to douse me with, or yell at me to give him ten for daring to challenge his authority. He drew in a breath and met my eyes. 'You are right. I apologise for jumping to conclusions and for throwing water over you. It was ungentlemanly of me and unprofessional.'

My mouth almost fell open. As impressive as my speech had been at this time of the morning, it was obvious I'd never have made it to the stupid gym. And the last thing I'd expected Winter to do was apologise. 'Well, then,' I blustered. 'That's settled.'

He nodded once. 'How did you know?' he asked.

'Know what?'

'About my military background.'

I coughed. I really didn't want him to know I'd been checking up on him. 'It was a guess. You look the type.'

He watched me. 'I never enlisted but my father is an officer. I grew up surrounded by the army and sometimes I forget how different civilian life can be.'

I sniffed. 'I get it.'

'Tell me again if I overstep the mark.'

This was going much better than I expected. I snapped out a sloppy salute. 'Yes, sir!'

Winter's eyes glittered and he leant towards me. 'Oh, but Ivy?'

'Mm?'

'This doesn't make me a soft touch. Our job is vital and I won't let anything compromise the security of the Order or of this country. You will train and you will work and you won't necessarily enjoy either.'

I registered the sincerity of his gaze. He truly loved his job and I felt uncomfortably that he very much had my measure. He'd realised that the stick approach wasn't going to work. His proffered carrot, however, was laced with tempered steel. Despite backing down, Raphael Winter was no pushover.

'Gotcha.' I thought of Eve's burglars – not to mention Harold who was probably getting hungry by now. I should probably check on them all. I grinned at Winter. 'Give me fifteen minutes and then I'll meet you downstairs.'

'Ten minutes.'

Arse.

IF I'D THOUGHT that other people believed this was too early to be out and about, I'd forgotten about the zeal of the Order members. Even though Winter and I arrived barely after dawn, the gym was still half full. Judging by the sweat on some of the faces around us, there were witches here who'd been working out for hours.

'Treadmill,' Winter barked. 'We'll start with a comfortable jog to warm you up.'

Horror settled in my bones. Since when was a jog ever comfortable? A slow stroll perhaps, preferably in broad sunshine with an ice-cream in my hand. Before I could begin to suggest we started more sedately, he shoved me onto a machine and started jabbing the buttons. 'Hey!' I protested. 'That's too fast!'

'It's barely a walk.'

'But…'

He glared. 'Continue complaining and I'll increase the speed.'

I gritted my teeth. 'I don't see,' I said, already beginning to pant, 'how jogging is going to make me a better witch.'

'How will you run down a suspect if you can't run?' Winter retorted.

The last thing I planned on doing was running anywhere. 'I'll zap him between the ears to stop him.'

'A good Order witch never relies on magic alone,' he chided.

I'd have reminded him that I wasn't a good Order witch but it was impossible to talk. I found it difficult to believe that people did this kind of thing for fun. It didn't help that, every minute or so, Winter increased the speed. In the mirror opposite I saw my face growing redder and redder. I was fairly certain I was about to have an aneurysm when he gave me a break and stopped the treadmill.

'Thank the heavens,' I wheezed. 'Can I take a shower now?'

There was a glint of amusement in his eyes. 'We've not even finished the warm-up yet.'

'I hate you.'

He smiled. 'You must have come here when you were a Neophyte.'

I like to think I had more sense. 'I was busy,' I said shortly, as he directed me to some terrifying contraption with heavy weights attached to its back.

'Cheating?' he asked mildly.

I grunted. 'Amongst other things.' I felt Winter's cool eyes on me and changed the subject. 'What does this do? It looks like some ancient torture device.'

'It will help your upper arm strength. You'll love it.'

Somehow I doubted that.

Winter adjusted the weight and corrected my posture. 'We'll start with ten reps,' he told me.

I began to lift. Ten? I'd be lucky to manage two. 'I need water,' I told him.

He flicked me a frustrated look. 'You didn't bring a water bottle?'

'I didn't have time.'

He sighed, as if all this were a great imposition. He should put himself in my shoes. 'Fine,' he said. 'Wait here.'

'Where else am I going to go?' He threw me a narrow look and I smiled sunnily. 'Thank you, Adeptus Exemptus Winter. You're *the best.*'

'Don't push it,' he growled.

I smirked. As soon as he turned away, I got to work. I reached back, focusing on the weights. This was a series of runes I'd used on many occasions. I hated lugging customers' bags in and out of the taxi, especially when they had heavy suitcases. Some people expected it; some demanded it because they enjoyed watching a girl heave their stuff around. There was a simple way around it. By the time Winter returned with a cup of water, I was all set to go.

I took the cup from him, drained it and smacked my lips. 'Thanks!'

'You're welcome,' he murmured. His eyes were suspicious. I'd have to give an Oscar-worthy performance.

'Ten reps?' I asked. 'You don't think maybe we should start with less?'

'Make it twelve.'

'Hey!'

He shrugged. 'Every time you complain, I'm going to add more.'

'Well, that sucks,' I muttered. At least I'd deflected his attention from the weights.

'Be careful with your breathing,' Winter instructed.

'Mm'kay,' I heaved, trying to look as if I were really struggling.

'Those weights aren't that heavy. You're not that weak.'

He was right; the weights weren't heavy at all. 'Says the man with muscles that Popeye would envy,' I muttered. I had to be careful not to overdo the straining or he'd get suspicious.

'Keep up remarks like that,' Winter told me, 'and all you'll get for lunch is boiled spinach. I got these muscles by working for them. You can do the same.'

Yeah, yeah. I glared; I also shut up. With the facial expression of someone in pain, I lifted ten times, clenching my jaw and holding my breath to make sure my cheeks stayed red. It might have looked as if I were giving it everything I'd got but it felt like I was lifting air. Ha! Take that, Mr Smarty Pants.

I couldn't cheat on every exercise. Some of the strange contortions he made me do were impossible to fake and sometimes he didn't look away long enough for me to cast a spell. All in all, though, it was a successful venture. Winter wasn't stupid; if he'd checked closely enough, he'd have worked out what I was up to. His trouble was that it didn't occur to him that I'd try to fake my way through getting fit.

I was lucky our binding would last only three months. I doubted Winter would fall for my tricks for long. But then, for all I knew I couldn't trust him any more than he could trust me. He may have had something to do with Bell End and his partner breaking into Eve's flat. They were all in the Order, after all.

Despite managing to fudge my way through most of the exercises, I was still exhausted by the end of them. My whole body was in agony.

Winter scratched his chin and cast a critical eye across my bedraggled and sweaty appearance. 'I was going to move onto sparring,' he said. 'But I think that's probably enough for today.'

'Great.' I was really looking forward to getting back home. I didn't even care if my sheets were still wet; right now I'd sleep almost anywhere.

'Take a quick shower,' Winter said. 'After that, we can hit the library.'

I went very still. 'Excuse me?'

'Why? What have you done?'

I glared at him. 'You know what I mean. Why do we need to go to the library?'

Honest-to-goodness surprise flickered in his eyes. 'So we can study.' Belatedly he seemed to understand what I was getting at and slowed his speech as if he were speaking to someone of very low intellect. 'The library is where books are kept. Books contain knowledge. If you read books, you can learn things.' Winter raised an eyebrow. 'You can read, right?'

I shook my head. 'Nope. Not a word. So there's no point going near any books.'

Winter remained deadpan. 'Hmm. In that case, we'll need to spend even more time in the library than I thought. We can begin with basic phonics.' Damn it. The corners of his mouth twitched. 'I'll teach you the alphabet song.'

'I hate singing.'

'It seems, Ms Wilde, that you hate everything and everyone unless it involves lounging around at home and doing nothing at all.'

I grinned. 'So now you understand why all this training is a waste of your time.'

He gazed at me with sapphire-hued promise. 'I don't fail, Ms Wilde. Ever. The Ipsissimus wants me to prove myself so that is what I will do.'

'I've told you before, my name is Ivy.' I put my hands on my hips. 'And failure is good. People who don't fail have no understanding of their own limits.'

Winter leant closer to me. 'People who don't succeed aren't trying.'

It was like talking to a brick wall. I suppose I should have been grateful that sometimes he showed glimpses of a sense of humour. I sighed. 'I'm going for that shower.'

'Fifteen minutes,' he called after me. 'Or I'll come in after you.'

That was too good to pass up. I turned round. 'You can come

now if you want. I'll soap your back. You can wash my hair. And then we can—'

'Shower, Ms Wilde,' Winter interrupted flatly. 'Now.'

Scratch that about his sense of humour. The man was no fun at all.

As before, Winter took off at tremendous speed. When it became clear that I wasn't going to sprint alongside him, he tutted loudly and slowed down to match my pace. I could tell it annoyed him from the way he kept clenching and unclenching his fists. This was fun.

'There are two main methods of performing magic,' he informed me.

'Casting runes and herblore.' I rolled my eyes. 'I'm not a complete idiot.'

'I never said you were. If you let me finish…'

I swept out a grandiose gesture. 'By all means.'

'Casting runes is effective for spells that need to be completed in a hurry. However, as I'm sure you know, First Level witches can only use basic runes to perform basic spells. Even Second and Third Level witches struggle to remember enough runes to act quickly and effectively under pressure.'

'So you're a herb lover, huh?'

'I use both types of magic equally,' he responded stiffly 'The point I was making, Ms Wilde, is that preparation is the key to magical success.' He glanced at me. 'How did you bespell speech upon your familiar?'

'You do realise that sometimes you speak like a Victorian, right?' Winter glared at me. I sighed and pushed back my damp hair. 'Runes.'

'So you did it when you were a Neophyte? You must have gained access to that knowledge through the library.'

'No,' I said distantly, focusing on a group of witches on the path ahead. 'I did that when I was around fifteen or sixteen.'

Winter stopped. 'You what?'

Too late, I realised what I'd said. 'Er … familiars live longer than common house cats,' I demurred, hoping to deflect his attention.

'If you were talented enough to achieve that at sixteen, then why would you feel the need to cheat a few years later?'

I shrugged awkwardly. 'Maybe I was too lazy to study.'

Winter's eyes narrowed. 'Indeed.'

I could tell him the truth; it was usually the easiest option and in any other circumstance that's what I'd have done. But I'd been down this road many times before and I knew he'd never believe me. Tarquin was too slick: I'd given up trying to tell the truth about my supposed cheating years ago. I'd railed and shouted and pleaded; it hadn't done me any good whatsoever and at some point I'd given up. It was too much effort to continually plead my innocence when the world thought otherwise. People believed what they wanted to. Whatever. It was their problem; not mine.

'It wasn't that big a deal,' I said. 'Really.'

'I consider myself a talented witch, Ms Wilde, but I'm not sure I could manage such a feat even now.'

'I got lucky,' I mumbled.

'There's no such thing as luck.'

It was my turn to stare in astonishment. Every witch I've met is superstitious. Hell, even I'm superstitious. *Of course* I'm superstitious – it comes with the territory. The last thing I'd pegged Winter for was a fortune sceptic. 'Four-leaf clovers?' I said.

He shrugged. 'Pretty plants.'

'Magpies?'

'They're just birds.'

'Itchy left palm?'

'Allergic reaction.'

I gaped. 'Half of what the Order believes in is rooted in super-stition.'

Winter looked at me. 'So?'

'I had you pegged as a full convert, worshipping at the knees of the Ipsissimus.'

'Oh, but I am,' he murmured, mockingly. 'But I don't blindly believe in nonsense.'

He could have fooled me. We started walking again. Winter was more of an enigma than I'd realised. We drew level with the group of witches, whose chatter immediately subsided in case I was in any doubt about what – or rather who – they were talking about. In their midst, Tarquin gazed at me and quirked an eyebrow. I blew him a kiss and kept on walking. As soon as we were past, the whispering started again.

'You know the way to stop all that?' Winter asked. His fingers brushed against the skin on the back of my hand and I felt a strange electric shock shiver through me.

I moved my hand. The whole lot of them could gossip and tattle all they liked. I didn't care. Much. 'How?'

He grinned. 'Succeed.'

CHAPTER SEVEN

THE LIBRARY WAS MUCH THE SAME AS I REMEMBERED. THE OLD rule about technology was still very much in place, with a total ban on anything that might hint at twenty-first-century know-how. Every so often some bright spark came up with a method to scan the old books onto a computer and, without fail, every time they tried the ink on the original pages vanished forever.

It is one of the reasons witch haters give for their ardent anti-magic protests: that the Order are antiquated and have no place in today's society. Sometimes I wonder if they have a point.

Nothing in the library building ever seemed to change. Even the smell was the same – that memorable aroma of ink and vellum and leather. Sure, some of the more dangerous books were bound in human skin and the like and rumour had it that some of the Cypher pages were written in blood. Most of what was here, however, was paper. The only thing the librarians seemed to fear more than mobile phones was fire.

Winter directed me to a study carrel that reeked of stale mari-juana. I was happy to wait while he ventured out to get me the books I was apparently required to read in order to be deemed good enough to work alongside him. I kicked off my shoes and leant back in the chair. Catnaps are good for the soul. Unfortunately, as seemed to be my lot these days, my opportunity for twenty winks was interrupted by yelling. A lot of yelling.

A few minutes later, Winter burst back in. 'Training is over,' he said.

I jumped up and clapped my hands. 'Excellent! You mean I'm free? I can go home?'

'Don't be ridiculous. It means we have an assignment.' Compared to his usual demeanour, he seemed positively aglow.

'Oh goody.'

Winter noted my lack of enthusiasm. 'We can go back to the gym if you prefer.' He flung a pile of books at me. 'And you still need to read those.'

'Gee, thanks.' I left the books where they were. 'What's the assignment?'

'The sceptre belonging to the Ipsissimus was on display up on the third floor,' he told me. 'It's been stolen.'

'Someone stole a big stick?' Who cared?

'A big gold stick encrusted with rubies and diamonds,' Winter said.

Oh. Okay then. 'Lead the way.'

Winter turned to leave. 'Bring the books, Ivy.'

'They're heavy. I'll fetch them later.'

'Be sure that you do.'

I was tempted to stick out my tongue at him. 'Do you ever get out?'

'Out?'

I waved my hands around. 'You know. To a pub? Or a party? Maybe even just to the cinema?'

He gave me a look as if to ask why on earth he would ever want to. Then he marched off, leaving me to follow in his wake.

There was still a lot of yelling going on. Perhaps the sceptre was sentient and the librarians thought that shouting and screaming would encourage it to return to its rightful place. One particular red robe went past us, his arms flapping and his robe billowing out so that I wondered whether he was about to take off and fly around the room. No witch had ever managed to fly before – not that many of us over the centuries hadn't tried – but this guy was making a good stab at it.

I caught up to Winter and nudged him. 'What's the big deal? I get that the sceptre thingy is probably worth a lot of money but this amount of panic is ridiculous.'

He glanced at me. 'You really didn't pay any attention when you were here as a Neophyte, did you? Objects belonging to the Order, especially valuable important objects, do not just go missing.'

Oh please. 'Why ever not? You can't tell me that no one's ever attempted to boost anything.' I waved an arm. 'Anyone could waltz in and take what they wanted. Non-witches who are criminally inclined aren't so intimidated by the Order that they wouldn't try to nick something. And if you're trying to suggest that Order members are too noble or worthy to stoop to stealing, then you're a naïve fool.'

His jaw clenched. 'You are treading in dangerous waters, Ms Wilde.'

Apparently so. He'd just started calling me Ivy and now we were back to the Ms business. 'If the shoe fits, Adeptus Exemptus Winter…'

His glare intensified. 'Most people know better than to insult me.'

I stopped walking and looked around, a confused expression on my face.

'What is it?' he ground out.

'I was just checking,' I told him airily.

'Checking what?'

'To see whether I was in a school playground rather than a library. I didn't insult you. I said that if you think the Order witches are too good to steal then you'd be a fool. I didn't say you *were* a fool. There's a vast difference. Besides, I'm only trying to understand.'

Winter muttered something then took a deep breath. 'You seem intent on testing my patience to its limits. One minute you are almost tolerable, the next I want to throttle you.'

'Most people feel that way about me,' I said cheerfully. 'But cough up the answer. I still don't get the panic.'

'Nobody believes that Order members are above reproach. After all, some of them are even prepared to cheat and assault their fellows.' Touché. 'And,' he continued, 'we are well aware that certain elements of society may wish to steal some of our more valuable items. That is why there are heavy protective wards in place to prevent thefts.'

I shrugged. 'No ward is infallible.' Some took more time and effort to break than others but where there was a will there was usually a way. Or so I'd heard.

He pushed back his hair. 'This library is vital to the Order. Many of the objects and books contained within its walls are highly volatile. I can assure you, Ms Wilde, that the wards surrounding this building are as strong as you'll find anywhere.'

'So what you're saying is that to steal the sceptre, you'd have to be a very powerful witch.'

Winter nodded grimly. 'Third Level or beyond. In fact, to take it out of the library without anyone noticing, they'd have to be one of the strongest witches we've ever seen.'

I absorbed this. 'Fair enough. At least that narrows down the list of suspects. Let's examine the crime scene, solve the crime and then we can break for afternoon tea.'

He frowned. 'Leave the investigations to me. You're an amateur and I'm the professional.'

While I didn't object to Winter doing all the work, I was still needled. 'I thought we were supposed to work in tandem?'

'As long as you're with me, the binding will be satisfied,' he said shortly. 'If you pay enough attention, you might learn something. Now let's get moving.'

'Yessir, Adeptus Exemptus Winter.' I crossed my fingers and hoped he was good at his job so the sceptre was recovered quickly. More to the point, then I could finally go back home. I did, after all, still have Eve's burglars to deal with. And *Enchantment* was on TV tonight.

THE THIRD FLOOR WAS BUSY. Most people were standing around and staring at the sceptre's empty display box. I'd seen enough episodes of *CSI* to know that these onlookers would be doing little more than contaminating the scene but Winter had made it pretty clear what my role was in all of this, so I kept my mouth buttoned shut.

'What are all these people doing here?' he barked. 'We need this area clear so that we don't lose any evidence.' Maybe he'd seen the same episodes I had.

'Come on everyone,' a nervous-looking red robe said. 'You need to vacate the area.' Unfortunately his voice was so quiet and lacking in authority that no one paid him any attention. He tried again. 'Everyone downstairs.'

For goodness' sake. 'Oi!' I yelled. Every face turned towards me, some pale and in shock, others merely confused. That was more like it. 'Everyone clear out! No one leaves the building until your details have been noted or you've been questioned.'

There was a dissenting murmur from several of the onlookers but they did as I asked, shuffling downstairs no doubt to congregate and gossip about the culprit. The librarian gave me a grateful nod while Winter raised an eyebrow. I shrugged. 'The sooner you investigate and solve this crime, Sherlock, the sooner we can leave.'

He looked like he was about to say something then thought

better of it and turned his attention to the display cabinet. As I watched, he circled round it a few times before pursing his lips and beckoning over the hapless librarian. 'Talk me through the wards,' he grunted.

The librarian's Adam's apple bobbed nervously. 'Well, you see, er, there's, um…'

Winter was obviously growing impatient. He tapped his foot and glared at the man. No wonder he was nervous. We'd be here all day at this rate. I stepped up. 'What's your name?' I asked softly.

'Philip. Philip Maidmont.'

'And you're a librarian here?' I questioned, ignoring Winter's frosty demeanour.

'Yes. Four years now. I'm Practicus but I never managed to proceed to Philosophus.'

'Those exams are a bugger.'

He tittered slightly. 'Yes, yes, they are.'

I ignored the question in his eyes about what level I was at and gently touched his arm. 'Philip, can you tell us what wards were in place around the case?'

His eyes widened. 'Oh, the very strongest. The Ipsissimus himself put them in place.'

'When did that happen?'

'After the swearing-in ceremony for last year's Third Level witches.'

I calculated: that would have been during the Winter Solstice, which was almost five months ago. The Order liked using auspicious dates to add to the pomp and circumstance of their ceremonies. 'And no one's opened it since then?'

'No, of course not.'

'Thank you, Ms Wilde,' Winter interrupted tautly. He focused on Maidmont. 'When was the last time you saw the sceptre?'

Maidmont swallowed again, his eyes shifting nervously as if Winter were accusing him of stealing the damn thing. This time, at least, he held it together to answer. 'Last night. I did the final rounds around ten o'clock.'

'Bloody hell!'

Both Winter and Maidmont turned to me. 'What is it?'

'The library closes at ten?'

Maidmont nodded.

'You have a thought, Ms Wilde?' Winter asked.

'I'm having several thoughts, Adeptus Exemptus Winter,' I returned. 'Who in their right mind is studying at ten o'clock at night? Clearly, they're several sandwiches short of a picnic.'

Winter's blue eyes filled with exasperation. 'You have the logbooks?' he asked Maidmont.

'Yes, yes, I'll get them for you. But everyone left.' He shot me a look. 'I made sure of it.'

'Just get us the books,' Winter demanded.

Maidmont half bowed and half curtsied, as if he couldn't make up his mind how to treat either of us, then skedaddled downstairs.

'You are not exactly helping,' Winter informed me.

I crossed my arms. 'I think I'm helping a lot. That poor man would still be trying to answer your first question if I hadn't stepped in. Softly, softly catchee monkey.' I shook my head. 'Getting things done quickly takes a gentle approach sometimes.'

A muscle throbbed in his cheek. 'I'm not interested in getting things done quickly, Ms Wilde. I'm interested in getting them done right. Now stay quiet and let me do my job.'

I rolled my eyes. Fine. I leant back against the nearest wall and let Winter go to it. Idiot man.

He withdrew a stick from the inside pocket of his jacket. It was similar to a chopstick in length, maybe a few inches longer. I stared at it then snickered. Was that supposed to be a magic wand? Winter ignored me. Using the wandy chopstick, he probed the display case. The moment the tip touched the glass there was a faint hissing sound and the stick turned green around the edges. It didn't take a Second Level genius to realise that vestiges of the original ward were still in place. All the same, as far as I could tell the sceptre had been lifted right out of the case with incredible ease. Some ward.

Winter poked around a little longer and then made for the stairs. I was perfectly willing to watch him go but, when he was almost out of sight, he called in an irritating voice, 'Come on then, Ms Wilde. Get a move on!'

No. I understood he had a job to do and that he treated the loss of the sceptre as a particularly grave matter but that didn't give him the right to talk to me like that. Keeping quiet was one thing; acting like Winter's obedient shadow was something entirely different. I dug in my heels and didn't move.

That was a good plan as far as I was concerned except that almost immediately the skin on my arms began to tingle, and not in a good way. I pulled up my sleeve. I was covered in goose-bumps, each hair standing on end. And I appeared to be turning a dangerous shade of purple. The tingling wasn't just painful; it was also bloody itchy. I stared after Winter. Was this because of him? Had he cast a damn spell on me?

I pushed myself off the wall and jogged after him. When I reached his shoulder, however, he merely grunted, ''Bout time. I thought you were in a rush to get this over and done with.'

I narrowed my eyes. He didn't seem to be carrying any herbs although he could well have cast a few runes. All the same, he wasn't acting any differently and my skin already seemed to be returning to normal.

'What's wrong?' he snapped. 'Is walking down a few stairs too much trouble for you now? Would you prefer to take the lift?'

It wasn't his doing then. No doubt it was a result of the binding. We might not have been far apart but the spell must have registered my intention to have nothing more to do with the investigation and reacted accordingly. That was … interesting.

Rather than admit to Winter what had happened, I deflected him. 'There's a lift?' I asked hopefully.

'Don't be ridiculous. This is a technology-free zone.' He continued downward.

I rubbed my arms and followed. Well, this was just shit. Apparently the binding was even tighter than I'd been led to believe. I suppose I should have been amused that the higher Level witches didn't trust Winter to work with someone else without enforced magic. If anyone else bore the brunt of this spell, it would have been funny. I was most definitely not laughing.

Winter strode down to the foot of the stairs and stopped. He took out his little stick and poked the air; this time it turned red.

'Abracadabra,' I muttered.

He didn't turn around. 'Go up and take a book from a shelf then come back down here.' I didn't move a muscle. He glanced over his shoulder. 'Didn't you hear me?'

I blinked. 'Oh, I'm sorry. Were you talking to me?' I clasped my chest. 'I thought I was just along for the ride and superfluous to your investigations. I'm just an amateur, after all.'

Winter's mouth tightened fractionally. I'd have hung around and waited for a 'please' except my skin began to tingle once more. 'Fine,' I snapped. 'Anything in particular?'

'Just get a book.'

I stomped back upstairs, swiped the nearest tome and stomped back down again, pausing only to read the spine. *Approaching Magic With Empathy. Volume Two.* Ha. Ha. Ha.

I thrust the book at Winter but he shook his head and pointed to the front doors leading to the outside world about twenty metres away. 'Take it outside.'

'Do you want to explain what this is about?'

He pinched off a headache. 'Ms Wilde, please just do it.'

I regarded him silently for a moment or two. 'You're wishing I'd been sent to jail now, right?'

He didn't answer. I shrugged and stepped forward, taking the book with me. Hot pain flashed through my body. 'Ow!' I yelped. 'What the hell?'

'Books have to be checked out at the desk before they can be moved beyond this point.'

'Well, why the hell didn't you say so? Are you trying to kill me now?'

The long look he gave me suggested great sufferance. 'The ward around the display cabinet had degraded so it would have been simple to break it. This ward is a different matter.'

The pain coursing through my veins confirmed that it was very much still in operation. 'So how did the thieves get past it?'

'I don't know.'

'How did they know that the first ward had degraded?'

'I don't know.'

'Do you know anything?'

Winter gritted his teeth. 'Investigations of this nature take time, Ms Wilde. There's no sudden eureka moment where all is revealed.' He paused. 'Return the book.'

I glanced back at the stairs. 'Sure,' I said casually. I lifted up one hand and sketched out a rune in the air then let go of the book. It floated upwards, making its way back to its original position.

'That was a waste of magic. The Order dislikes unnecessary and lazy spells.'

I clapped my hand over my mouth dramatically. 'Gee. If only I'd known.'

He sighed in irritation. 'Come on. There are more wards to test.'

Oh goody.

This time at least, Winter stepped up to the plate. He grabbed an old mixing bowl on display by the wall situated past the first pain-inducing ward. The card next to the bowl informed us that it was sixteenth century. A perverse part of me hoped Winter would inadvertently break it while trying to get it past the second invisible ward. All that happened, however, was a faint hiss emanating from under his breath as he tried to pass with the bowl in his hand. I peered more closely. It looked like his lips had turned a faint shade of blue.

'I think you should try again,' I suggested. 'You know, just to be sure.'

Winter carefully replaced the bowl on its stand. He didn't bother answering me this time; instead, he walked beyond the first two wards and glanced about for a suitable object to filch. I got bored watching him and headed to the front door, gazing at the people outside. They looked happy. The bastards.

Eventually Winter picked up a gold-tipped quill from a shelf. 'This will do,' he muttered. He threw it towards me.

I didn't even attempt to catch it; I simply stepped back and let it fall to the ground. I grinned. 'Oops.'

'Pick up the pen and try to take it through the front door,' he commanded.

I shook my head. 'No way.'

Winter smiled at me wolfishly. 'You won't get hurt. The final ward is ... different to the others.'

I really didn't like the sound of that. 'I'm still not doing it.' I ignored the prickle that ran across my skin again. This was becoming ridiculous. Winter could do it; it didn't have to be me.

'As I have to keep reminding you, Ms Wilde, I am in charge here. You will do as I say.'

'Yesterday you said I wouldn't have to do anything apart from follow you around. Less than a day later you seem intent on torturing me.'

He raised an eyebrow. 'I thought you wanted this done quickly.' He came over to me and picked up the quill. 'I'll do it. But I'm in no rush.'

I looked into his eyes. I had the impression that he'd happily hang around for hours before testing the ward, simply to make a point.

I muttered a curse under my breath and snatched the quill from him. 'Fine. When I'm convulsing on the floor, you'll be sorry.' I twisted round and headed for the door. I was barely three feet away when the most god-awful shrieking started up. It was less like an alarm and more like a pack of harpies surrounding me, intent on making my ears bleed. I clamped my hands over my ears and kept going. A moment later there was a whoosh and I was surrounded by ten-foot iron spikes that sprang from nowhere. I was well and truly trapped.

'All this for a damn quill?' I screamed.

Beyond the ring of spikes, Winter shrugged. 'Missing stationery accounts for a lot of the Order's budget. It's important to track every item to avoid unnecessary loss.' He turned away.

'Hey!'

Winter didn't miss a step.

I shouted louder. 'Hey! You need to let me out!'

'I can't. Only the librarians can release you. You'll need to wait.' He looked over his shoulder and smirked. 'Don't worry. Once I've questioned them all, I'll send one over to get you out. Look on the bright side. This way we get some peace from each other.'

The plonker. He'd done this deliberately. I kicked at the nearest spike; it didn't budge. I should have chosen prison. Anything would be better than this.

CHAPTER EIGHT

It took bloody Winter ages to send someone to rescue me. It got to the point where I tried to expend my own energy to break through the iron circle but the ward was far too strong. No matter what I threw at it, it stayed firmly put. I wasn't big-headed enough to believe that I could beat down any magic thrown in my path but I wasn't without ability. Whoever had got past this with the sceptre in their hand was definitely an incredibly powerful witch.

Philip Maidmont, who performed the spell to remove the spikes, wrung his hands together. 'The investigation isn't going at all well,' he confided. 'No one knows anything.'

'Whatever,' I snapped. I was no longer in the mood to be nice to him. He looked hurt for a second and I felt a surge of guilt but I pushed it away. He was a part of the damned Order just as much as the Ipsissimus and Winter and Tarquin and all the other geeks. And I was done with the lot of them. I spun round to leave the library. Nothing was worth this. No more Miss Nice Ivy.

Unfortunately for me, the binding spell had other ideas. 'God-damnit!' I yelled as my skin flared up in pain once more. Why the bejesus didn't Winter get these crappy side effects? Why was I the one who had to suffer? 'Where is he?' I ground out. 'Where is Winter?'

Wide-eyed, Maidmont raised a shaky finger and pointed to the right. I nodded. Enough was enough.

I marched through the library with the Wicked Witch theme music from *The Wizard of Oz* pounding through my head. I was done. I no longer cared what the consequences were. I slammed open the door to the room where Winter was questioning a pale-faced Neophyte.

'That will be all,' he said as I entered. 'Thank you for your time.'

I strode up to him and took a deep breath to prepare for my angry tirade. The Neophyte noted the look on my face and made a quick exit. Smart move.

'Good to see you again, Ms Wilde,' Winter said, before I could open my mouth. 'We need to get hold of bakuli pods, rosemary, tansy, sweetpea and aconite.'

For a moment, his words barely registered. When they did, I froze. 'Say that again,' I said slowly.

He ticked off his fingers. 'Bakuli pods. Rosemary. Tansy. Sweetpea. Aconite.'

I stared at him. With the exception of aconite, which I'd never heard of, I'd come across that combination very recently. 'Aconite?'

He nodded. 'It smells like death but it can be very potent.'

Bingo. 'And,' I said carefully, 'do you use these particular herbs often?'

Winter pursed his lips. 'On occasion. They can be useful.'

'Useful for what?'

'Are you suddenly taking an interest in the investigation?' he enquired.

'Just answer the question.'

Rather than being offended by my manner, Winter appeared curious. 'What is it?'

I wasn't prepared to answer him. Not now he'd become a very real suspect in Eve's burglary. If it was a burglary; I was starting to wonder if the incursion was something far more nefarious. 'What are the herbs for?' I repeated.

His blue eyes were thoughtful. 'It's easier to show you than tell you.' He continued to watch me. He obviously knew something was up but he wasn't sure what. He was probably also wondering why I wasn't screaming blue murder at him for trapping me downstairs. Right now, however, the herbal coincidence seemed far more important.

'Great,' I said. 'Show me.'

BY THE TIME someone brought us the herbs, it was growing dark outside. Even on my longest taxi-driving days I'd never spent this much time away from home. I stifled a yawn. It didn't help that Winter still seemed to possess boundless energy. He strode around the library floor, barking orders and making notes. He managed to question and release everyone who'd been present that morning and had made appointments to talk to the others from Maidmont's logbooks who had been studying last night. It made me tired just watching him.

Truth be told, I found it hard to imagine he'd had anything to do with masterminding the break-in at Eve's. For one thing he was far too upright and focused on the Order. For another, it didn't make any sense. But I didn't like the coincidence and I wanted to know what those damned herbs were for.

I already felt guilty enough that I'd taken Eve's coveted spot. I might not want it but that didn't mean she wouldn't be devastated. If I could figure out what Bell End and his partner had been doing in her flat, at least I'd have something to offer her.

'So Herb Master,' I intoned. 'Let me see a demonstration of your powers.'

Winter's eyes narrowed, as if he weren't sure whether I was taking the piss or being deadly serious. 'It's important,' he said stiffly, 'to pay attention to both the order and the amount of herbs which are used. Different quantities can have different effects.' Damn. 'For these purposes, we begin with one part rosemary added to three parts sweetpea.'

I watched as he measured them into a small cast-iron bowl. I wasn't the only one fascinated by his actions: Maidmont and several of the other librarians also gathered round. If having such a rapt audience disturbed Winter, he didn't let it show.

'Next, you add a pinch of aconite.' Using his forefinger and thumb, Winter added a small amount of the pungent herb. I recoiled from the stench; the others drew nearer. 'Then,' he continued, 'one part tansy and four bakuli pods.'

I waited three beats. Nothing happened. 'Well, it's hardly dramatic, is it?'

'Hush,' Winter commanded. 'You are far too impatient for your own good.' He took a long-stemmed spoon, held it up towards the display cabinet and gently blew. The combination of herbs scattered across the empty glass frame. 'Everyone stand back.'

The group of librarians leapt about three feet in the air, clearing a large space around the cabinet. 'There,' Maidmont breathed.

I twisted round. He was right. A shadowy figure edged up. His features weren't clear and his body was a barely visible facsimile rather than anything solid. He was, however, definitely male.

'What is this?' I asked, fascinated despite myself.

'It's a shadow of what's gone past,' Winter murmured.

'So this is the guy who took the sceptre?' As I spoke, the figure hunkered down by the cabinet and ran sausage-like fingers around its rim, as if searching for weaknesses. He turned away, his lips moving. Winter cursed as he vanished from sight.

'What?' I asked. 'Where did he go?'

Winter folded his arms across his broad chest and glowered. 'He's vanished. He cast a spell to stop himself from being tracked like this. That means only one thing: the thief is definitely from the Order.' There was a harsh note in his voice, as if he were personally hurt that a fellow Order witch would stoop to such an act.

'So that's it?' I cocked my head, disbelievingly. 'We've waited for two hours to get a bunch of herbs together which told us nothing more than that there's one of them and he's a male witch.' I threw my hands up in the air. 'What a waste of time. Can't your herbs counter their runes?'

'Obviously not,' Winter said grimly. 'And just because we can only see one doesn't mean there is only one.'

'There must be some other way of—'

'Ms Wilde! Enough of this.'

I sighed. He really was very upset. 'Okay, okay.' I paused. The thought that Eve's two intruders had cast this very same spell to see what she'd been up to in her flat was creepy as hell. It was like the witchy version of a secret camera. 'What happens if you use the same herbs but with different amounts?' I enquired.

'It's not going to change anything,' Winter replied stiffly. 'We won't see any more than we just have.'

'Humour me.'

Maidmont answered for him. 'If you add more aconite and use it as the last ingredient, you can see future actions.'

I blinked. 'You can tell the future?'

'Even in its strongest form and applied by the most talented witch, it only shows you the next twelve minutes and it's hopelessly unreliable,' Winter said. 'If you saw yourself doing a jig in about six minutes' time, all you have to do is not do the jig and then you won't be jigging.'

His explanation was convoluted but I thought I understood. 'The future's not immutable, you mean.'

'Exactly.'

I pondered this. 'And are there any other applications? Any other uses?'

Again, it was Maidmont who answered. 'If you increase the number of bakuli pods then the herbs can be used to track people.'

'Track?'

Maidmont's expression was animated. He seemed to really enjoy playing the role of knowledge-giver. No wonder he was a librarian. 'If you can get close enough to someone to sprinkle some of the concoction onto them, you can use the remainder to follow where they go. It's similar to the breadcrumb theory but far more advanced. Naturally.'

'Naturally.'

Winter snorted. 'It's a stupid application. Any witch beyond Second Level can easily create long-term guards against such spells.'

'But, Adeptus Exemptus Winter,' I pointed out, 'not everyone is a witch.'

'If anyone is worried about being followed in this manner, all they need to do is pay the Order to ensure they are warded against such a spell.'

Assuming they knew it existed in the first place. Seeming to read my thoughts, Winter jumped in before I could argue my point. 'How do you know all this?' he asked Maidmont. 'This is higher Level magic.'

The librarian shrugged awkwardly and looked embarrassed. His librarian buddies also looked away, as if sharing in his apparent shame. Clearly Maidmont spent his free hours reading books that were normally off limits to lower Level witches. I suppose there had to be some benefits to lugging cartloads of books around all day long. The Order probably turned a blind eye to things like that. After all, it was one thing knowing such spells; it was quite another to have the ability to perform them. No doubt that was why they employed Level One librarians; even if they were curious enough to flip through the more complicated and dangerous spells, they wouldn't be able to do anything with them. The Order seniors could be sneakily clever when they wanted to be.

I filed all the information away for future use and got back to the matter in hand. 'Well, it's obvious who our main suspect is.' Everyone stared at me. I rolled my eyes. 'The ward spell around the display cabinet is degraded,' I reminded them. 'The Ipsissimus is the one who bespelled it in the first place. No one else would believe that they could steal the sceptre so easily. And very few others would have the know-how to bypass the other wards.'

Winter grew very still. 'You're accusing the Ipsissimus, the esteemed Order leader, of stealing his own sceptre?'

I shrugged. 'It's not really his sceptre, is it? It belongs to the Order. He only uses it for ceremonial occasions and then it gets passed along to the next Order Head when they take office.'

'You're an idiot,' Winter dismissed.

I pointed at him. 'Call me names all you like. You know there's a chance I'm right. I can see the doubt in your eyes.' Actually, I couldn't see anything beyond the brilliant blue of his irises but I liked to pretend I could read him like a book. I glanced at Maidmont. 'Would anyone expect the ward to be dissipated so quickly?'

He shook his head. 'No. Not at all.'

I smiled smugly. 'There you go. The Ipsissimus is the prime suspect.'

Winter glared at me. 'We are not interrogating the leader of our own Order!'

'Oh,' I said, the very picture of innocence. 'I thought you liked to make sure your investigations were done right. You know that getting through the three wards downstairs would take the skills of someone Third Level or above. I think the Ipsissimus falls into that category, don't you?' I paused. 'But if you're too scared of him or too intimidated to question him…'

Fire sparked in his eyes. 'I am not intimidated.'

'Sure. Whatever you say.'

Winter ground his teeth. 'Fine. I'll make an appointment to see him first thing tomorrow – but I will do the talking. You, Ms Wilde, will keep your mouth shut.'

I beamed. 'Brilliant. We should skip the gym tomorrow morning too.' I fluttered my eyelashes in a manner that I hoped was vaguely appealing. 'Now can we go home?'

CHAPTER NINE

I was unlocking my door when my phone started to ring. Hoping that it was Iqbal with information about how I could break the binding, I experienced a surge of energy and bolted in to answer it. I leapt for the handset, ignoring the puzzled look I received from Brutus at my uncharacteristic speed.

'Hey,' I said breathlessly. 'This is Ivy.'

'Ivy! How are you? How are things going?'

My heart sank. Eve. What the hell was I going to tell her? With any luck, someone had already been in touch and I wouldn't have to break the bad news that I'd effectively stolen her dream job. 'Things are … interesting,' I said, prevaricating. 'How about with you?'

She sighed. 'It's a real mess up here. First of all, the coven here didn't know I was coming. Secondly, they've got themselves into terrific trouble involving some frogspawn. Honestly, you really don't want to know the details. It's quite horrific.'

She was right; I really didn't want to know. 'Have you heard from the Order headquarters?' I asked, in an overly casual tone.

'Nothing.' She sounded put out. 'Given that I'm up here trying to sort out this mess alone, they should have been in touch. It's not normal for First Levels like me to complete this kind of assignment on their own.' She dropped her voice. 'I think it's a test. If I do well, they'll let me take the exam and proceed to Second Level. Or maybe it's to gain entry into Arcane Branch.'

I winced. 'Mmm.'

'Anyway, I can't stay on the line for long. I just wanted to check how Harold is doing.'

'He's fine. In fact, I'm just about to go and check on him now.'

'Brilliant.' She sounded relieved. 'I know he's not as smart as Brutus but I love him to bits. I hope he's not too lonely without me.'

I could tell her that he had company so he probably wasn't feeling lonely at all but somehow the phone didn't seem the right way to break the news to her. That, and the fact that I was a total coward. 'I should probably go,' I said awkwardly.

'Right, yeah, yeah. Thank you so much for all this, Ivy. I don't know what I'd do without you.'

I grimaced as she hung up. I doubted she'd still be singing my praises in a few days' time when she returned. This is exactly why I hate keeping secrets: they are always trouble in the long run. Skulking around just doesn't suit my temperament.

Brutus gazed at me narrow-eyed. 'Bored.'

I reached for a piece of paper, screwed it into a ball then tossed it in his direction. He immediately brightened and attacked it with immense vigour. Then he tapped it underneath the sofa and swung balefully round in my direction, as if blaming me.

I shrugged. 'Sorry. I'd retrieve it for you but I need to check on Harold and his new housemates.' I was almost convinced that Brutus rolled his eyes. I gave him a look to suggest there was nothing I could do and vamoosed into the bathroom, snagging up my pyjamas, a towel and some shampoo. With my boiler still out of action, the only shower I was likely to get in my own flat would be ice cold. At least this way I could kill two birds with one stone.

Harold had moved from one end of the sofa to the other. When I entered, he didn't even twitch. I was pleased to note, however, that he had one slitted eye on the pair trussed up in the middle of Eve's floor.

'Hey y'all,' I said cheerfully. 'How's it going?'

Nobody answered. Dumping my things on a chair, I dealt with Harold first, giving him a big fuss before making sure he had enough food and water. If he was annoyed at being cooped up all day long on babysitting duty, he didn't show it. I received several head butts and a deep-throated purr. 'Why can't Brutus be as sweet as you?' I asked, tickling him under the chin. Harold's purr increased. He knew where his food was coming from – at least for the next few days.

When I was satisfied that Eve's familiar was content, I moved over to Bell End. I peeled off his gag and offered him some water. He glared at me with the ferocity of a captive bear but he still took it, gulping down several mouthfuls. Once he was done, I waved one of the burgers I'd picked up on the way home. I'd made Winter stop before he dropped me off. Fortunately, he hadn't commented on the fact that I bought three separate meals but his expression told me exactly what he thought of me. Whatever.

'Want this too?'

Bell End nodded reluctantly. Feeding him like a baby was too much trouble so I undid his restraints and let him eat it himself while I kept a close eye on him for any sudden movements. His partner twitched the entire time. I even heard her stomach grumble. Tough. She could wait.

Once Bell End was finished, I re-tied his bonds and patted him on the cheek. 'There now. Isn't that better?'

He scowled. 'You can't keep us here forever.'

'Tell me what you were doing here and I'll let you go.'

He looked away. I replaced his gag and moved to the woman. 'What's your name?' I asked. She didn't answer. 'Tell me your name and I'll give you food and water.' I wafted my hand in front of her face. 'Mmm. Smells good, doesn't it?' Her eyes followed the burger in my hand. Yep, she was pretty hungry. I unwrapped it and started to eat. 'Yum.'

Resignation flickered in her face. I grinned, grabbed the final burger and raised an eyebrow. 'It's Alice,' she said. 'My name is Alice.'

Bell End sagged against her. I didn't know why he was upset; he was the one who'd been stupid enough to come out with identification on him.

'Alice what?'

'Fairclough.'

'You're in the Order.'

She nodded reluctantly.

I took an educated guess based on the magic she'd used against me during our fight. 'Adeptus Minor?' I asked. 'You seem Second Level to me.'

'Yeah.'

I pointed over to the pile of herbs. Harold helpfully leapt up beside them, his tail whipping from side to side. He apparently thought I should get on with it. 'What are they for?'

'Just give me the damn food,' Alice snapped. 'I told you my name.'

True. Never let it be said that Ivy Wilde went back on her word. I undid her bonds and she lunged for the burger, cramming into her mouth with gusto. I watched, fascinated. She didn't even seem to chew.

Alice was still on her final mouthful when she made a move. She shifted to the right slightly, dropping her hand behind her knee where it was just out of sight. Before she could finish the rune, however, I grabbed her hand and held it up. She squirmed.

'That's just rude,' I told her, tying her up again. 'But at least you're more interesting than your partner.' I sat down cross-legged in front of her. 'Did you break in to foretell Eve's future?'

She stared at me as if I were nuts.

'No,' I murmured, 'I didn't think so. Twelve minutes of her future self wouldn't get you very far.' I wiped away some ketchup from the corner of my mouth. 'Perhaps you wanted to see what she's been up to in the past.' I doubted it would be very interesting. Eve was a workhorse. If anyone wanted to spy on her, they'd see someone studying, keeping fit, practising magic and maybe, just maybe, sleeping occasionally. I smirked at the idea of someone trying it on me. The report would involve me wandering to the fridge, turning on the kettle and shifting around on the sofa.

Alice Fairclough's expression remained studiously bland. 'So,' I said, 'you must have wanted to track her.' It would have been fairly easy to manage. Neither Alice nor Bell End had expected Eve to be home, so they must have been planning to sprinkle the herbs in the right places so they'd brush off on Eve's skin. As a First Level witch, Eve wouldn't have had guards in place to combat such a spell. I leant my head to the side curiously. 'The question is why.'

Alice pressed her mouth shut. She obviously wasn't going to say anything more. Her choice. I felt like I was inching closer to the truth. It was just as well because between these two and Winter, I had my hands full. Another day or two and I reckoned I'd get what I needed. I replaced her gag and smiled. If I was feeling kind I might let them have a pee break soon. I was all heart.

'Not to worry. You two stay here. I'm off for a shower and I'd hate to think you were peeking at me.'

Alice glared at me. I nodded slowly. 'Oh yeah. You can't move, can you?' I grinned. It was a hard-knock life.

THE NEXT MORNING, every single alarm I possessed went off at the same time. It was the only way I could be sure that I wouldn't fall asleep again. My early start had nothing to do with the upcoming thrill of watching Winter question the Ipsissimus and everything to do with lulling my sapphire-eyed partner into a false sense of security. If I could make him believe that I wasn't quite as lazy as he thought, I reckoned I'd be able to get away with more – by which I actually meant less – in future.

I stumbled around, bleary-eyed. The sun rose for a reason. It wasn't natural to crawl out of bed when it was still dark outside. I muttered irritably to myself as I tried to get ready. My limbs were stiff and unyielding and the more I moved around the more they seemed to hurt.

Winter had told me that I should dress appropriately for our appointment with the Order head. The only clean clothes I could find, however, were so wrinkled that I wasn't sure even an industrial strength iron would make them look presentable. I shook out yesterday's T-shirt and frowned at it. It didn't smell *too* bad. Then my gaze fell on the box that Winter had procured for me. Hang on a minute. This could work.

I rummaged around, pulling out the red robe that was folded neatly on the bottom. As much as I hated dressing like all the Order geeks, this would satisfy Winter and it would mean I didn't have to bother getting dressed. I could just shrug it on over my pyjamas and no one would be any the wiser. I grinned. I bet other witches did this all the time.

Smoothing down my hair as best as I could, I gave Brutus a sloppy kiss on the head, spat out the fur that inevitably ended up in my mouth, and headed for Eve's flat. I double-checked that its occupants, both feline and human, were alright and gave them enough refreshments to last the day. I'd be relieved to get them out of my hair. Hopefully, Bell End and Fairclough would cough up the answers I wanted before too long. They were becoming a drain on my time that I could do without.

Once I was satisfied they'd been dealt with, I went downstairs. Winter had insisted on picking me up again. It suited me; it meant I'd be able to nap on the drive in and catch up on some of my precious lost sleep.

I made it to the corner about twenty seconds before he pulled up. He stuck his head out of the window and blinked at me. 'You're here.'

I made a show of checking my watch-less wrist. 'I've been waiting for at least fifteen minutes.'

He frowned. 'I'm bang on time. We said six am. It is six am.'

'I didn't want to miss you,' I told him, clambering into the passenger seat. 'You were grumpy enough yesterday to last a lifetime.'

'I was not grumpy,' he growled.

'Yes, you were. Throwing water over an innocently sleeping woman is not the action of someone with a sunny attitude.'

Winter's mouth twitched. 'The last thing I would ever call you is innocent.' He put the car into gear and began to drive.

'If the opposite of innocent is experienced and worldly-wise,' I commented, 'then I'll take it.'

'You certainly seem experienced at sleeping.'

'Oh,' I purred, 'when it comes to the bedroom, I have lots of experience. In fact, I'd go so far as to say I'm very skilled.'

Unfortunately, Winter wasn't easy to embarrass. 'Is that so?' he murmured. The faintest hint of mocking disbelief coloured his words.

It was on the tip of my tongue to tell him I'd give him a demonstration if he so wished but somehow it didn't seem like a good idea. If he were anyone else, I'd have continued with the banter but with Winter it made me feel slightly uncomfortable. Goodness knows why.

'Now buckle up,' he instructed.

I smiled slightly, grateful for the change of subject. 'Are you concerned for my safety?'

'If you end up splattered against the windshield, the paper-work would be a pain in the arse. Not to mention the cleaning.'

'See?' I said smugly. 'You don't enjoy extra work any more than I do.'

He rolled his eyes. I clicked in the seatbelt and grinned. Some-times Winter was almost human.

'WE SHOULD BE grateful that the Ipsissimus has agreed to come in early to answer our questions,' Winter informed me.

Should we? I opened my mouth to say as much but Winter held up a hand to forestall me. 'It's good that you dressed appro-priately. He will be pleased that you're showing that you're willing to be a real part of the Order for the next hundred days.' I pressed my lips together tightly. 'But, as I said yesterday, it's important that you let me do the talking. This is a delicate situa-tion which requires careful diplomacy.'

Considering I hadn't seen much yet in the way of careful diplomacy from Winter, I was amused by his words. All the same, I could let him worry about the stupid sceptre and the Ipsissimus and spend my time thinking about what to do with Bell End and Alice. Or better still, daydreaming.

'Adeptus Exemptus Winter,' I began.

'You really don't have to keep calling me that.'

'Adeptus Exemptus Raphael Winter,' I said instead, 'do you know everyone in the Order?'

'There are thousands. Of course not.'

I arched an eyebrow. 'You strike me as the kind of person with his finger on the pulse.' Truthfully, I'd imagined him being conscientious enough to pore over the names, photos and identi-ties of each and every Order witch. He seemed that kind of person.

Winter sighed. 'Who is it you're looking for?' His eyes

narrowed slightly. 'Do you want to know more about Philosophus Villeneuve?'

He was referring to Tarquin. I shook my head. 'No. Do you know Alice Fairclough?'

'Second Level Adeptus Minor,' he answered instantly.

Ha! I knew he'd be aware of her. 'And what kind of person is she?'

'I know her name, Ms Wilde. I don't know her shoe size or whether she's an adept witch or not. She is Second Level, however, so I assume her abilities are reasonable.'

It appeared that Winter lived and died by the Order's hierarchy. He wasn't denying knowledge of her; if he had anything to do with her shenanigans at Eve's, I'd have expected him to deny having heard of her. 'Does she have a partner?' I enquired. 'Or a mentor?'

'Adeptus Exemptus Diall.'

Hmm. Something about Winter's tone suggested that he didn't think much of Diall. That was interesting.

'How about Matthew Bellham? Have you heard of him?'

Winter turned to me. 'What exactly is all this about?'

'I'm just curious.'

'No,' he answered. 'I have not heard of him.'

Probably because Bell End was First Level and beneath Winter's consideration. I nodded amiably. 'Thanks.' Winter looked shocked. 'What is it?' I asked.

'You thanked me. You have manners after all.' He shook his head melodramatically. 'I never would have believed such a thing were possible.'

I suppressed a grin. 'Hey, if you want manners, then you've got manners.' I dipped into a low curtsey, just as the door opened and a tired-looking witch peered out. 'The Ipsissimus will see you now.'

Winter pushed off the wall. 'Excellent.' He walked in through the open door. 'Come on, Ms Wilde.'

I coughed. 'I need a bit of help.' I was still in the curtsey. Unfortunately I'd over-estimated how low I could go without toppling over or requiring a hand up. I blamed the gym session yesterday; my muscles were still in agony.

Winter looked as if he were trying very hard not to laugh.

The other witch offered his hand. I grabbed it gratefully. 'Note to self,' I muttered. 'Perform fewer acts of obeisance.'

'This is why you need to get fit.' Winter smirked and headed in. I glared at his back. Yeah, maybe he had a point. But that didn't mean I had to like it.

THIS TIME AROUND, we weren't in the grand meeting room but in the Ipsissimus's study. I could only imagine that Winter had suggested this meeting should be conducted in private so that we didn't accuse him of stealing from his own Order in front of all his minions. He was seated behind a grand desk, with a delicate china teacup in front of him. There was also a toweringly large pile of paper. Somehow, I didn't think it would be fun to have his job.

Winter and I took our places in front of the desk. I opened my mouth to speak but received a hard jab in my ribs and an irritated glare. Miming a zip, I closed my mouth once more. Yeah, yeah. Winter could do all the talking if he was that desperate.

The Ipsissimus took off his half-moon spectacles and looked at us. 'So,' he said, 'what can I do for you?'

'First of all,' Winter began, 'thank you very much for coming in at this early hour to talk to us.'

The Ipsissimus gestured at the paper in front of him. 'It's no trouble. I might as well come in early and make a start on this lot.' He smiled pleasantly, although there were a hard questioning expression in his eyes. 'Have you made any headway with the theft of the sceptre?'

'We have made some progress,' Winter answered. 'There's nothing concrete to report yet but I'll write up our findings this evening to keep you abreast.'

The Ipsissimus inclined his head. 'Excellent. And how are things working out between the two of you? Ms Wilde?'

I didn't say a word. Winter jabbed me in the ribs again. 'Oh? I'm allowed to talk now?' I asked. I beamed. 'Things are just peachy. Adeptus Exemptus Winter is an absolute joy to work with. He's a little ray of sunshine in my otherwise grey and dull life.'

I could feel the man in question getting ready to throw me out of the room. The Ipsissimus merely smiled again, as if oblivious to my sarcasm. 'I'm thrilled to hear it. We are very proud to have him in our ranks.'

'Thank you,' Winter murmured before I could leap in and say anything else to embarrass him. He paused. 'I am here to ask about the warding spell you had in place over the sceptre. It had degraded quite badly.'

The Ipsissimus grimaced. 'So I've heard. I can only imagine that I didn't reset it properly after last year's ceremonies. It was my error.'

I thought Winter would leave it at that but now that I'd called the Ipsissimus's integrity into question, he was going to prove that he'd examined every possibility. 'Is that typical?' he asked.

The Ipsissimus let out a short laugh. 'I certainly hope not. I admit, however, that I pay less attention to such spells than I should. Generally speaking, the belief that strong wards are in place is enough to deter sticky fingers.'

Winter nodded. 'And there were still strong wards in place on the ground floor. It must have been an incredibly powerful witch who breached them to get the sceptre.'

'Yes. I'm told also that there are no apparent weaknesses. It's very unusual to pass through a ward in that manner and leave it untouched. Among other things, the second ward requires crushed cypress leaves picked at midnight on midsummer's day. Those are not easy to obtain.'

'Or to use,' Winter pointed out.

'Indeed.' The Ipsissimus appeared amused. 'So I imagine your list of potential suspects are high Level witches.'

'We are looking at Third Level only,' Winter agreed.

The Order Head took a sip of his tea. 'On the night in question, I was attending a soireé at number ten. The Prime Minister wanted advice on introducing magic to border controls.'

Winter threw me a look of triumph. He had a point; I reckoned that was a pretty rock-solid alibi. I'd never really believed the Ipsissimus nicked his own sceptre but this had been kind of fun. And it had given me a good reason to avoid another sweat-inducing session with the weights and treadmills.

'I will ensure that every Third Level witch clears their schedule in order to meet with you and discuss their movements,' the Ipsissimus said. 'The sceptre might only be ceremonial but it does have value and it is certainly worrying that it's gone missing. I've instructed every ward to be reset this afternoon. It will take time, effort and energy but it will be worth it. We cannot have more items walking out of high-security buildings.'

'That is wise,' Winter said. 'I admit that I'm very concerned that someone could achieve this, even if the display cabinet's ward was no longer effective.'

The Ipsissimus knitted his fingers together. 'Do you think that the sceptre is recoverable? It will be a blow to the Order if we cannot find it intact.'

Winter heaved a sigh. 'Frankly, I have no idea. It's not even clear why someone would take it because it has no real power beyond the ceremonial. The trouble and effort they have gone to is extraordinary. Whoever is responsible, they must have had good reason to go to such lengths.'

I understood that the sceptre was intrinsically valuable, considering it was made of gold and encrusted with jewels, but this all seemed ridiculous to me. I thought about saying something but I had my orders.

At my side, Winter frowned and began to scratch at his arm. The Ipsissimus didn't notice. He had embarked on a long speech about the merits or otherwise of the other library warding spells. 'The fact that there was no blood spilt or that these thieves managed to circumnavigate…' He paused mid-sentence and glanced at Winter, who had now yanked up his sleeve to stare at his mottled skin. 'Is something the matter?'

Winter cursed. 'An allergic reaction perhaps.'

The Ipsissimus tutted. 'That's no allergy.' He swung his gaze to me. I smiled meekly in return. 'What is it, Ms Wilde? The binding is making its presence known and I can only assume that it is as a result of you.'

Winter turned and glared at me. I held up my hands. 'Hey!' I protested. 'I've not done anything. In fact, I'm doing as I've been told and staying quiet.'

'The nature of the binding requires that you work *in tandem* with Adeptus Winter. It will not permit you to stay silent when you have a salient point to make.'

Well, well, well. So the binding worked both ways.

'Out with it,' Winter growled.

I raised my shoulders. 'Make your mind up, buddy.' I tilted up my chin. 'It's obvious, isn't it? The amount of effort needed to remove the sceptre negates any actual value it could possibly have.'

'What's your point?'

I glanced at Winter. 'Easy. The sceptre hasn't yet left the building. It's still there.'

'Don't be idiotic. It was removed from the case. Maidmont and the other librarians would have noticed if it was simply shoved behind a shelf somewhere.' His voice hardened. 'Not everyone is as lazy as you are.'

'It's not about laziness.' Well, actually it was. 'It's about what makes sense. Even a Third Level witch would need to sleep for several days after performing the kind of spells you're talking about. Hence, the sceptre must still be in building.'

Winter gritted his teeth. 'It cannot still be in the building. That's impossible.'

'It's a big place,' I argued. 'It could have been hidden away anywhere.'

'To what end?'

I was getting irritated. I didn't have all the answers. 'How the hell should I know?'

The Ipsissimus cleared his throat. 'Enough.' Winter and I fell silent. 'I can see that your partnership is going to prove … interesting.' Winter let out a snort of derision. 'Ms Wilde does make a good point. I suggest that you return to the library and scour it for any sign of the sceptre. It's possible that what we are looking at is nothing more than a First Level prank.'

Arse. 'The librarians know the area best,' I suggested. 'They should look for it.'

'This was your idea, Ms Wilde. Take ownership.'

I sniffed. 'I'm not sure that's entirely necessary…'

'Deal with it.'

So much for Mr Nice Ipsissimus. Winter had stopped scratching and his skin had returned to its natural tanned colour. Next time I should really keep my bright ideas to myself.

CHAPTER TEN

'This is stupid,' I grumbled to Winter as I came out of the last study carrel on the third floor. 'I don't know where all the library hidey-holes are.'

'Quit complaining.'

'I've got sore feet.' I pulled up a chair and sank into it while he examined a bookshelf, apparently on the off-chance that the metre-long sceptre was hiding behind a volume of ancient witch poetry.

'You need to check the bathrooms,' he told me.

'I think someone would have noticed by now if the sceptre had been hidden in a loo stall. Have you seen how much coffee this lot drink?' I waved a hand at the studious-looking witches seated near us.

Winter turned. His eyes drifted down to my legs and I realised that the red robe had sneaked its way upward, revealing my lace-edged pyjamas underneath. I sprang to my feet before remembering, through a spasm of pain, that my body still ached all over from yesterday. I grimaced.

'Are you wearing your pyjamas? Did you not bother getting dressed this morning?'

I folded my arms. 'Does it matter?'

Winter heaved a sigh as if the woes of the world lay across his broad shoulders. 'I suppose not.'

He walked away from me, heading towards the small room where the Cypher Manuscripts were kept. He really was leaving no stone unturned. 'Stay there,' he snapped.

Suited me. I didn't want to taint the ancient magical archives with my presence anyway. I closed my eyes. A moment or two later, Winter reappeared. 'The sceptre's not there.'

'Are you sure?' I asked. 'Maybe you should double check.'

I opened an eye and peeked at him. He was staring at me with undisguised exasperation. 'Come on. There's still the basement to go through.'

Whoopdeedo. I heaved myself up and trailed after him, wishing I were just about anywhere else in the world. At least when I was driving the taxi I got to sit around for most of the day instead of just the odd minute or two.

We made our way downstairs, pausing at an unassuming door on the ground floor. Winter rattled the doorknob. When it appeared to be stuck, he shoved his shoulder against the door to force it open. I glanced down and realised I was standing on a crack in the marble floor. I jumped to the side and let out a hiss. Damn it.

The door finally banged open and I peered around Winter into the darkness beyond. 'Maybe we should take a break first,' I suggested. 'Tea and tiffin.' Suddenly I felt a prickle across the back of my neck and half-turned. Standing on the other side of the room was Tarquin, his dark eyes fixed on me. 'Forget I said that,' I muttered. 'Bring on the basement!'

'What on earth are you wittering about?' Winter asked.

'Nothing.' I nudged him. 'Come on. Let's investigate!'

'Sometimes, Ms Wilde, I wonder whether you are entirely there. You don't seem able to concentrate on any one thing for more than a minute.'

'It's because my mind is filled with so many great and important matters,' I informed him airily.

Winter snorted. 'Like tea and tiffin?'

Ah. So he had heard me. 'Let's just get this over and done with.'

The corner of his mouth crooked up. 'Your wish is my command.'

If only.

The staircase leading down was narrow, as you'd expect from somewhere heading into a dingy dungeon type of place. I half expected to be attacked by vampire bats or giant cobwebs. The overhead light buzzed annoyingly and the steps were so uneven that I almost tripped and collided with Winter's back. There wasn't a soul, animal or human, in sight.

After what seemed like an age, we reached the foot of the staircase. The space in front of us was cavernous, filled with endless stone archways. There were also a lot of old boxes and filing cabinets. From where I was standing, I counted dozens of the darn things. We'd be here forever.

'You're an Adeptus Exemptus,' I said.

'Yes.'

'So you must have a few runes up your sleeve for tracking objects. Can't you do something so we can be out of here by next century?' I was sure I'd heard of such spells; if only I'd bothered to seek them out. But then, why go to such trouble when Adeptus Exemptus Winter could do it for me?

'If such spells existed and were reliable,' Winter answered, 'don't you think I would have already tried them to find the sceptre?'

I shrugged. 'Maybe they only have limited reach. Surely you know something that will be successful in an enclosed space like this.'

'There are runes which could work. But only around thirty per cent of the time.' His tone was brisk and brooked no nonsense but I wasn't ready to give in yet. Where magic was involved, there is always an easier way.

'Aw, Winter baby,' I coaxed. 'It's worth a shot. Even if only to flex your magical muscles and show me what you're really made of.'

'Winter … baby?'

I couldn't tell whether he was annoyed or amused. 'Well, you keep telling me to stop calling you Adeptus Exemptus.'

He stepped towards me until he was barely inches away. 'And,' he said in a low voice, 'if you call me baby, what should I call you?'

I considered. 'Boss would work.'

'Not happening.' He leant closer. 'How about honey?'

I met his eyes. I felt surprisingly hot and bothered. 'Are you flirting with me?'

'Trust me, Ivy. When I flirt with you, you'll know all about it.'

I couldn't help wondering whether that was a threat or a promise. I licked my lips. 'Those runes…'

He moved back, the mention of work making him return immediately to his usual business-like self. 'I suppose they're worth a try.' He glanced at me sideways. 'Watch carefully. You might learn something.'

I fixed my gaze on his hands. He raised them, using not one but both to sketch out the rune. This was complex stuff indeed. No wonder he was held in such high regard. Not that I was going to let him know I was impressed. 'Nothing's happened,' I remarked.

Winter rolled his eyes. 'The spell only works for me.' He paused. 'But then you knew that, didn't you?'

I grinned.

He walked forward, swinging his head from side to side as he passed each stack of boxes. I had a fairly good idea how this would go down. Nothing would register and we'd still have to search the place from top to bottom. All the same, I ambled along behind him, taking the opportunity for some momentary peace and quiet to relax.

About halfway along, Winter halted, his back ramrod straight. It was so unexpected and I was so lost in the swirl of my own chaotic thoughts that I didn't notice until I was almost past him. 'What is it?'

He swivelled round to his left where a shabby pile of card boxes lay, stacked in an untidy heap. It was a wonder they'd not toppled over.

'No way,' I breathed. 'Was I actually right?' I bellowed a laugh. 'Is the sceptre really here?' I started bopping around. 'The non-Order witch saves the Order's hide. Who's the boss now? Eh? Eh?'

'Shut up.'

I supposed I wasn't acting like a particularly gracious winner but it still felt good. I stopped talking but I was still bouncing.

Winter strode over to the boxes and started pulling them off the pile, one after the other. After the first four or five, he turned and glared at me. 'I suppose it would be too much to ask for a little help?'

'As you've already said, the spell doesn't work for me. I have no way of knowing which box the sceptre is hiding in. So it's probably better if you do the heavy lifting.'

Even from several feet away, I could see Winter grit his teeth. 'Except,' he muttered, 'I don't think it's in any of the boxes.'

I eyed the pile. 'It's underneath?' No wonder the stack resembled the Leaning Tower of Pisa. Although you had to wonder at the First Level witches who would go to such lengths for a prank. Surely they'd have made their point if they'd simply left the stupid thing on the top?

'Just get over here.'

I took my time shuffling over. Winter was picking up and discarding boxes so quickly, he already had a sheen of sweat across his brow. I reached out and placed my hand on his arm.

'Allow me,' I said kindly. I drew the same rune I'd used yesterday in the gym that made all the boxes, regardless of their size or weight, feel as light as air. Winter reached for another one and almost fell backwards at its unexpected lightness.

'What did you do?' he asked.

'Just a little spell I picked up during my time out in the wilderness,' I said smugly. I grabbed a box and lifted it up, using only the tip of my index finger. I pretended to groan and strain.

'You did this yesterday, didn't you? You had the same expression on your face when you were lifting weights.'

Uh oh. 'Nooooo.' I shook my head. 'I wouldn't do such a thing.' I tossed the box to one side, put my hands behind my back and began to whistle, avoiding Winter's glare.

'Unbelievable.'

I cocked my head. 'Is it though?'

'You probably expended more energy avoiding exercise than doing the exercise itself.'

Somehow I doubted that. 'Chill out,' I drawled. 'You need to realise that the path of least resistance is always the best.'

'This is like dealing with a toddler.'

I raised my eyebrows. 'You're the one throwing your toys out of the pram.'

'Whenever I think that we might be able to make this work, you revert to type. You're almost entirely untrained and yet look at the talent you've got. You're wasting it all.' He seemed genuinely angry.

'Well, look at you!' I shot back. 'Ninety per cent of the time you're a sad sack jobsworth who can't crack a smile unless it's on Order instructions. Then you show flashes of fun and a sense of humour and genuine thoughtfulness. It doesn't last though, does it? All work and no play makes Jack a very dull boy.'

'All play and no work makes Jack a mere toy,' Winter retorted. 'I didn't ask for this, you know. I didn't even want a partner.'

'Is that supposed to make me feel better?'

Winter turned away, shoving his hands into his pockets. He was very, very pissed off. And to think that a few minutes ago we'd almost been flirting. I grimaced and reached out, gently touching his shoulder.

'I'm sorry,' I said gruffly. 'Obviously, we're just opposites who've been thrown together through no fault of our own. We rub each other up the wrong way. My priorities are different to yours.' I sighed. 'I won't cheat again.'

'Is that what you said eight years ago?'

I bit my lip. Winter cursed and looked back at me. 'Let's just find the sceptre and get out of here. Alright? We'll worry about this … partnership later.'

I nodded. 'Yeah. Okay.' I paused. 'Should I undo the spell on the boxes?'

'Don't be ridiculous.' And then he closed his mouth and stopped speaking altogether.

In silence, we made short work of the rest of the boxes, tossing them to the side and clearing the way. Despite having been moved round the previous day, they still kicked up a lot of dust, making me sneeze violently on several occasions. The rest of the time, I kept my head down and avoided looking at Winter.

We finished moving the boxes and stared down at the dusty floor. There was no shiny golden sceptre waiting to be rescued – but there was a trapdoor. A single padlock, which was obviously brand new, gleamed up at us. I didn't need to glance at Winter to feel his tension.

Reaching into his pocket, Winter crouched down and took out a small amount of dried knotweed. He blew it into the padlock and released the lock. He unclipped it and placed it carefully to one side, while I lifted up the trapdoor and gazed downwards into the dark, dank hole that had been revealed. It was little more than a foot and a half wide and there was a rope ladder stretching downwards. The air that rose up from beneath felt humid. I was betting that somewhere down there was water.

Knowing my luck, this led directly to the Order sewers. How lovely.

Determined not to complain again and give Winter more cause to snap, I twisted round and began to climb down, swaying dangerously on the first few rungs until I found my balance. It was difficult to keep going, not least because the further I went the darker it got. Above my head, I felt Winter test the ladder's strength then, apparently deciding that it wouldn't hold both of us, he pulled back and waited while I continued to descend. I looked neither up nor down; I simply kept ploughing on. I'd wanted to be anywhere other than the library and this was what I got. Be careful what you wish for indeed.

The basement light from above was only just visible by the time my feet landed on solid ground. I tugged on the rope ladder to let Winter know he could come down then used a rune to magic up enough light to see. It definitely looked like a sewer. It smelled a lot like a sewer too.

There were concrete paths on either side of a small, unnatural looking river of gunk. From behind me there was a skittering sound as a rodent of some kind darted along on its merry way. I shivered; mice were one thing but sewer rats were entirely different. The curved walls on either side were covered in dark, slimy moss that only added to the atmosphere of despair. If the person who'd stolen the sceptre had brought it down here, I'd certainly award them a gold star for determination.

I edged forward and peered into the gloom, half expecting to see the eyes of some tunnel-dwelling monster staring back at me. As far as I could tell, I was completely alone. Then something touched my back.

I leapt about a foot in the air, banging my head on the low ceiling and almost slipping into the smelly river below. The only reason I didn't was because Winter grabbed my arm and hauled me to safety. I blinked at him in acknowledgment. I'd have expressed my gratitude but he was the one who'd scared me in the first place.

He turned to the slime on the walls and immediately began bagging some of it up, no doubt for some spell he was planning later. This is one of the many reasons why I prefer focusing my energies on runes rather than herbs. If you have to climb into a sewer to get the ingredients you need, I reckon it's probably never going to be worth it.

Winter jerked his head downstream, in the opposite direction to which I'd been facing. I nodded and gestured at him to proceed. With his face set in a grim mask, he moved off. For once, he wasn't marching along like an army colonel. One false move and he'd be on his arse. As entertaining as that might be, the last thing I wanted was for him to bring me down with him.

I followed gingerly, matching him step for step. My light spell continued to illuminate the way but all we could see was more of the same.

We traipsed along for a good eighty metres. We had to be getting close to the end of the building by now. The sceptre might have been taken down to the very bowels of the earth but the wards preventing it from leaving the walls of the library without permission would still hold. It couldn't be far away. I cursed whoever had sent us on this wild goose chase. If Winter spent his days investigating trivial matters like this, I couldn't understand why he took his work so seriously. Arcane Branch: what a waste of time. I was just about to tell him so when he stopped abruptly and pointed across the river to a gap in the wall. Some broken bricks were lying underneath it as if it had been created deliberately.

I flicked my fingers, making the illumination spell drift over so we could see for sure. The light hovered, its glow bouncing off the tip of the sceptre, which was barely visible inside the hole. I eyed it thoughtfully. Considering the lengths the so-called thieves had gone to in order to bring the sceptre down here, they hadn't done a particularly adept job of concealing it. Even with Winter's locator spell we could have walked right past it if they'd replaced the bricks.

Without waiting for me to say or do anything, Winter leapt over the river, landing with a barely audible thump on the other side. Well, that was a manoeuvre I wasn't likely to copy any time soon; chances were I'd miss and end up waist deep in whatever nasty gunk was beneath us. I peered down. Whatever was down there, it included some incredibly large objects. Didn't some heartless people flush baby alligators down their toilets? Was that a long snout or a branch?

My brow creased. Whatever it was, it was moving strangely as if fighting against the flow of water rather than being carried along with it. That didn't make any sense unless…

I whipped my head up just as Winter reached into the hole in the wall to grab the sceptre. 'Stop!' I yelled.

He pulled it out, holding it lightly in one hand and turned to frown at me. 'What?'

It was too late. There was a faint rumble, almost like distant thunder. If this were Hollywood, there would have been time to make a run for it. Unfortunately, we were in real life. There was barely time to blink before the wall of ferociously churning water hit us.

I was immediately swept off my feet. I thought I heard Winter yelling my name but I might have imagined it in the roar. I couldn't see anything and, no matter how frantically I tried to kick or swim or grab for the side, the gush of water was simply too strong. It was freezing cold, already chilling me to my very bones. The temperature wasn't the most pressing danger, however – it was the flotsam and jetsam crashing along with the water. Something metal scraped along my thigh, sending a bolt of flaring pain up through my body. Something else slammed into the side of my skull. And the water kept coming.

I had no way of knowing which way was up and which way

was down. My lungs were burning and I needed air. The red robe I was wearing snagged on something and my body was yanked backwards, momentarily halted against the flow of water. It was enough. I twisted and turned, swallowing water as I desperately sought oxygen. Then my head broke upwards and I could breathe. I took in a scant two mouthfuls before the fabric of the robe ripped and I was cast away again.

This time, the robe wasn't helping me. Instead it was dragging me down, a sodden mess that would end up pulling me into a watery grave if I didn't get rid of it. My fingers scrabbled at the buttons, desperately trying to undo them, but it was too cold and the current was too strong. Completely disorientated again, I tumbled this way and that, blood thumping in my head like the bass drum of a crazy thrash metal band screaming out an anthem for death. I gasped for air once more and then held my breath, squeezing my eyes shut and trying to concentrate. It was next to impossible to manage a rune here but I still had to try.

I moved my right hand, feeling the magic course through me as I threw all my energy into it. Then another object slammed into my back and I was thrown off course, the power of the rune fizzling away before I could complete it.

A feeling of complete calm overtook me. The tiny logical part of my brain that remained knew that this was my body preparing itself for the inevitable. I no longer minded. This was where it was going to end. I couldn't really complain; I'd had a fairly good innings and the good thing about dying young was that I'd probably get a decent number attending my funeral. I hoped someone would be sensible enough to look after Brutus for me. I hoped Bell End and Alice didn't starve to death in Eve's flat.

'The sceptre! Ivy, grab the sceptre!'

Winter's barely audible yell registered dimly. Good grief. The man really did take his job seriously if he was drowning and still worried about that stupid thing. I opened my eyes, catching sight of him a few metres ahead of me before another wave of water crashed over my head. Why wasn't he moving?

He thrust the tip of the sceptre in my direction and, without thinking, I took hold of it. Then my body slammed against an invisible wall and pain flared through me, expelling even the cold from my veins.

'Don't let go!'

I groaned. 'What?'

Winter's face swam towards mine. 'Don't let go!'

My grip tightened as the pain increased. Of course, I thought dully, the ward. The water had carried us from one end of the building to the other and, because Winter hadn't released his hold on the sceptre, the magic was preventing him from going any further. He was holding one end of the sceptre while I held the other and, as long as we were touching it, the avalanche of water around us couldn't break through. The downside to all this was the agony of the ward itself. I howled, swallowing more foul water as I did so. It was excruciating. My very atoms were screaming.

'The water!' Winter shouted. 'It's stopping. Just a few moments longer, Ivy. You can do this.'

No, I didn't think I could. I gritted my teeth and tried to cling on. It was like being stabbed by a thousand knives all at once, while standing in an arctic tsunami. I couldn't do it. I couldn't do it. The water was still sucking me under, dragging at my useless robe. The Order were going to kill me after all. Death by dangerous dressing.

Then Winter's hand grabbed me. 'You see? It's going down. We're alright, Ivy. We made it.'

He was right: the water level was sinking rapidly, from my shoulders down to my torso. What had been Hokusai-inspired waves were now gentle undulations. I gasped and gulped and finally let go of the sceptre. My body jerked a few feet, still pulled by the under-current, but it wasn't long before I could stand up.

I reached for the side, my hands clinging to the warm concrete. I tried to heave myself over the edge and back to safety but the damn robe was still in the way. With shaking fingers, I undid enough buttons to push it over my shoulders and down to my waist. I kicked it free of my feet and hauled myself onto the walkway. I rolled onto my back and tried to calm my breathing.

Winter's hands reached for me, pulling me backwards until my back was against his body. 'We're both too cold,' he muttered. 'We need to warm up or we'll freeze before we can get help.'

I pushed back into him, seeking his warmth as he sought mine. Then I sketched out the rune for fire and, right by our feet and without any fuel, flames roared to life, casting heat in our direction. Winter was shivering as much as I was but we clung to each other. Shivering was good. Shivering meant we were still alive. And against all the odds, as well.

CHAPTER ELEVEN

I DON'T KNOW HOW LONG WE STAYED LIKE THAT; IT WAS QUITE some time before I felt Winter stir. 'I'm sorry,' he said. 'This was all my fault.'

'You weren't to know.'

'I should have known that it was a trap of some kind. They rigged the sceptre to the water, staunching its flow until someone came along and moved it. Then everything that had been held back was released all at once. It was designed to kill us,' he said grimly.

'Not *us* specifically,' I consoled. 'Whoever was assigned to investigate the sceptre's disappearance. It was just dumb luck that we were in the library when they realised it was missing.'

For a moment, Winter was silent. 'I'm sorry, Ivy,' he said again. 'It wasn't dumb luck. This is my remit. I was re-assigned just before you were bound to me. When anything is misplaced or stolen, I'm the first port of call. It might seem that we were in the right place at the right time but even if I'd been on the other side of Oxford, I'd still have been the lead investigator.'

I absorbed this. 'So what you're saying,' I said, wanting to be absolutely sure that I understood him properly, 'is that you still believe it was an Order witch who took the sceptre. And that the thief knew you would be brought in to investigate, so they laid that trap knowing that you would be the one to trigger it.'

'Not just me.' He paused. 'Us.'

I pushed away from him and turned round, meeting his eyes for the first time. 'Are you trying to tell me that someone is deliberately trying to kill us? That because human resources made a stupid mistake, I should be afraid for my life?'

'Maybe they didn't realise you were working with me.' He scanned my face anxiously. 'The Ipsissimus has been keeping your, um, recruitment quiet. You were probably right the first time around. It must just be me that's being targeted.'

I sprang up, shivering again as both my magical fire vanished and I lost the last of Winter's body heat. It didn't matter; there was enough angry fire inside me to keep me warm for a while yet. I spun on my heel and began to march off. Idiots with guns in the back of my taxi were one thing – I could deal with them. This was entirely different.

'Where are you going?'

'To find someone to complain to!' I stomped off towards the door.

It didn't take Winter long to catch up. 'Ivy,' he began.

'Don't say anything.' I marched up the stairs, hell-bent on my mission. 'I need to do shouting right now.'

'Shout at me.'

I turned to face him. 'I can't shout at you.'

'Why not?'

'Because first of all, you were the target of that drowning as much as I was. Probably more than I was. And second, when I shout at you, you shout back and you usually make sense.'

Despite our situation, Winter chuckled. 'That bothers you?'

'Yes,' I snapped back. 'I don't want sense. I don't want pragmatism or calm thoughts or anything logical.'

'You just want to shout.'

'You got it.'

He pressed his lips together and pointed upwards. 'Well, then,' he said. 'Go for it.'

I glanced at his hands. 'You still have that silly sceptre?'

'That silly sceptre saved our lives.'

My lip curled. 'I still hate it.'

Winter leant in. 'Me too.'

For a moment we grinned at each other. Then, slowly, Winter's smile began to leave his face until his expression was something else entirely different. His eyes drifted downwards to my mouth and he raised his thumb, brushing it gently against my bottom lip. 'Stray slime,' he said softly. I shivered.

'I still need to shout,' I whispered. Someone had tried to kill him. No-one, I decided, was allowed to do that other than me. My rage was only building.

His nod was barely perceptible. 'Go get'em, bruiser.'

I sucked in one deep breath then whirled round. I was most definitely on a mission.

When I reached the top of the stairs, I had to use considerable energy to force the door open. That meant that when it finally budged, I went flying out and landed at the feet of two startled Neophytes.

Maidmont hurried towards us from the other side of the hall. 'What happened? Why are you all wet?'

I looked at the librarian. He was wringing his hands and seemed very concerned by our sudden, bedraggled appearance.

'We have retrieved the sceptre,' I heard Winter say behind me. I sniffed and picked myself up. He could return the stupid thing to its stupid display cabinet. I couldn't shout at Maidmont; I'd already tried that once today and it was like kicking a puppy. I needed to find someone else.

I left Winter to explain what had happened and continued my march, storming out of the library and round the back to the next Order quadrant. There were many, many people staring. I couldn't give a shit.

I flew along the pavement, ignoring the sudden chill wind that whipped at my wet hair. I was a tornado of fury and I was going to find someone to vent all that fury on. I had a good mind to head straight for the Ipsissimus. When I passed the sign pointing towards human resources, however, I changed my mind. At least with this lot I wouldn't be kept waiting.

I made an abrupt turn left towards their small annexe. Slamming open the door so that it rattled violently in its frame, I pulled my shoulders back and stamped inside.

'Hello,' the brunette at the front desk called. 'Isn't it a wonderful day, today?' Despite her words, her voice remained flat and unenthusiastic, as if she were merely repeating her welcome by rote. 'Just look at all the sunny…' She faltered as she took in my appearance.

'All the what?' I snapped. 'All the witches conspiring to steal from the Order? All the witches conspiring to kill me and my partner? Or,' I said, leaning forward with a dangerous glint in my eyes, 'the people who fucked up and put me in this position in the first place?'

The woman recoiled. I realised, somewhat belatedly, that I probably smelled bad but I really didn't care. 'Who's in charge here?' I demanded.

She sniffed. 'Adeptus Major Price. But if you want to see him you'll need to make an appointment. He's not here.'

Price. I'd heard that name before. I searched my memory until I remembered that was who Tarquin was supposedly running errands for. My eyes narrowed. The plot thickened.

'Well, that's convenient,' I said. I was betting that Price was actually here. She just didn't want to trouble him with a sodden, pyjama-wearing crazy woman. Tough.

I turned but, instead of leaving, headed straight for the door to the offices beyond.

'Hey!' the receptionist protested.

I ignored her. I stalked down a corridor until I reached a large, open-plan office filled with red robes. The witch nearest me, seated at a large desk with a pile of paper in front of him, sniffed the air, made a face and looked up. As soon as he saw me, his eyes widened with alarm. I bent down. 'Where,' I said icily, 'is your boss?'

'He … he's not here.'

I folded my arms. 'Where is his office?'

The hapless witch raised a shaky finger and pointed behind him. I spotted the door at the side of the room. Nodding, I abandoned the witch. If Price really wasn't in, I would wait. Or I'd yell at every single person in this bloody office. Frankly, it could go either way.

I stomped over as more and more of the HR witches took notice. I paid them no attention and focused on the door. It was slightly ajar and I could hear voices from within. Aha.

'If Price finds out that you screwed up like this,' a female voice said, 'he'll chew up your insides. He's in a lot of trouble with the Ipsissimus over this.'

I had a sudden mental image of the nervous-looking witch from the boardroom meeting. Adeptus Major Price didn't seem likely to chew up anyone's insides; in fact, from what I remembered, he appeared more likely to run and hide in the corner.

'Price won't do anything,' returned a familiar voice with an even more familiar sneer. I tensed. You had to be kidding me. 'He barks a lot but he's got no real power. Don't tell him. This will go better if he doesn't find out.'

'Why did you even send her up there?'

'I told you,' Tarquin said. 'They've been having a lot of trouble.'

'Eve Harrington is First Level. She should never be sent anywhere on her own like that. Anything could happen.'

'Eve's very talented. I'm sure she can handle whatever is

thrown her way. Besides, Adeptus Bawdrip has gone after her now. She won't be on her own for much longer.'

That was some good news, I supposed sourly. Tarquin was right on another point too: Eve *was* very talented. I kicked open the door and strode in. Both Tarquin and his companion jumped and turned guiltily.

'Ivy?' Tarquin looked me up and down. 'What the hell have you been doing? Swimming in a sewer in your pyjamas?'

I marched up to him and jabbed him in the chest. 'Funnily enough,' I snarled, 'that's exactly what I've been doing.'

He blinked. 'Oh. Adeptus Exemptus Winter really has been working you hard, hasn't he?'

'And I bet that really pisses you off.' I crossed my arms. The little snippet I'd overheard was more than enough. 'It wasn't a paperwork mistake, was it? You deliberately sent Eve away because you knew she was your competition to be Winter's partner. With her gone, the field would be clear for you to make your move.' I glared at him. 'You really screwed up there, didn't you?'

A guilty expression that I knew only too well crossed his eyes. 'I don't know what you're talking about.'

'You've not changed a bit over the years, have you? You're still just as conniving and devious as ever. Still overly ambitious and reaching above your station.'

Tarquin looked at the woman. 'It's probably a good idea if you let me deal with this.'

She stared at him and in that instant I knew he was sleeping with her. All the better to pull the wool over someone's eyes. Tarquin was good at that. I should know.

'Yes, love,' I agreed. 'Why don't you piss off?' She wasted no time rushing out of the room and closing the door behind her.

Tarquin looked at me, amused. 'There's no need to get jealous, Ivy.'

I snorted. 'That'll be the day. She's welcome to you. Although I imagine that once she finds out what a snake you are, she'll run for the hills.'

He tutted. 'Such venom.'

He could tut all he wanted; now I knew the truth. 'If I'd known you worked for HR, I'd have realised it sooner. You sent Eve away and blamed it on a mistake. You've probably done something to make sure that Price takes the fall for it. You reckoned that Winter would come running to you when he realised she wasn't around.'

'You have no proof. All you have are your own ravings, the ravings of the witch who cheated in an exam by copying from me and then assaulted me when things didn't go her way.'

'Everyone believed you then. They won't believe you now.'

'I only did what I had to. My father's been breathing down my neck. You know what he's like. If Eve had partnered with Winter, he'd have wanted to know why I failed. Winter's the most talented witch in the Order. He's going places. My father wanted…'

'Oh, shut up. Stop using your dad as an excuse. This is all *you*, Tarquin. You're the one who keeps doing this to people.' I glared. 'How many others have there been over the years? How many more people have you stamped on so you could rise to the top?'

'It's not like that.' A calculated expression passed fleetingly over his face. 'You don't need to be like this, Ivy. We can work together, you and me. You can get your revenge on the Order for booting you out. They're the ones at fault here, not me.'

Pah. I ignored his pathetic attempt to bring me into the fold. 'What I don't understand is why, after you'd already failed, you sent Bell End and Alice after Eve. What was the big plan there? Follow her and hope she screws up so you can still take her place after I'm gone?'

Tarquin frowned. 'Eh?'

'Matthew Bellham and Alice Fairclough,' I said through

gritted teeth. 'Haven't you been wondering where they've got to? Weren't you worried that they'd vanished?'

Tarquin looked at me. 'Isn't Fairclough Second Level? An Adeptus Minor?'

Something about his tone rang true. 'You don't know her.'

'I know she's Second Level. Why has she disappeared? And who's the other guy?'

I shook my head. 'You idiot. You absolute sodding plonker. You sent Eve away and then you kept it quiet, didn't you? You didn't want anyone to know that she'd gone. Even the Ipsissimus has been trying to keep it under wraps so people don't realise how messed up the Order can be. Eve is up in the middle of nowhere, on her own, dealing with goodness knows what.' And the news that she was gone and I'd taken her place hadn't reached the bad guys in time. They thought her partnership with Winter had gone ahead.

Winter had told me that he had magical guards in place to avoid being tracked – and that every Second Level witch did the same. Eve wasn't Second Level yet; Bell End and Alice wanted to use those herbs to cast a spell to follow her, so that they could also follow Winter. The only reason I could think of why someone would do that was related to the sceptre and the fact that Winter had almost just died. As had I. But surely the sceptre's value wasn't worth all this trouble – was it?

The door opened and Winter appeared, filling the entire doorway with his muscular figure. Compared to him, Tarquin looked small and weedy. I wondered how things would have gone down between them if Tarquin's plan had worked. Somehow I didn't think Tarquin would fool Winter for long.

Winter's blue eyes flicked from Tarquin to me and back again. 'Have you finished shouting?' he enquired.

I tilted my head and considered. My desire to vent loudly had dissipated in the face of certain truths but there were still some hard questions that needed answering. For now, I nodded.

I could almost feel Tarquin about to burst with nerves as to whether I'd dob him in or not. It was very tempting; I'd have loved to wipe that smug smile off his face once and for all. Despite what he might believe, however, I wasn't that vengeful. I'd worked through my issues with him a long time ago and decided he didn't deserve any sleepless nights. I hoped that Eve felt the same because, in the end, she was the one who'd been genuinely wronged by Tarquin's actions. I was just the bystander who'd been drawn in by accident. I'd let Eve decide how to deal with him when she got back. It was only fair.

'I think I'm good,' I told Winter. 'But I'm starting to get a bit cold.'

'I thought you might be.' With another hard look in Tarquin's direction, he tossed me a clean robe. I never thought I'd be happy to put on one of those things but I sighed contentedly and pulled it round my shoulders.

Winter smiled. 'I think you gave half the Order heart attacks walking around like that. People are still talking about the woman in transparent wet pyjamas storming through the buildings. It made following you very easy.'

Transparent, huh? I grinned. 'Well, you did make it very clear that I was to dress appropriately for my position.' He was also wearing a robe. Rather than clashing with the brilliant blue of his eyes, the red rather suited him. 'I thought I'd prove that I have nothing to hide.'

'Adeptus Exemptus Winter,' Tarquin began. 'I think you should know that your partner…'

Winter took me by the elbow and propelled me out of the room, leaving Tarquin gaping like a guppy. Together we strolled out of HR as if we'd merely popped by for a convivial cup of tea and were now leaving for an afternoon picnic.

'Can you give me a lift home?' I asked, once we were outside. 'Unless there's more work you'd like us to do first.'

A ghost of a smile crossed his face. 'I think you've probably done enough for the day.'

I'd say. Unfortunately, I wasn't finished yet. For now, however, I chose the easy option. 'Thank you,' I said softly. 'For helping me down there. I'd be dead if it weren't for you.'

'You wouldn't have been in danger if it weren't for me.'

I inclined my head and didn't argue.

We walked in silence for a few minutes. There were still a lot of people staring at us. I flicked back my hair and added a little strut. If I was going to look and smell like the creature from the black lagoon, I ought to own it.

'Was he your boyfriend?' Winter enquired, out of the blue, obviously referring to Tarquin.

I blinked. 'Uh, yeah. A long time ago. I was still a teenager when we were together. It didn't last. He's also the one I assaulted,' I added helpfully.

'Because he dumped you or because he cheated and you got the blame?' I shot Winter a surprised look. He frowned at me. 'I'm an investigator, Ivy. This was hardly a difficult case to crack.'

'No-one believed me before.'

He scratched his chin. 'I think they probably did,' he said finally. 'But Tarquin's last name is Villeneuve and his father has donated a vast amount to the Order. His great-grandfather was Ipsissimus. Their magic runs strong.' He gave me a sidelong glance. 'I'm not blind to the Order's faults, Ivy,' he said softly. 'And no single person or organisation is perfect.'

I grunted. Even so, there was a warm glow inside me. I leaned into Winter, enjoying his reassuring solidity. He was a good guy. A *very* good guy.

CHAPTER TWELVE

It was still light when we pulled up outside my block of flats. That made a pleasant change these days. I didn't unclip my seatbelt immediately and I could feel Winter's curiosity growing.

'Is everything alright?' he asked. 'You should probably get inside and get out of those wet things.'

'Yeah,' I agreed. 'I should.' A shadow passed across the dashboard and I looked up, counting seven magpies wending their way over us towards the small copse of trees on the other side of my estate. No choice, then. I took a deep breath. 'There's something you should see first.'

'I've already seen quite a lot, thanks to those wet pyjamas,' Winter deadpanned.

I managed a weak smile. When I didn't immediately return a saucy remark, Winter's gaze grew more serious. 'What is it, Ivy?'

'It's easier if I show you.'

We headed inside. As a measure of how guilty he was feeling for what had happened in the depths of the library, Winter didn't comment when I veered towards the lift. Instead, he simply waited until it arrived. I had a feeling that his sudden amiable temperament was about to change dramatically.

Rather than heading for my own flat, I led him towards Eve's. Winter raised his eyebrows but said nothing. I took out her keys and placed them in the lock. Before I turned them, I faced him. 'This happened after that first day,' I informed him. 'Maybe I should have told you earlier but they're from the Order and I wasn't sure if I could trust you. One of them was carrying the same combination of herbs that you used in the library to evoke the past.'

Winter didn't move a muscle. 'Ivy,' he said, his voice sounding strained, 'have you killed someone?'

'It's not quite as bad as that,' I replied with a nervous laugh. I unlocked the door and let Winter enter in front of me.

Harold, apparently surprised to have yet another unfamiliar intruder in his home, let out a soft growl and darted for the underbelly of the sofa. Winter paid the cat no attention; his focus was on Bell End and Fairclough. They'd obviously been trying hard to free themselves, judging by the mess they'd created as they'd shifted around in a bid to break their bonds. All the same, they remained as trussed up as before.

'Adeptus Minor Fairclough,' Winter said. He looked at me. 'This is why you were asking whether I knew her or not.'

I nodded. For her part, she angled her head away as if the curtain of her hair would be enough to hide her. Bell End took a different approach. He struggled violently against his bonds, an urgent expression in his eyes. I walked over and loosened his gag.

'Help us!' Bell End burst out to Winter. 'This crazy woman attacked us and is holding us hostage!'

Winter walked round, stood beside me and stared down at him. 'Matthew Bellham.'

Bell End nodded vigorously. 'Yes, yes! That's me. Have I been reported missing? We've been held here for days against our will.' He held up his wrists. 'Untie me!'

'You're a Practicus,' Winter murmured. 'Although you're

clinging on by the skin of your teeth after several complaints against you. It's been alleged that you were responsible for the attack on several young Neophytes last year.'

I watched Winter. 'I thought you didn't know him.'

He raised a shoulder. 'I looked him up after your enquiries.'

I was impressed. There must be benefits to being a workhorse who jumped on every little detail.

'So?' Bell End yelled. 'Those were trumped-up charges!' He jerked his chin in my direction. '*She* has kidnapped me.'

Winter knelt down and I wondered if he was going to free him. Instead, he returned the gag to its original position. 'He's quite annoying,' Winter murmured.

I could only agree. Winter straightened up. 'So,' I said, 'they broke in. I went to confront them and,' I shrugged, 'they ended up like this.'

He nodded as if I'd just told him that it was raining outside. I let out a silent sigh of relief. I hadn't realised how important it was that he believed my version of events until right at this moment. 'It's smart that you didn't tell the police. We need to keep this within the Order.' He looked around. 'Where are the herbs they were carrying?'

I pointed to the side table. Winter picked up each bag and examined it carefully. A muscle throbbed in his cheek. I hoped that it wasn't me he was angry with. Returning the herbs, he moved to Alice. She was still shying away. Winter gently unfastened her gag and tilted her head towards him. 'You were here to bespell Eve Harrington.' It wasn't a question. 'Tell me why.'

Alice wouldn't meet his eyes; she was genuinely afraid of him. I glanced at Winter with renewed interest. Apparently his reputation was greater than that of a talented investigator who worked too hard.

'Come on, Alice,' he coaxed.

It looked as if she would remain as stubbornly silent with him as she had with me but then her chin wobbled slightly and her shoulders dropped. It all came pouring out. 'It was Diall,' she said, referring to Eve's mentor. 'He told us to come here and sprinkle around enough herbs to attach themselves to Eve so that she could be tracked wherever she went. We knew there was only a short window of time when we could do it.' She flicked her eyes towards me. 'We thought she was still out at work. Our intention was not to hurt anyone.'

Considering how much of a fight the pair of them had put up when I'd confronted them, I found that difficult to believe.

'What reason did Diall give for this?' Winter asked. There was a dangerous edge to his voice that made me step backwards. No wonder he was a skilled investigator; all he had to do was ask a question and his air of menace encouraged immediate and full disclosure. Handy trick.

'He wanted to know what you were doing,' she admitted. 'By tracking Eve we could track you. He'd found out about the binding spell that was going to be put on you and he knew its terms. There was no chance that you'd work separately.' She sighed. 'I don't know where Eve Harrington is. If you're worried about her, I suggest you start questioning that one.' It was obvious she meant me. I snorted. I wasn't the evil witch around here.

'Why, Alice?' Winter probed. 'Why did he want to know what I was up to?'

She looked away. 'Diall said you were getting too big for your boots. That you had your eye on the Ipsissimus's job and that you had to be watched. He thought maybe you were passing Order secrets to the military and that you were plotting to bring down the Order once and for and all.'

This time my snort was much louder. You only had to meet Winter for a minute or two to know that was about as likely as a snowman enjoying a sauna. Alice Fairclough's reluctant tone suggested that she knew it was bullshit as well.

Winter leant back on his heels and rubbed his forehead. He was probably as dog-tired as I was. We'd both been to hell and back only a few hours ago and now I was bringing him conspiracy theorists and kidnap. Yep. He was definitely ruing the day he met me – and that had only been Thursday.

'When is Ms Harrington due back?' he asked me.

'Monday.'

He absorbed this and stood up.

'Can I ask a question?' Alice said. We both looked at her. 'Why do you smell like a toilet?'

I rolled my eyes but Winter didn't react. He replaced her gag and nodded in the direction of the kitchen. I did as he requested and walked in with him. Harold emerged from underneath the sofa and joined us then Winter shut the door.

'The legal thing to do is to inform the Order and the police immediately. You could get into a lot of trouble for holding these two here, Ivy. You've also made me a co-conspirator by default.'

I folded my arms. 'They're dangerous,' I protested. 'As soon as I let them go, whether it's to the police or the Order or the damn Knights of the Round Table, Eve will be at risk. So will I. And so will you. She says it was Diall who put them up to this and maybe it was but we don't know if he was working alone. There might be others who want to silence us. The entire Order might be compromised. Not to mention that it's highly suspicious that all this stuff with the sceptre and the attempt on our lives just happened too. They might not be related, there's no proof, but it's a hell of a coincidence. In fact...'

Winter put a hand on my arm. 'I was going to let you keep going until you ran out of steam,' he said drily. 'But I was worried that you'd not taken a breath and you'd end up passing out.' He sighed. 'What I said was that telling the Order and the police would be the legal thing to do. It wouldn't be the *right* thing to do.'

I blinked. 'Are you also saying that *I'm* right?'

'Don't let it get to your head.'

I held up a hand towards Harold. 'High five!' Harold started washing his ears.

Winter gazed at me expressionlessly. 'We need to keep these two here until we know what's going on. I'll set up a perimeter spell. If anyone comes looking for them then we'll know who it is and we can use it as evidence against all of them.'

Huh. That was actually a good idea. 'Brill.' I pressed my lips together.

'What is it?'

'I suppose now you want to go all gung-ho and storm off after Diall.' My muscles screamed their reluctance to do anything other than have a hot bath and go to sleep.

'You're right, that is what I want to do – but it's not what we're going to do. Both of us need to be fresh and alert for our next move.' He ran a hand through his hair. 'If we go out again now, we'll end up making mistakes which could cost us dearly.' He paused. 'I'll sleep on your sofa. That way if anything untoward happens at least there will be two of us to deal with it.'

I squashed down my sudden, inexplicable thrill of glee. 'Brutus will want to talk to you all night.'

The corner of Winter's mouth crooked up. 'If I can handle you, I can handle a snarky cat.'

Famous last words. 'I should tell you that my boiler's broken so it's pretty cold in my flat.' I twiddled my thumbs. 'And there's no hot water.'

Something akin to despair crossed Winter's face. 'No wonder it was freezing when I was there before. I'll fix it.'

'Really?'

'I'm a witch of many talents.' He raised an eyebrow. 'And so, apparently, are you.'

I felt a twinge of suspicion. 'What do you mean by that?'

'Fairclough might only be Adeptus Minor,' he said, 'but she

scores higher than almost everyone else in magical aggression. You did well to bring her down.'

I wasn't blushing. Nope. Not even a tiny bit. I coughed. 'Well, then. I'll give this lot some food and we can go.'

CHAPTER THIRTEEN

For once, I woke up early without using an alarm clock. I wiggled my toes, enjoying the warmth both inside and outside my duvet, and listened. In the other room, Winter appeared to be having a fruitless argument with Brutus.

'I've given you lots of attention. Now let me have some peace.'

'Pet.'

'The last time I did that you scratched me.'

'Pet.'

'Fine. But keep those damn claws to yourself.' There was a pause followed by a hiss of pain. 'You little bastard.'

I could almost hear Brutus sniggering. I grinned and pulled my aching body out of bed. If I thought I'd feel refreshed after a good night's sleep, I was sorely mistaken. I hurt more today than I had yesterday. How was that even possible?

I yanked on some clothes and padded into the living room. Winter, whose hair was adorably mussed up, handed me a cup of coffee. 'I hope you don't mind,' he said. 'I made myself at home.'

'Not as long as you bring me hot drinks,' I said cheerfully. I was particularly enjoying the fact that he was wearing casual jogging bottoms and a tight T-shirt that he'd pulled from his gym kit in the boot of his car. It made a nice change from his immaculate suits. Not to mention that his new attire showed off a great deal more of his body than he normally displayed. 'You can make me breakfast too, if you like.'

'I would but all that seems to be in your fridge is a wrinkly apple and three slices of rather unappetising looking pizza.'

I immediately brightened. I'd forgotten about the leftover pizza. Yum. I took a gulp of coffee and headed into the kitchen to heat it up. Brutus followed me, giving me a baleful glare.

'My sofa,' he hissed. He was obviously annoyed that Winter had dared to stretch out and sleep on his territory.

'It's not your sofa. I paid for it.'

'My sofa.'

'You really don't need to repeat every single thing several times over, you know. I'm perfectly capable of hearing you the first time.'

He jumped onto the counter and, with his eyes fixed on me, pawed at the cup of coffee I'd just put down. Before I could stop it, it slid onto the floor. The cup smashed and I yelped as hot coffee splashed over everything, including me. Brutus twitched his whiskers and sauntered away while Winter, alarmed, ducked his head in. 'What happened? Is everything alright?'

'It's fine.' I grabbed a cloth and began dabbing ineffectually at the mess. In the end, I gave up. There were more important things to worry about. 'Look, I keep thinking about the sceptre. It doesn't make sense that Diall or anyone else would go to this much trouble for it. Unless the ulterior motive was to kill you, stealing it was pointless. And frankly, there would have been easier and more reliable ways to put us both down than a sewage tsunami.'

Winter gave me a grim look. 'I've been thinking the same thing.'

'Do you think—' I began, before hesitating and cocking my head. 'Hang on. Can you hear that?'

Brutus, from the corner, arched his back. With dilated pupils, he leapt onto the floor and darted for the front door.

'Don't worry,' Winter said. 'I know who this is.'

Puzzled and more than slightly wary, I followed him. From the other side of the front door there was a faint scratching sound. Brutus was now on full alert, the fur across his spine on end and his tail puffed up like an old-fashioned feather duster.

'Winter,' I cautioned.

He turned and grinned at me, his features suddenly boyish. 'Don't worry.'

I watched as he unbolted the door. Brutus scarpered to the other end of the small hallway, his claws scratching the wood floor in his haste, although he was obviously determined not to hide. A moment later, with a small kittenish meow, a white, long-haired Persian strolled in, head butting Winter's legs and demanding attention. My mouth dropped open. 'Is that…?'

'My familiar.'

I scratched my head. 'I thought you lived on the other side of town.'

'She's pretty smart. I called to her last night after you went to bed.'

This was some dedicated moggy. Despite her fluffy, delicate appearance, her temperament was clearly similar to Winter's. She also had extraordinarily blue eyes to match his.

'What's her name?' I asked, finding my voice.

'Princess Parma Periwinkle.'

I tried very hard not to giggle. It didn't work.

'I've had her since I was ten,' Winter informed me sniffily. 'When my magic abilities first appeared. I was rebelling against my parents and I had a vivid imagination.'

'Mmm.' The fact that familiars live far longer than normal house cats means that their names are often amusing – but rarely on this scale.

Winter pointed at Brutus, who was still glaring suspiciously at the princess in question. 'Like you can judge.'

True. 'Is she here to stay?' I enquired.

'It makes sense. If I'm going to hang around here until this mess is sorted out, she should be here too. She can give Harold a break as well.'

'Brutus and I are thrilled,' I said drily. Actually, I was; it had been reassuring to know Winter was here all night. Plus, a problem shared was a problem halved and all that. The presence of Bell End and Alice in Eve's flat bothered me less now that I wasn't the only one who knew about them.

'Anyway,' Winter said, while Princess Parma Periwinkle made a move towards a very unhappy Brutus. 'What were you going to say?'

My attention was momentarily diverted as I watched my cat decide what to do next. He threw me a look. 'Bitch,' he hissed. Then, seemingly without another thought, he flopped down on the floor and presented the new arrival with his belly.

Winter lifted an eyebrow. 'You didn't do that for me.'

Recovering slightly, I gazed at him mischievously. 'I will if you want me to.'

Winter seemed on the verge of responding, his blue eyes darkening, then he shook himself. 'We have work to do. There was something you were going to say.'

I took a deep breath. 'Yes. But you're not going to like it.'

His good humour vanished in an instant. 'Go on.'

'We can assume that the sceptre wasn't the real target.'

'Agreed.'

'If we assume that you weren't the target either but just a bonus side scheme for entertainment…' Winter's eyes flashed '… then there's another motive behind all this.'

He smiled. 'You see? You've been thinking about this all night, haven't you? This is why this line of work is so satisfying. The more you chew over a problem, the more interesting it becomes.

When a possible solution emerges, even if it's at three o'clock in the morning, the feeling is like no other.'

I stared at him. I'd slept like a baby; the idea had come to me while I was brushing my teeth. 'Yeah,' I said unconvincingly. 'Sure. Anyway, you're the lead investigator when it comes to theft and missing objects. So if you're out of the picture, the Order would have to scramble to find a replacement. Maybe the trap was simply to clear the field for more theft.'

'You mean the sceptre was stolen in order to cover up something more valuable being stolen?'

'Exactly.'

The colour drained from Winter's face. 'The wards,' he said. 'Maidmont and the other librarians were going to reset the wards across the whole building. Yesterday afternoon, while we were being half drowned in the sewer.'

'Yeah. It would have been the perfect opportunity for a thief to steal something else from the library. The question is, what is more valuable than the sceptre and worth all this effort?' I already knew the answer but I wanted to hear Winter confirm it. If it was true, then all hell might be about to break loose.

He clenched his fists. 'The Cypher Manuscripts.'

I sighed. Arse. 'Great minds think alike.'

UNFORTUNATELY, Winter didn't pause to make me another coffee. He all but sprinted for the car. The only way I delayed him slightly was by reminding him that I needed to check on Harold, Alice and Bell End. All the same, he tapped his foot impatiently while I gave them food and water and a loo break then ensured everything was shipshape.

Princess Parma Periwinkle, whose name I was going to have to change soon because it was such a mouthful, nudged Harold with her little pink nose before settling into a comfortable spot in the corner to watch the trussed-up pair and let him have a break. Eve's cat didn't quite roll over the way Brutus had but it was a close-run thing.

When we eventually set off, Winter tossed me his phone and told me to get in touch with Arcane Branch so they could send someone round to keep an eye on Diall. I jabbed in the number and leant back, kicking off my shoes and propping my feet on his dashboard as I waited for someone to answer.

'Ivy,' Winter said stiffly. 'Just because we have come to a truce after our shared near-death experience, that does not mean you can get away with whatever you want.'

I turned to him. 'What do you mean?'

He gestured in irritation at my feet. I waggled my toes in return. Winter was not amused. Unless I almost drowned again, I reckoned I'd used up all his goodwill towards me. For the sake of a quiet life, I dropped my legs to the floor. We had more important things to worry about.

'I'm sure you don't permit your customers to treat your taxi like that,' he said,

Actually, it was much better for me when my passengers were more relaxed. Before I could say as much to Winter, someone finally picked up the phone. 'Arcane Branch, Practicus Smythe speaking. How may I help you?'

I put on my poshest voice. 'Oh, good morning, Practicus Smythe. How charming to talk to you.' Winter gave a long-suffering sigh. I ignored him. 'I am here with the esteemed Adeptus Exemptus Raphael Winter.'

I could almost hear Smythe sitting bolt upright. 'Winter?' He coughed. 'Yes, of course, what can I do for him?'

'He would very much like it if you could send someone around *tout suite* to Adeptus Diall. He needs to be brought in for immediate questioning.'

'Diall? But…' Smythe paused. 'Yes, of course. And if he refuses to come?'

'Use all force necessary.' I hung up. I could get used to this; having all manner of uptight witches at my beck and call was rather fun.

Winter tsked. 'Diall is still a respected member of the Order.'

'A respected member of the Order that sent out two of his minions to perform an illegal action against a younger witch,' I pointed out. 'And who more than likely just tried to have you killed. If he has the Cypher Manuscripts in his possession...' The consequences could be catastrophic.

'There are protocols to follow. We can't act like the Gestapo and drag away whoever we choose.'

'Why not?' I arched an eyebrow in his direction.

'There's paperwork to be filled in.'

'In triplicate?'

He seemed to be counting to ten. 'No, but...'

The ringing phone interrupted his words. He smiled triumphantly. 'See? That'll be Smythe calling back to confirm.'

Winter didn't seem to realise how seriously the rest of the Order took him. Even from the short conversation I'd just had, I knew that Smythe wouldn't dare to question his orders, whether they were second hand or not. He was probably already on his way to Diall's with an army of Arcane Branch goons as we spoke. I dug into my pocket and pulled out my own phone. 'It's for me,' I said smugly. 'Not you.'

I pressed the answer button. 'This is Ivy,' I chirped.

'Hello, gorgeous.'

I beamed. 'Iqbal! How are you?'

'Good. I've got some news for you. And for me. I see karaoke in your future.' He started to sing, not very tunefully.

I sat up, not looking at Winter. 'Go on.'

'There is a loophole to your binding. I found a temporary measure but it won't last more than a day or two. I figured you were looking for something more permanent so I kept on searching and I think I've found just the thing. It's not going to be easy but if you can get hold of some ossombe root then I have the spell for you.'

'I've never even heard of the stuff.'

'I'm not surprised. The only reference I found to it was an old text from the seventeenth century. It's certainly not a typical ingredient.'

'Where would I find it?'

'It only grows in one place in the world.' He paused. I could almost hear the drumroll. 'The foothills of Mongolia. You're welcome.'

An odd sensation of relief trickled through me but I quashed it. I was probably mistaking it for disappointment. 'Iqqy, honey, I can't get to Mongolia any time soon.'

He was silent for several seconds. 'Oh,' he said finally. 'I didn't think of that. Maybe you can source it somewhere else.'

'Have you any idea where?'

'Um, no.' He pondered this conundrum. 'Ebay?'

Pah. I cupped my hand over the receiver. 'Have you heard of ossombe root?' I asked Winter.

There was a line forming between his eyebrows and his expression was tight. 'No.'

If even Winter hadn't heard of it, then it was highly unlikely that such a rare ingredient would be easy to find. And I didn't know any Mongolians. 'Thanks,' I said drily to Iqbal.

'You're welcome!' he trilled. 'So how does next weekend suit?'

'For what?'

'Karaoke, of course.'

'The binding is still in place,' I said. 'And you don't know where to get ossombe root from. Ergo, you've not fulfilled the terms of our agreement.'

'Oh yes, I have. I've told you what you need to do to gain your freedom.'

I shook my head. 'Nope.'

'Ivy…'

'You really should get back to that thesis. It won't write itself, you know.' I ended the call.

Winter drummed his fingers against the steering wheel. 'What was that about?'

My phone rang again. Iqbal's name appeared on the screen and I turned it off. 'I asked someone to look into our binding,' I said, trying to sound casual. 'To see whether there was any way of breaking it before the hundred days were up.'

'And?' Winter asked stiffly.

'Ossombe root.'

His mouth tightened. 'But you don't know what ossombe root is or where to get it?'

'No, I don't.'

'That's a shame,' Winter commented. He didn't look at me.

'Yeah,' I agreed. 'It really is. We could be free of each other if only we could find some.'

'Hmmm.' Winter put his foot down on the accelerator, narrowly beating the next red light. Neither of us said another word until we reached the library.

CHAPTER FOURTEEN

WINTER CRACKED HIS FINGERS AS WE ENTERED THE LIBRARY'S front doors. I guess he wanted to show that he really did mean business. He strode up to the front desk and barked at the man behind it. 'This entire area needs to be closed off immediately. Make sure everyone leaves.' He checked his watch. 'You've got two minutes.'

Just when I thought he'd been softening up. The man stared at him. 'Adeptus Exemptus Winter,' he began, his left eyebrow twitching furiously.

'I'm sure we don't need everyone to leave,' I said helpfully. Winter glared at me. Somewhat belatedly, I realised I'd called his authority into question in public. Oops. I hastily backtracked. 'What I mean is it would be fabulous if you could stay on this desk,' I said, addressing the man. 'You seem like an excellent gate-keeper and someone who can keep everyone away from the library for the time being.'

The man's chest puffed up slightly. 'I could do that,' he sniffed. 'But what I can't do is kick everyone out. There are a lot of people carrying out important research here. Unless there is a health and safety issue, I can't simply order them off the premises.'

Thinking about it, I suppose that it was vital to the Order – and by extension, Winter – that no one discovered the Cypher Manuscripts might have been compromised. There was the potential for mass panic if the news got out; even I felt shaken by the possibility and I didn't care whether the Order lasted one more day or one more millennium.

'Sorry,' I muttered to Winter. 'Don't forget I'm new to all this.'

If my words appeased him, he didn't show it. He crossed his arms. 'Ninety seconds.'

Flustered, the man picked up a phone. His fingers were trembling and he had trouble finding the right numbers. He appeared to be wilting under the pressure of Winter's impatient glare and he was starting to make me feel uncomfortable.

'Don't worry. I've got a better idea.' And it would mean a lot less hassle. I held out my right palm and, using my left, sketched the rune for fire. I knew how much fire was feared in the library; this would have them running for the hills before I could toast a marshmallow. I was becoming a dab hand at this rune. By the end of the week, the Scouts would be looking to hire me as their personal mascot – or better still, the fire brigade. I pictured myself on their annual calendar, surrounded by broad-chested firemen. Now there was an idea.

A second after my tiny flame flared into life, a god-awful screeching filled the library. From all corners, red-robed witches came rushing forward looking like they were ready to do battle.

I extinguished the flame. The siren, however, kept up its alert. 'Evacuate the building!' I shouted. 'Fire!'

'Ivy,' Winter said over the racket, while rubbing his forehead as if he were in pain. 'This isn't an office block. In the event of fire, every witch in the vicinity is trained to come here to try and prevent the flames from spreading. You've just achieved the opposite of what we wanted.'

Oh. Now that I thought about it, that made sense. *I* would run from fire; these idiots would run towards it.

A witch standing nearby raised his palms. His eyes were closed and he seemed to be concentrating hard. 'There's the source of the fire,' I heard him mutter. Before I could react, he drew the rune and drenched me from head to foot in ice-cold water. Oh bloody hell.

Winter flicked his fingers, performing a rune so nimble and fleeting that I barely caught it. The front doors to the library sprang open, then his voice boomed out as if from a loudspeaker. Cool. 'There is no fire but everyone must leave the building for safety purposes until we discover who set off the alarm.'

The witch who'd just doused me in magical water frowned. 'She started the fire. She set off the alarm.' To emphasise his point, he sent out another ice-laden gush of water in my direction.

She was soaking wet yet again and starting to get mightily pissed off. I shook off the worst of the water and hissed, 'Plonker.'

'Ivy,' Winter warned. He took the watery witch by the elbow, drew him into a corner and murmured something in his ear. The witch paled, nodded, then immediately left the library like a good little boy.

Through the window I saw a crowd of red-robed witches running towards the library from all directions. Winter's reckless spell-casting witch began to yell at them, gesturing at them to go back. 'It's not fire!' he shouted. 'It's a black cat!' He paused a beat for dramatic effect. 'And she has a litter of kittens!'

I looked quizzically at Winter. He shrugged. 'All those Order superstitions have got to be good for something. Until the Ipsissimus says otherwise, and until we know for sure that the Cypher Manuscripts have been taken, we need to keep this on a need-to-know basis.'

I was impressed by Winter's quick thinking. All around us the witches who had remained in the library decided they weren't taking any chances. They streamed outside, willing to do anything to avoid a black cat – or indeed several of them – crossing their path. The Order normally went to great lengths to keep black cats away from their grounds. Despite my own superstitions, I felt a bit sorry for the cats; they couldn't help their colour.

'Adeptus Exemptus Winter is such a hero,' I heard one of the departing witches murmur to a friend. 'He'll make sure the cat is kept away from us even if he has to risk his own safety.'

'You know,' I said to Winter, 'people will avoid you for weeks after this in case they're tainted by your potential bad luck.'

'Then at least I'll be able to do my job unimpeded,' he growled. He glanced at me. 'Doesn't it bother you that you'll be treated the same way?'

I snorted. 'Hardly.' I shook myself, sending a spray of water in Winter's direction. He stiffened fractionally but didn't comment.

'Do you think,' I asked hopefully, 'that I could go home and change first?'

'Your wet condition is your own fault, Ivy. Besides, those witches out there shouldn't be kept away from the library any longer than is necessary. The Cypher Manuscripts might be untouched.'

'Yeah,' I said, knowing I sounded unconvinced. Perhaps these repeated soakings would give me a cold then I'd have an excuse to stay at home for a few days. Every cloud, etc.

The last witch was Maidmont. He approached us, his brow furrowed. 'There's no cat, is there?'

'No.'

He looked momentarily relieved. That wouldn't last. 'So what is it?'

Winter gave him a hard look. 'If I tell you,' he said, 'you are under oath to keep it quiet until further notice.'

Maidmont nodded vigorously. 'Is it asbestos?'

'We think the Cypher Manuscripts might have been stolen,' Winter said, without any preamble.

The words didn't seem to register immediately. Maidmont gazed at us both blankly. 'Wh – what?'

'The only reason that we can think of for the sceptre's theft, other than trying to assassinate my good friend Winter here, was to cover up another more serious crime,' I offered helpfully.

Maidmont blinked rapidly. 'But the Cyphers?' He wrung his hands. 'That's impossible.'

'When you reset the wards yesterday,' Winter asked, 'did that include the ones around the Cyphers?'

The poor librarian scratched his head. 'Um, yes. We did all of them.' Panic appeared on his face. 'Did we do wrong? Oh God, this is all my fault. The Cyphers…'

'We don't know they've been taken yet. Let's confirm that first of all.'

Maidmont licked his lips. 'Yes, yes. Good idea. Let's do that.' He didn't move a muscle.

Winter tapped his foot. 'Let's go then.' His mouth flattened. 'The more trustworthy witnesses we have while we check, the better.'

He had a point. Given my reputation within the Order, I wouldn't be surprised if the coincidence of my return and the Manuscripts' disappearance would end up being linked. I'd go down in history as the most infamous, evil witch that ever dared to walk the earth. Not to mention that I'd be locked up for the rest of my natural life.

The three of us headed up to the third floor. Part of me hoped that Winter and I had got it wrong and someone merely wanted to send us to cold, desolate graves. Right now, that was more comforting than the thought that someone had stolen the Cypher Manuscripts and all the power they contained within their ancient scrolls. If they had, the amount of work Winter and I would have to do would be never-ending.

Winter had permission to enter the warded room where the Cyphers were kept but I had to wait outside until Maidmont released the ward. Rather than make him go to all that trouble, I stepped out of the way; I could watch from the doorway. At least then there would be no chance that my fingerprints would compromise the scene.

Winter opened the door and he and Maidmont strode inside. My eyes searched beyond them. There were a lot of oak shelves; even from here, I could see that several of them still contained Cypher documents. I let out a sigh of relief.

'It's alright! They're still here.' I wiped my brow. It was difficult to tell whether the dampness was sweat or drips from the water spell. Either way, the world wasn't about to end.

Winter slowly examined the shelves. Although he was still frowning, I sensed he felt the same relief. We'd been jumping at shadows. As soon as I thought that, however, Maidmont let out a small cry. 'Volume 9,' he gasped. 'It's not here.'

Winter leapt towards him. 'Show me.'

The librarian pointed shakily. With both their bodies blocking the view, I couldn't see anything but it didn't matter; there was no doubt that the librarian would know whether it really had gone missing or not.

'Could it have been checked out?' Winter demanded.

Maidmont stuttered, 'N−no. No one apart from the Ipsissimus himself is allowed to remove the Manuscripts and he's not been in here for several months.'

'Double-check the room,' Winter growled. 'Maybe it's just been returned to the wrong shelf. Ivy, get in here and look around too.'

'I can't,' I said unhelpfully. 'The ward won't let me.'

Winter flicked his fingers at me with another lightning-quick rune. The slight pressure that had been holding me back immediately vanished. I wrinkled my nose and inched forward. The less involved I was with all this, the better. I really didn't want to go inside.

'It's not here,' Maidmont whispered. 'It's definitely not here.'

I released a breath. 'I don't suppose you know what Volume 9 contains?'

A deeply troubled voice sounded behind me. The Ipsissimus. 'Authority,' he said. 'Volume 9 includes all the spells for increasing power and authority over others.'

I bit my lip and turned towards him. 'Well, things could be worse, right?'

His pale eyes looked at me. 'If you'd be happy to live in a magical dictatorship, where the leader goes permanently unchallenged and can do whatever they want to, including torture, death and corruption of the highest order, then yes, Ms Wilde, things could be worse.'

Ah. Well, when he put it like that…

CHAPTER FIFTEEN

THE FOUR OF US REGROUPED IN THE IPSISSIMUS'S STUDY. 'IT WAS wise to keep this matter to ourselves,' the Order Head said to Winter. 'We will have to allow the witches to return to the library or it will raise suspicion. Let's make sure that the Cypher room is sealed off from everyone.'

'Agreed,' Winter said. 'Until we know who is responsible for the disappearance of Volume 9, we have to assume everyone is a suspect.'

The Ipsissimus rubbed his chin. 'Indeed. This is worrying. Most worrying.'

'Why would those kind of spells exist?' I asked. 'And why would they be written down where anyone can access them?'

'We don't generally believe that our witches have the desire to rule the world, Ms Wilde,' he answered. 'And witches who have access to any of the Manuscripts are carefully monitored. We can't go around destroying ancient artefacts because we don't like what they contain. One cannot unknow what is already known. Once the atom was split, it could not be undone.'

'Nobody goes around teaching nuclear physics to children

though, do they? It's bullshit. The Cyphers could have been locked away in a sealed room. People would forget about them.'

'We live in the free world, Ms Wilde. We are not in the business of concealing knowledge. Besides, that volume contains information that is still used today.'

'Such as?'

'The less powerful spells include details on subjects such as how to gain the attention of a room,' Maidmont interjected. 'They can imbue the caster with confidence. There are also a few spells for dealing with bullish familiars who are unwilling to do as they're ordered.'

I imagined how Brutus would react if I tried to put a spell like that on him. There would be feline carnage and my corpse would be left undetected in my flat for months.

The Ipsissimus drew back his shoulders and stared at Maidmont. 'Have you read it?' he enquired icily.

'Oh no,' the librarian denied, suddenly alarmed. 'I wouldn't. I'm simply well versed in the catalogue. Besides, my skills aren't high enough for the spells to have any effect.'

Winter sighed. 'And therein lies the rub.' I looked at him questioningly. 'Only high Level witches can absorb the magic and cast the spells from the more complicated Cypher pages,' he explained. 'If a less able witch tries them, they're liable to destroy themselves in the process.'

'And,' the Ipsissimus added, 'just in case you think that we give anyone access to the Manuscripts and the opportunity to abuse their power, all Order witches are only allowed to view the Manuscripts for short periods of time. It would take days to fully understand and utilise the higher Level magic.'

'Which is why,' I pointed out, 'they were probably stolen in the first place. So the thief could study them at leisure and implement the spells without fear of being stopped before they finished.'

Everyone fell silent as we absorbed this. Frankly, it was all becoming a little too worrisome for me. 'Ipsissimus,' I began, 'do you happen to have any ossombe root?'

Winter stiffened. The Ipsissimus frowned. 'It's not an ingredient I'm familiar with,' he admitted. 'Why? Will it stop our would-be megalomaniac?'

'No,' I said cheerfully. 'But it'll enable me to get as far away from here as possible.'

If anything, he was now even more confused.

'That's enough, Ms Wilde,' Winter barked.

So we were back to Ms Wilde again? Before I could say anything, the Ipsissimus regained control. 'I hope, Adeptus Winter,' he said, 'that you have a plan for tracking down this witch, whoever they may be.'

'Assuming there's only one,' Winter growled. 'I have a few ideas.'

'You have carte blanche but time is of the essence. It's imperative that you find them before they can absorb all of the magic they are after. If that happens, we will be helpless.'

I met Winter's eyes. It was obvious where to begin; we both knew that Diall was mixed up in this somehow. We could probably have him under lock and key in the next hour – if eager Mr Smythe hadn't already brought him in. It was possible – just – that this entire catastrophe could be solved by teatime.

There was a knock on the door. 'I said I wasn't to be disturbed!' the Ipsissimus roared. I jumped. Had he partaken of a little of Volume 9's magic himself?

A woman put her head round the door. 'I apologise, Ipsissimus,' she said. She didn't look in the slightest bit sorry. I already liked her. 'But there's a witch here to see Adeptus Exemptus Winter. A Practicus Smythe. He says it's an emergency and he won't take no for an answer.'

Winter's face shuttered. The Ipsissimus frowned and gestured to the woman to let him in. A moment later, a bespectacled witch shuffled in. He was wearing a red robe and looked as skinny and pale as most Order witches. There was also a distinct aura of panic about him. I examined him more closely. There were a few odd stains around the cuffs of his robe. It was difficult to tell for sure given the robe's colour but I had a horrible feeling I knew what they were.

Smythe bowed several times then shuffled his feet and twitched. 'I'm so sorry, I wouldn't have bothered you if it weren't important. I was told to bring in Adeptus Diall for questioning.' He was doing everything he could to distance himself from responsibility. It was a tactic I knew well.

'And?'

He licked his lips. 'Maybe I should talk to Adeptus Winter on his own?'

'Is that a question?' the Ipsissimus snapped. 'Because the answer is no. Tell us what the problem is.'

Smythe took a shaky breath. 'Well, I went to Adeptus Exemptus Diall's home as instructed. Not just me, there were three of us from the Arcane office.'

Dread snaked its way down my spine.

'And?'

Smythe seemed to shrink into himself. 'He's dead. Diall, I mean. It looks like he's been stabbed.'

DURING MOST OF the journey to Diall's home, Winter was silent. His face was a grim mask and the stiff way he held himself showed his tension. Truthfully, I felt the same way. Maybe Diall had died whilst trying to master the more dangerous Cypher spells but I somehow doubted the Manuscripts rose up and shoved a knife into his heart.

'How are you doing?' Winter asked, as we pulled into a wide, leafy driveway leading up to Diall's house.

My fingers plucked at my sleeve. 'I'm drying off,' I said. 'So that's something.'

'I meant are you going to be able to cope with what's about to happen?'

I knew he was referring to seeing Diall's corpse. I might watch a lot of crime shows on television but real dead bodies would be far more gruesome and chilling than their fictional counterparts. Clever make-up on a breathing actor was one thing; a very dead witch was something else entirely.

'What's the alternative?' I asked softly. 'You have to go and check Diall's body. The binding means that I have to investigate with you. I'll have to cope.'

'If it's going to be too much, I can get a verbal report from one of the other Arcane Branch members. We can proceed without viewing the body.'

Winter really was concerned about me. Given how seriously he took his job and how vital this investigation was, I was touched. 'I'll manage.' I ran my tongue around my mouth. I could probably do with a stiff whisky first, though. 'How many dead bodies have you had to deal with?'

'Too many. A while back I worked with the police on Arcane secondment. There's a lot of misery in this world, Ivy. Why do you think I do what I do?'

This wasn't the time for blithe remarks so I simply nodded and looked out of the window. Diall's place was nice.

We got out of the car and walked up to the couple standing at the entrance – one policeman and one witch. This was murder; there was no chance that the Order could avoid involving the coppers, but I had a feeling that the red robes were going to take the lead.

The witch bobbed her head at Winter and murmured his name to the policeman. It was clear from the curious flicker in her eyes that she recognised me. She knew enough to keep her mouth shut. This wasn't the time for gossip or pointless questions.

My foot was barely over the threshold when I smelled it. If I thought I knew what death smelled like, I'd been sorely mistaken. Diall probably hadn't been dead for long and still the reek was overpowering. The sewer had been a rose garden compared to the sour, faeces-ridden stench that now confronted me.

There were Arcane Branch witches all over the place. They acknowledged Winter and ignored me. That was fine. We weren't even in the same room as Diall's corpse yet and already I felt like throwing up. Holding a conversation with anyone, even just saying my name, seemed like a step too far.

I breathed in through my mouth. I could do this; I didn't want Winter to think I was a complete wuss – even if I was.

We were directed into the kitchen. It was a cook's delight, with a marble-topped island, copper pans hanging from the ceiling in a neat row and a view out towards the sunny garden. It would have been a beautiful room if it weren't for the dead body lying askew on the tiled floor. Winter walked over to him and knelt down. I told myself not to start heaving and edged over to join him, although I remained standing and wrapped my arms round my body.

There was no doubt what had killed Diall: the large kitchen knife protruding from his chest was a dead giveaway. There was an incredible amount of blood splattered over the pristine kitchen cabinets as well as pooling underneath the body. Diall's hands lay by his side; he was not clutching the knife as I might have expected. His head lay to the side but I could still see the scream on his face. And his eyes were wide open.

I gulped and took a step back. Focus on Winter, I told myself. He's the expert here.

I watched as he examined Diall. He didn't touch the body but his eyes roved over every aspect of it. He paused as he looked at the mortal wound and studied the knife from all angles. He also took his time over Diall's face until I wondered whether he was willing the corpse to open its mouth and start speaking.

'I don't suppose you know necromancy?' a plain-clothes police officer enquired, half-jokingly.

Half the witches in the room sighed. I guess they got asked that a lot. Yes, necromancy was theoretically possible but no one in living memory had been able to master it. It was well known that even just attempting necromancy could consume a person, body and soul if you didn't get it right. Ironically, I was fairly certain that the ability was described at length in the Cypher Manuscripts. Not in the missing Volume 9, though.

Winter merely grunted. He stood up and circled the body a few times, making sure he didn't tread on any vital piece of evidence. When he was done, he beckoned the police officer. 'The murder weapon,' he said. 'Is it from here?'

The officer nodded. 'As far as we can tell. There's a missing knife from the block on the counter.'

So we could assume that this wasn't a premeditated murder; it had been the result of circumstance – unless the killer knew Diall's kitchen well and had planned to use one of Diall's own knives against him.

'Was he married?' My voice was weak and thready, barely audible to anyone but Winter. I cleared my throat and tried again. 'Adeptus Diall,' I said. 'Was he married? Did he have a partner?' Most murders were committed by someone the victim was already close to. Considering the circumstances, it was unlikely that a jealous spouse had done this to him but it was worth asking.

The police officer shook his head. 'Divorced. We checked on his ex-wife. She's been living in Spain for the past three years. We're sending the local police round to her villa but we think we can rule her out.' He glanced at me. 'She's not one of yours.' Probably not a witch then. That was unusual but not necessarily suspect.

'Have we uncovered anything?' Winter asked, addressing the other witches.

The nearest one shook his head. 'Unsurprisingly Adeptus Exemptus Diall had strong wards in place. No spell we can use will work here.'

Typical. Bloody Order witches and their desire for security. It seemed to bite them all back in the end.

'There are no fingerprints except for those of Mr Diall and his housekeeper,' the policeman said.

'Adeptus Exemptus Diall,' Winter growled.

I rolled my eyes. Even now, he remained a stickler for Order protocol. While the policeman bristled, I jumped in to fill the gap. 'Has anyone found any, um, papers?'

One of the witches said, 'There's the *Daily Express*.'

'Uh, no, I mean magical papers.' I ignored Winter's frown. If Diall had taken the missing Cypher Manuscripts either they were here or his murderer had left with them.

The witch pursed her lips. 'Nothing beyond what you'd expect. A few interesting treatise on the workings of Myomancy but nothing unusual.' Her eyes grew sharp. 'Why?'

Winter coughed. 'On the way here Ms Wilde was wondering whether a layman might have broken in to steal some magical artefacts or books.'

'We can't say for sure whether anything is missing but nobody appears to have rifled through his possessions. There are no obvious gaps on his shelves.' She paused. 'We did find this, however.' She held out a piece of paper in her gloved hands.

I glanced down, confused. It just looked like random numbers to me.

'It's the…'

'Coordinates for the library,' Winter finished. He pointed towards the last few numbers. 'And here, minus three at the end.' He pressed his lips together.

'That could mean three levels down,' the witch interjected

helpfully. She flipped the paper over and I realised it was a picture of the sceptre. I drew in a sharp breath. As usual, Winter didn't react but he had to be thinking the same as me.

'And herbs?' Winter asked. 'Any sign of what magic he might have been working on?'

She shrugged. 'Some brimstone and foxglove. There are some more jars in his office but we've not had a chance to look at them properly yet.'

Diall's corpse took that opportunity to let out what I can only describe as a massive belch. I yelped and jumped, banging into Winter's hard body. He reached out an arm to steady me. 'That's quite normal,' he assured me.

Normal? Ickity ick ick. 'I'll have a look through his office and see what's there,' I said hastily.

A faint smile settled on his lips. 'Good idea.' He turned back to the others and started asking more questions.

I darted out of the kitchen, pausing only to ask a red robe where the office was. My shirt felt tight and uncomfortable and I was sure that Diall's heating was turned all the way up. On the plus side, I'd kept the contents of my stomach where they belonged so things could have been worse.

Diall's office was like a cupboard. It was crammed full of books and papers and, although there was a desk, the place was cramped and dingy. I sat down on his chair and contemplated where my life had gone wrong. This time last week I was driving happily around the streets of Oxford dropping off old ladies and businessmen. I sighed. Being a key part of a murder investigation was not what I'd dreamed of.

I ran my eyes along the shelves but nothing caught my attention. There was no flashing neon sign pointing towards the stolen Volume 9. I leant back and fiddled with the drawers. The first one contained a set of quills and a stained inkwell. The second was filled with small glass jars of dried herbs. Interested from a purely professional standpoint, I rifled through them.

Some looked more than slightly past their sell by date. Helpfully, Diall had labelled each one – and they were in alphabetical order. Musk. Myrtle. Nettle. Oak blossom. Ossombe root. Parsley.

I froze and went back for a second look. Ossombe root. I lifted up the jar and stared at it. The jar contained three or four ounces of dried brown stuff. I unscrewed the lid and took a quick whiff. Well, it was certainly pungent.

It didn't seem relevant to the investigation that Diall had this particular herb in his possession and he certainly didn't need it any more. I placed the jar on the top of the desk and looked at it. It wouldn't be missed. I weighed up my options then, without thinking about it any further, shoved it in my pocket. It would be good to be free from the Order – and it would certainly be good to be free from Winter and his tiresome work ethic.

Right?

CHAPTER SIXTEEN

'Diall has to have taken the Manuscript. And hidden the sceptre.'

'Of the sceptre, we can be almost certain,' Winter replied. 'But of the Manuscript, there's no actual proof, although it does seem the likeliest scenario. It's definitely not at his house though.'

'How about his office at the Order?'

'The Ipsissimus has people searching it right now.'

I gnawed on my bottom lip. 'Do they know what they're looking for?'

Winter ran a hand through his hair. 'They will if they find it.'

And if they didn't find it, the Order were going to have to tell the world that it was missing. They couldn't keep something like that hidden for long. Instead of pointing out the obvious, I focused on something else which had been bugging me. 'You didn't like Diall, did you?' I said quietly.

He pursed his lips. 'For someone who professes not to care about the Order, you certainly pay attention.'

I didn't comment. It might be entirely irrelevant to our case but I still wanted to know the reason behind Winter's antipathy for his now dead colleague.

He sighed. 'Second Level witches like myself are involved in the recruitment and promotion of others. For example, we sit on the board that decides whether witches like your neighbour are permitted to move into the next Level. Obviously the Third Level members have the final say but our opinions still carry weight. Adeptus Exemptus Diall had a bad habit of speaking up for those whose skills were not always up to par. I've been pushing to launch an investigation into his machinations for quite some time.'

I was intrigued. 'Why would Diall do something like that? If he recommended someone who couldn't do the job, it would surely come back to bite him in the arse.'

'I have a theory.' Winter fell silent.

I waited for him to elaborate further; when he didn't, I prodded him. 'Well? What's your theory?'

'It's moot now.'

'You don't know that.'

'I have no desire to speak ill of the dead. Or of a fellow witch.' Winter's manner was stiff and unyielding. No, that wasn't going to work.

'Winter,' I said, 'this might have something to do with our investigation.'

He snorted. 'Unlikely.'

'You're too close to the subject matter because you're emotionally involved. You need an objective ear.'

'As much as you enjoy objecting, Ivy, I don't think it could ever be said that you're objective.'

The blue-eyed one certainly had a way with words. 'Go on. I won't tell anyone.' I crossed my fingers and held them up to prove it. 'I promise.'

Winter muttered something under his breath. 'Fine,' he said. 'Diall was ambitious.' He said it with a flourish, as if it would explain everything.

'Er, I hate to break it to you, but just about every Order witch is ambitious.'

Winter rolled his eyes at my inability to understand his point. 'He was encouraging lesser members into positions they shouldn't have held so that in the future they would be more likely to support him in return.' He paused. 'Or so I believe. Adeptus Exemptus Diall could be very persuasive when he wanted to be.'

I considered this. 'So couldn't one of those so-called lesser members have killed him?'

'Why would you bite the hand that feeds you?'

'Because,' I said softly, repeating my earlier point, 'every Order witch is ambitious.' I skipped round him to avoid a ladder propped up against the wall of my building.

Winter's mouth twitched. 'It's a possibility,' he finally conceded.

'Ha ha! You see? I can do this.' I stretched out my arms. 'I can be an investigator extraordinaire.'

'It's a theory. And not a very plausible one either.' Winter stopped walking for a moment. 'It's important not to believe too strongly in any one idea without concrete evidence. Otherwise you start looking for evidence to fit the theory rather than the other way around. There are no shortcuts in this line of work. And ambition isn't a bad thing. The desire to succeed and do better is what drives society forward.'

'Not everyone can be Ipsissimus. What drives society forward is having a strong backbone of people willing to do the jobs that their leaders don't want to dirty their hands with.'

'Like driving taxis?' he asked drily.

'Okay, maybe not that. I was thinking more like cleaners and binmen and herb collectors. Those sorts of jobs, although people do need to be able to get around when they need to. But you have to see what I mean.'

'I do,' he answered. 'But you have to see what I mean too.' He opened the main door and held it for me while I ducked inside.

I wrinkled my nose. 'Yeah, okay, I suppose I do.' I glanced at him and smiled. 'Look at us,' I marvelled. 'Next we'll be skipping along hand in hand.' I turned left for the lift while Winter went immediately for the stairs. Oh well, you couldn't have everything.

We re-grouped upstairs then walked into Eve's flat. Although Bell End and Alice barely stirred, Princess Parma Periwinkle and Harold sprang apart. It looked to me as if they'd only been grooming each other but I couldn't be sure. I reckoned Brutus would be pretty annoyed if he knew. That was until he emerged yawning and looking pretty darned self-satisfied from behind a nearby cushion. Alrighty.

Winter looked from the cats to me and back again. We shared a moment of amusement and then got to work. I went for Bell End while Winter focused on Alice.

'How's it hanging?' I enquired. Bell End glared at me. I smiled, entirely without humour. 'Let me guess. You want to be freed immediately. This has all been a terrible misunderstanding.'

Winter loosened Alice's gag. 'Would you like something to drink?'

She licked her lips. 'Just let us go.'

'We've been to see your boss,' I told Bell End. His eyes flew up to mine. My smile grew. 'I thought that would get your attention.'

'Did you tell him about us?' Alice demanded. 'Does he know we're here?'

'Unfortunately not,' Winter replied. 'On account of the fact that he's dead.'

While Winter studied Alice's reaction, I did the same to Bell End. He appeared momentarily alarmed then he relaxed, as if he'd decided that we were lying.

'It's true,' I told him softly. 'Look into my eyes. You'll be able to tell.'

'Was it you?' Alice asked. 'Did you kill him?' To her credit, there wasn't so much as a quiver in her voice.

'No. We did not.' Winter continued to watch her. 'But it looks like whoever did already knew him. He was found in his kitchen with one of his own knives sticking out of his gullet.'

Bell End moaned. He believed us now.

'I'll ask again. Why did he send you here?'

As his gag was still in place, Alice answered for him. 'You know why. We were to cast herbs so we could track Harrington and Adeptus Exemptus Winter.'

'And Diall asked you personally to do this.'

'Yes,' she said tiredly. 'We've been through all this.' She seemed genuinely upset about Diall and I almost felt sorry for her. Her shoulders drooped. 'Take us into the Order. We'll admit to it all.' She sighed. 'Just don't keep us here any longer.'

I met Winter's eyes. He nodded. Removing Bell End's gag, I moved closer to him. 'Did Diall ever mention the Cypher Manuscripts?'

He screwed up his face in response. 'What? Why would he?'

'Did he ever ask you to go and look at them for him?'

'No.'

'Did he spend any time studying them?'

'For fuck's sake!' Bell End blasted. 'You stupid bitch! How many times do I have to say the same thing?'

Winter abandoned Alice and came to my side. He knelt down and regarded Bell End soberly. 'If you ever call her that again,' he murmured, 'you will live to regret it.'

It wasn't Winter's words, it was the way he said them. A shiver ran down my spine and I wasn't even the one he was threatening. Feeling the sudden urge to create some space between Winter and me, I took his place next to Alice.

'How about you?' I asked. 'Was there ever a time you heard your boss talk about the Cyphers?'

Her eyes spat fire. She didn't like me very much. Shocker. 'He might have mentioned them in conversation once or twice,' she said through gritted teeth. 'I really don't remember.'

'Well,' I told her, 'you really should try harder.'

'He said once that they should be more accessible. He wanted to be able to take them out of the library and study them in more detail.'

Finally we were getting somewhere. 'And did he mention which volumes in particular he was interested in?'

'No,' Alice replied flatly. 'He did not.'

'Can't you ever keep your mouth shut?' Bell End grunted from the other side. 'It was Volume 9, okay? He wanted Volume 9.'

Over their heads, Winter and I exchanged looks. Well, well, well.

'IT DOESN'T PROVE ANYTHING,' Winter argued, once we were back in the privacy of my flat.

'Of course it does! You said how desperate Diall was to get more power. He stole the Manuscript. Someone else came along, saw he had it and took it from him, killing him in the process.' I dusted off my palms. 'I think our work is done here.'

Winter folded his arms across his chest. I pretended not to notice the way his muscles bulged. 'Except we don't know who killed him and we don't know where the missing Manuscript is.'

I held up my index finger. 'If I recall, our task was to find out who stole the sceptre and recover it. We've already achieved far more than that. I think it's time we passed this to someone else. It's a murder investigation now, not stolen property.'

'We have a long way to go yet, Ivy. Don't you want to know who tried to kill us?'

'Diall, of course. And now he's dead. I'd call that a win.'

'It might not have been him. Diall is just one piece of the puzzle.'

I opened my mouth to argue but the expression on Winter's face stopped me. I supposed it had been worth a try. 'If we recover the Manuscript,' I asked hopefully, 'do you think we'll get a holiday as a bonus?'

'You've only been working for three days. Why on earth would you need a holiday?'

Given what we'd been through, that was an inane question. 'If you have to ask then you'll never understand.'

Winter arched an eyebrow in my direction. 'You're enjoying this, aren't you?'

'Hell, yes. Getting half-drowned and seeing dead bodies is the most fun I've had in *years*.'

Amusement flickered in his eyes. 'I mean pretending to be lazy and needing a break.' He leant forward. 'Secretly, you love this. You just don't want to admit it.'

'I don't love it,' I declared, a tad too loudly. 'I love sleeping and watching TV and reading books and occasionally getting up to make a cup of tea.'

'Yeah, yeah.' His eyes gleamed. 'Methinks the lady doth protest too much.'

I tutted. He was being utterly ridiculous. I did shift my gaze away from his knowing blue eyes, however.

With a mutter, I left Winter where he was and went into the bathroom. Only then did I pull out the jar containing Diall's ossombe root. For one brief moment, I examined it carefully. Then I gave a shrug. I didn't have to use it now. There wasn't a sell-by date. I opened the bathroom cabinet and carefully placed it behind an old bottle of shampoo. As far as anyone knew now, it didn't even exist.

CHAPTER SEVENTEEN

Despite Winter's admonitions, it was obvious he was of the same mind as I was: Diall had to be involved in this somehow, even if he wasn't the sole culprit. There was no chance that he was simply an innocent party or that his death was unrelated. Solve Diall's murder and we'd find the missing Manuscript. It sounded easy when I thought of it that way.

'We'll start with the other people in Diall's department,' Winter declared decisively as we headed back to the car. I was starting to feel like a yo-yo with all this going in and coming out again. 'We already know he sent two of them to commit a crime against Ms Harrington. Perhaps he has done the same to others and they will lead us to more clues.'

'Great!' I beamed. 'Can we stop along the way? I want to pick up a magnifying glass.'

'No.'

'But all the best investigators use them. It'll help us hunt for clues. I was thinking perhaps I should get a gun as well.'

'This is not a television episode. And it's obvious that you have the skills to defend yourself if you need to.'

I thought mournfully of the gun used by my would-be taxi

mugger. I could have used that but the police would have impounded it by now. That's what I got for trying to stay on the right side of the law. I could magic up something into a gun but it wouldn't be like the real thing. Transmogrification was never perfect, especially when technology was involved.

'A gun takes less time to use than magic.' I formed my fore-finger and thumb into an imaginary weapon. 'Bang. You're dead.' I grinned. 'I win.'

'That is not necessarily true.' Winter glared at me. 'I'll prove it. You be the bad guy with the gun.'

I clapped my hands in delight. 'Role-play? Do I get to dress up?'

'You're fine as you are.'

'But…'

'Ivy.'

I rolled my eyes. 'Fine,' I muttered.

'Walk towards me,' Winter instructed. 'When you decide the time is right, you can shoot me with your … gun.'

I mimed placing my weapon in my pocket. 'This is going to be a piece of cake.' I started strolling; to add to the atmosphere, I also started humming. Nothing to see here, just a plumpish blonde out for a walk. Less than fifteen feet away, Winter pulled back his shoulders and headed in my direction. It was like the world's worst-ever game of chicken.

Although I stayed on the balls of my feet, I forced myself to look relaxed. Even though he knew it was coming, I still wanted Winter to think I was going to wait until he passed me before I reacted.

I didn't look directly at him but I could see him with my peripheral vision. When we were almost shoulder to shoulder, I spun to my left and started to pull out my imaginary gun. Winter also turned, checked my hand, then drew a rune. Before I could bring my hand up to chest level, I was thrown backwards by an immense force. I landed on my back, winded and in considerable pain.

'Shit!' Winter jogged over to me. 'Are you alright?'

I lifted my head weakly. 'It hurts,' I admitted.

'Where?'

I pointed to my back. 'I'm not sure I can move.'

He bent down. 'I'm so sorry, Ivy. I never intended to—'

I lifted up my hand again and this time managed to get my 'shot' off. 'Bang.'

For a moment Winter stared at me then he growled under his breath, 'You cheated.'

'No, I didn't. I took advantage of the situation.' I grinned at him. 'I still won.' I stuck my hand into the air and waved it around. 'Help me up.'

He tutted. 'You're incorrigible.' He reached down, grabbing my palm with his left hand. What I hadn't realised was that he'd pulled out a smattering of herbs from his right pocket. As he hefted me upwards, he blew them into my face.

'What the—?' A cloud of choking black magical smoke enveloped me. I let go of Winter's hand and tried to waft it away. Hearing him chuckle, I spun round as if in the throes of panic. Then I launched a sharp kick, catching him on the shin.

Unable to see him, I leapt backwards, thinking I'd be out of his reach. Winter was faster than I expected, however, and he lunged towards me and barrelled me to the ground. He landed on top of me, just managing to brace himself to avoid crushing me completely. Not that I reckoned I would have minded that much. His blue eyes pierced mine and I shivered.

'Are you cold?'

'No.'

We stared at each other. His head dipped down further until I could feel his hot breath against my skin. 'Ivy,' he began, his voice strained.

'Good afternoon! Do you need some help there?'

I turned my head to the side. It was Mrs Burridge, the woman who lived on the floor above me. 'We're fine,' I called out.

Winter's mouth twisted, then he shifted his weight, pulling himself upright.

'Are you sure? Because I know a great spell.'

'Don't worry, Mrs B. It's all good.'

She peered at us both. 'If you're sure.'

I coughed. 'Yep.'

She smiled benignly and continued on her way.

'I don't know her,' Winter said, no longer looking at me. 'She's a witch?'

I stood up and dusted myself off. 'She thinks she is. The most magic she's ever managed was to avoid paying the building main-tenance fees for three years.' Admittedly, I wished I'd accom-plished that.

Winter let out a non-committal grunt. 'We should go.'

I coughed. 'Yeah.' I hesitated and he looked at me question-ingly. 'I still won though.'

'No, you didn't.'

I folded my arms smugly. Yeah, I did.

DIALL WORKED at the Geomancy Branch, a section of the Order that probably sounds a whole lot more glamorous than it actually is. Geomancy is the magical equivalent of the more spiritual Feng Shui. When new houses are built, the Geomancy Branch are brought in to ensure that everything is planned and structured to avoid disturbing any untoward magical forces. The stronger the Geomancy magic, the more majestic and inspirational the final buildings. As an example, St Paul's Cathedral is surrounded by Geomantic magic. It is said that more than five hundred witches worked with Christopher Wren on that particular project. Walk through the doors and you can still feel the old magic buzzing in the air.

These days, of course, they work on suburban houses and estates. There is little Geomancy called for when it comes to fitted kitchens and underfloor heating. The more technology that is incorporated in new buildings, the more it conflicts with Geomancy. I'd heard on the grapevine that their latest big project involved cowsheds. Admirable, to be sure: cows deserve somewhere decent to sleep just as much as humans. But it wasn't exactly romantic, interesting work. Still, it made some sense that Bell End and Alice were from Geomancy. If you want to be a thief and break into people's houses, understanding the magic that binds them would be very handy.

Winter and I walked into their showy building in the far corner of the Order campus. As if to prove their worth, the Geomancy worker bees had gone to considerable effort to make the place look grand. Like most of the neighbouring university buildings, this one was made out of local Headington stone but it was an odd mish-mash of styles, as if each generation had sought to put their personal stamp on the structure. There were sweeping curves coupled with harsh gargoyles and perpendicular modern lines. Although it was a mess, I rather liked the way it had been put together. I particularly liked the marble floor in the entrance because it was shiny enough for me to slide across without bothering to pick up my feet.

'How old did you say you were?' Winter enquired.

'Twenty-seven.' I pushed out my arms. Perhaps if I was more streamlined, I could slide to the next pillar. I turned my head and grinned at him. 'If you're trying to make the point that I'm childish, thank you very much. The only reason that most adults don't do things like this is because they're too concerned about what others think. Or they're so worried about their problems they can't think about anything but themselves. Or they no longer see

169

the wonder and joy in sliding across a floor or down a banister. I think that's sad, not immature.'

'Hmmm.' Winter scratched his chin. Rather than frowning at me in disapproval, he shocked me by flinging himself forward and trying to glide along himself. He didn't get very far. 'This is stupid,' he muttered.

'Your shoes are too sensible. They probably have expensive non-slip soles. Now if you took them off and tried in your socks…'

He tilted his head. 'Don't push your luck, Ivy.'

I winked at him. 'You gave me the opening, *Raphael*.'

For a long moment he was silent. When he spoke, I barely heard him. 'Rafe.'

'Pardon?'

Winter cleared his throat. 'It's Rafe. Not Raphael. I'm not an angel.'

'You just look like one,' I said, the words out of my mouth before I could stop them. 'I mean…' Ah, darn it. I shrugged. 'You're a remarkably good-looking guy.'

He met my eyes. I thought he looked rather pleased. 'You're not so bad yourself.'

'I'll take that,' I said cheerfully. 'It beats being told I need to go on a diet.'

Winter had the grace to redden slightly. Before he could apol-ogise – and end up embarrassing us both even more – I pulled back my shoulders and stopped monkeying around. 'We should get going.'

He nodded. 'Yes.' Then, 'You're becoming a bad influence on me.'

I patted him on the shoulder. 'Then there's hope for you yet.'

We walked, rather than slid, towards the reception desk. A smartly dressed man without a hair out of place greeted us. 'I've always wanted to do that,' he confided in a delighted tone.

Winter, embarrassed at having been caught doing something

that didn't involve marching like a sergeant major, frowned. 'I'm Adeptus Exemptus Winter,' he said. 'And this is my associate, Ivy Wilde.'

Much as I liked being described as Winter's associate, I needed to come up with a title for myself so that I sounded as grand as Winter. Supinus Wondrous, perhaps. Both Winter and the receptionist looked at me strangely and I realised I must have said it out loud. Oops. I grinned and stuck out my hand. 'Nice to meet you.'

The perfectly coiffed man smiled back, although a touch more nervously now that he knew who he was dealing with. Winter seemed to have that effect on a lot of people. 'We've been expecting you,' he said. 'I'm to take you to one of our meeting rooms.'

He stepped out from behind the desk and led the way. I was tempted to start sliding again but the moment had passed. Instead I decided to fill the silence with something more helpful. 'What's your name?'

He didn't turn around. 'Michael Weathers.'

'And did you know Adeptus Exemptus Diall well?' I enquired.

'He didn't speak to me very often,' Weathers answered. 'But I'm only a Neophyte and I don't have much aptitude for magic. I mean,' he said hastily, with a backward glance at Winter, 'I can do the basics but I'm not that talented.'

'Maybe you just need to find your niche,' I suggested.

'I thought I was doing well,' he said in a low voice. 'But Adeptus Diall set me straight. I have a lot to learn. I'm not sure I'll ever progress.'

I nudged Winter meaningfully. Maybe Diall hadn't just worked on elevating those whose talent was inferior; he might also have tried to keep down those with genuine abilities. So much for Order honour.

Winter nodded, acknowledging my meaning. 'What have your duties been?' he asked Weathers.

'Manning the desk. That's what I do.'

'You've not been sent out on any recent errands?'

Weathers let out a humourless laugh. 'No. I don't go anywhere.'

No doubt Winter would insist on double-checking this but I was certain that the receptionist was telling the truth; we weren't going to find anything more useful from him.

'You know,' I said, feeling sorry for the young man, 'we would make a great team. The three of us, I mean. We'd be Wilde Wintry Weather. We should start our own agency immediately.'

Winter raised his eyes to the heavens. I shrugged. I thought it was a *great* idea. Judging by the way Weathers' shoulders were shaking, he did too.

Weathers deposited the pair of us in a pentagonal meeting room; another acknowledgment of the abilities of Geomancy no doubt. Seemingly from out of nowhere, Winter pulled out a sheet of paper with a list of names on it. I peered over his shoulder. There had to be at least twenty people. I heaved a silent sigh of despair. We were going to be here forever.

'You should take the lead in the interviews,' Winter said, surprising me.

I blinked. 'Why?'

'Because people seem to like you. You have a way of getting them to open up. Look at that man there. Weathers. I thought he was going to tell you his whole life story.'

I pursed my lips. 'I've been a taxi driver for quite a few years,' I said. 'And people like to chat. Maybe it's rubbed off.' I grinned. 'That, or I'm supremely talented.'

Winter smirked as if the idea were ridiculous and I punched him in the arm. He yelped, startling the first interviewee who almost backed out of the room again.

'Come in, come in!' I called out cheerfully. 'I'm just beating up my associate.'

The woman shuffled into the room, throwing me a wary

glance. She sat down on the chair in front of us, perching on the edge in case she had to make a run for it. So much for my winning ways.

I knitted my fingers underneath my chin and relaxed. 'Hi.' I checked the sheet. 'Bethany.'

'Hi,' she responded.

I thought about how to start. Given how many names there were on the list, and that I wanted to get home again before the next millennium was up, I decided there was no point in beating around the bush. 'Have you ever stolen anything for Adeptus Diall?'

Shock rippled across her face. 'What? I … what? No!'

'What was the last thing he asked you to do?'

'Make him a cup of coffee.'

I leant forward. 'How did he take his coffee?'

'Three sugars.' She stared wildly at Winter as if praying he would rescue her. He didn't.

'You may go now,' I said, dismissing her.

'But…'

'Go! Shoo!' I waved her off. 'Send in the next one.'

As soon as she left the room, Winter leant across to me. 'Ivy,' he said patiently. 'The reason I said you could take the lead is because you're nice to people. It encourages them to tell the truth. I don't think the approach you just used is going to do that.'

'We're on a clock though, aren't we? We need to find the missing Cypher Manuscript before whoever's taken it grasps all of its magic.'

He looked at me suspiciously. 'Is that the only reason?'

'Of course!' I smiled innocently.

'Why did you ask her how Diall takes his coffee?'

'To see whether she was lying or not. The devil is in the detail. She didn't hesitate. She's nothing more than a coffee flunky.' I amended this slightly. 'At least as far as Diall was concerned.' I paused. Hang on a second.

The next witch was edging into the room. I held up my hand and he halted in mid-step. 'Bring Bethany back.' He didn't say a word but turned on his heel and did as I asked.

'Actually,' I murmured in an aside to Winter, 'this power thing is kind of fun. If we get Volume 9 back maybe I should keep it for a while. It's not as if you lot can look after it safely.'

Winter tutted as Bethany, looking more nervous than before, came back in. 'Sit down, please,' I told her.

She did as I asked. 'What is it?'

I leant forward. Bethany leant back. 'I'm going to assume that you make coffee for a lot of people in this office.'

Her eyes darted to Winter. He was watching me intently. 'I suppose.'

'That must be a bit shit. You're just as much of a witch as them, right?'

Her nose twitched like a rabbit's. I was right. 'Yeah,' Bethany admitted cautiously. 'It's a pain but I don't mind that much.'

I pointed towards the door. 'That guy.' I glanced at Winter's sheet of paper. 'Bill January. How does he take his coffee?'

'He doesn't,' she answered. 'He prefers tea. Weak and milky.' Her expression told me exactly what she thought of his preference.

'How much of your time do you spend by the kettle?'

She looked wary, as if I were trying to accuse her of something. 'Quite a bit.'

I pressed ahead. 'I bet that when you give them their drinks, they barely even notice you.'

'Sometimes they say thank you,' she muttered.

'And sometimes they don't.' I smiled. 'Sometimes they're in mid-conversation and they barely pay you any attention at all.'

Her bottom lip jutted out. 'Yeah.'

My smile grew. 'As a result, you probably know more about what's going on under this roof than anyone else. You hear things. Lots of things.' She didn't say anything. 'Bethany?'

'Was that a question?'

I liked her. 'Am I right?' I asked softly.

She shrugged. 'I guess.'

'Are there any illicit romances going on?'

Winter sucked in his breath but didn't stop me. That was good. I knew what I was doing. Sort of.

Bethany's eyes shifted. 'Deborah from marketing is having an affair with Tony.' She hesitated then dropped her voice. 'He's married. They think I've not noticed but they share looks all the time. Brush against each other when they think no one is paying attention. That kind of thing.'

She clearly disapproved. To encourage her, I pursed my lips and shook my head. 'Awful.' I crossed my legs. 'You have an eye for detail.'

The compliment pleased her. 'I do.'

I kept my voice soft and went in for the kill. 'Have you noticed anything unusual lately about anyone here? Anything at all? You could really help us out. Winter will put in a good word for you. He's terribly important but he doesn't let it go to his head. In fact, he's made coffee for me and I'm a nobody.'

Bethany thought about it. 'The HR Head. What's his name? Adeptus Price? He was round here looking for Adeptus Diall. He seemed quite desperate to talk to him.'

'Did he say why?'

'No. He was pretty frantic though.'

I exchanged glances with Winter. 'Anything else?'

Bethany shrugged. 'Some people are missing. We've not seen them for days. No one's saying anything because they think that they're on some kind of secret mission for Diall. But I know they weren't expecting to be away for so long because I've had to field calls about their missed appointments.'

'Who? Who's not here?'

'Matthew Bellham and Alice Fairclough. They work together as partners. They left three days ago without telling anyone where they were going or what they were up to and we don't know where they are now.' Oh, yeah, them. I grimaced slightly but Bethany wasn't done. 'And another witch has been gone for ages. A First Level witch called Oscar Marsh.'

A triumphant trumpet sounded in my head. 'Tell me about him.'

'He's a drunk,' she said dismissively. 'Adeptus Diall seemed to like him but he's useless. And he's a bastard.'

'What makes you say he's a bastard?'

'He was born out of wedlock, of course.'

I blinked. 'Er…'

Bethany ignored my startled reaction. 'He doesn't hold with the old ways. He brings a laptop into work.' Her eyes grew saucer-wide. 'A laptop,' she repeated, obviously shocked at such a heinous infraction of the rules.

'Unbelievable.'

She nodded fervently in agreement.

'When was the last time you saw him?'

'He left an hour or two after Bellham and Fairclough. He's not been back since.'

'Bethany,' Winter said, 'could you get us his personnel file?'

She seemed surprised. 'Oh, I don't have it. All those sorts of things are kept over at HR.'

I frowned at Winter. 'Is that typical?'

'I suppose so.'

I couldn't help wondering whether Tarquin was involved with this too. He was in HR and I certainly wouldn't put it past him. 'Thank you so much, Bethany. You've been extraordinarily helpful. You may go.'

'Sure.' She stood up and pushed her chair back before bobbing her head and leaving. Once she'd gone, I got to my feet as well. 'Now that,' I said with a dramatic flourish, 'is how to conduct twenty interviews in five minutes. Let's get out of here.'

Winter didn't move. 'There are still nineteen people to go.'

'Yeah, but we've got what we needed. Bethany has her finger on the pulse.' I grinned. 'Never underestimate the tea lady.'

'It's important to talk to everyone.'

'It'll take hours, days probably. We don't have that kind of time and we already have a new lead. Stop being such a stickler for the rules, Rafe. We can come back if we need to.'

'This is not the way things are normally done.'

'You should be happy.'

'I am.' He didn't look it. He seemed rather disturbed.

'You're not smiling,' I pointed out. He didn't smile all that often and he really should because his eyes crinkled up and he looked approachable and warm rather than – wintry. 'Don't worry about Bethany. There are people like her in every office up and down the land. I'm sure she'll be thrilled that you could talk to someone about giving her more responsibility but she probably loves knowing all the gossip too. She'd be great at the reception desk,' I mused. 'Then Michael Weathers could go off and improve his magic.'

Winter still didn't smile. 'And what if someone whose parents dared to have sex before marriage shows up?'

I shrugged. 'She's old-fashioned. And yes, a bit odd. But we can't lock everyone up for that. If we did, I reckon the two of us would be top of the list. Besides, this is the Order. Weird goes with the territory. Along with power hungry, overly ambitious and downright irritating.'

Winter sighed and pushed back his hair. 'Let's find the file for this Marsh fellow and pay him a visit. We should probably talk to Adeptus Price too and find out why he was so desperate to speak to Diall. But we need to make a detour first.'

I wrinkled my nose. 'A long detour?'

'We can take fifteen minutes out.' His jaw hardened. 'It'll be worth it.'

'Will it involve stairs?'

I didn't get an answer.

IN THE END, I was rather thankful for Winter's side mission. It was grey and blustery outside, with a chill that penetrated my bones. It was the sort of day when, by rights, I should have been curled up on my sofa with my duvet and a vast mug of steaming hot chocolate. I moaned at the thought; that garnered me a strange look from Winter.

We ended up in a large unsignposted building. I must have passed it on numerous occasions when I was a Neophyte but I'd never wondered what it was. 'What is this place?' I enquired, trotting to keep up with Winter's long-legged march. 'And can you slow down?'

'I promised you fifteen minutes. I would hate to go back on my word.' He still didn't tell me where we were.

We swerved round the corner and came out into a vast atrium. I gasped. It was really quite something. Even with the grey skies outside, the light filtering in through the glass was extraordinary. There were plants everywhere, some of which I recognised, some I didn't. Every shade of green was represented and the earthy smell that filled the space was incredibly alluring. It almost made me want to start my own allotment. Almost.

'Let me guess. This is for herb lovers like you?'

'Try again.'

There was a strange chattering sound. I spotted a squirrel with an impressively bushy tail disappearing into the under-growth. 'Hey!' I exclaimed. 'That squirrel was red!' I turned to Winter and realised he was watching me carefully.

'Yes,' he said. 'It's part of a programme we're undertaking to help the red squirrels return in full force to the countryside now that we're over-run by greys.' He pointed to a patch of tall plants. 'Look at these.'

'Wheat?'

'Yes. Magic is being used to strengthen their roots and their ability to grow in difficult terrains. There's already been considerable success and farmers across the world are reaping the benefits. Literally.'

Okay, I was impressed. I opened my mouth to ask Winter another question but my attention was caught by a gaggle of uniformed children heading our way. I raised an eyebrow. 'Getting the magically inclined in while they're young?'

He shook his head. 'Wrong again.' He gestured to the red-robed witch leading the way and she ambled over.

'Adeptus Exemptus Winter! What a pleasure.' She presented her cheek for him to kiss then kissed him back. I banked down the trickle of anger I felt at someone else's lips touching the cheek of *my* partner. What a ridiculous thing to be annoyed about.

'This is Ivy Wilde,' he said. 'Ivy, meet Adeptus Major Goldstein.'

There was a flicker of curiosity in her gaze as she smiled at me and inclined her head. 'Pleased to meet you.'

'Why don't you tell Ivy what you're doing?'

Goldstein lit up. 'My pleasure. I'm with this group who've come from London.'

She was interrupted by a boy of about ten who tugged impatiently at her sleeve. 'I need to go to the toilet.' He spoke in an oddly stilted manner and wouldn't look her directly in the eye.

'Of course.' She beckoned another witch from the back of the pack who led the boy away.

'He's autistic,' I said.

She smiled. 'Yes, in this group they all are. We use magic to boost their development and help them make sense of the world. It's a slow process but we're seeing some real results. Yesterday, we had a great bunch of kids in who were all suffering from cancer. We haven't found a way to beat their disease but we were able to show them the progress we've been making in the labs.'

179

I licked my lips. 'Wow. That's … that's really good.' The words sounded stupid. Talk about an understatement.

One of the younger children reached out and touched a rose stem, drawing back and howling when a thorn pierced his skin. Goldstein hurried over to him while I turned to Winter. 'So that's today's lesson, is it? That the Order does a lot of good?' I'd been dimly aware that there were projects like these but I'd never given them much thought.

'You were only here as a Neophyte for a couple of months, Ivy. Your focus would have been on initiation and basic studies.' A trace of a smile crossed his mouth. 'Although I'm pretty certain you skipped the fitness components.'

'Hey!' I protested. 'They were voluntary.'

'Everything we've experienced so far – and everyone we've met – has suggested that the Order is big and bad and thoroughly inward-looking.' His gaze grew more intense. 'Yes, witches here are ambitious but they have good reason to be. It's not all murder investigations and stolen objects. The people here aren't all evil power seekers or downtrodden receptionists. You've seen the sordid side because that's what the Arcane Branch is involved with.' He shrugged. 'That's part of our job description. But you need to understand what we are fighting for. I know things turned sour for you all those years ago, and I know we're probably not making much of a positive impression on you now, but I promise that most of what the Order achieves is for the betterment of everyone, regardless of whether they are witches or not.'

I met his eyes. 'Why isn't this kind of thing advertised more often? If more people knew what the Order was doing, they'd be more inclined to think well of you.'

'Nothing is secret. Anyone can petition to find out what we're up to. But good news doesn't make headlines and, regardless of what you might think, we don't like to boast.'

My gaze swept across the impressive space. 'Why are you showing me this?' I asked. 'I think I've proved that I've invested.

I'm taking the investigation seriously and not simply hanging onto your coat-tails.'

'I know,' he answered quietly. 'I suppose I wanted you to see it because I want you to love the Order as much as I do.' His hand brushed feather-light against mine and I shivered. Winter licked his lips and gazed at me with an intensity which sank all the way down into my very soul. My mouth went dry. Then he cleared his throat. 'We should go and find Oscar Marsh now so we can save the world.'

'Yeah.' As disappointed as I was that the moment between us had been so fleeting, the thought that an Order witch might be doing something to jeopardise the kind of operation which happened here was making me feel sick.

CHAPTER EIGHTEEN

THE ATMOSPHERE INSIDE THE HR OFFICE WAS CONSIDERABLY different to last time. Clearly everyone was on their best behaviour; they had their heads down and grim expressions on their faces.

We were allowed in immediately, which didn't make the receptionist happy. She glowered at us both for daring to interrupt her peace and quiet. She was hardly a good advertisement for HR but she wasn't my problem and she didn't really interest me.

When Winter and I strolled into the main office, several people straightened their spines and I clocked more than one nervous glance in our direction. Whether that was from guilt or something else, I had no idea.

I spotted Tarquin in the far corner, seated at a choice desk next to the window. Given the rain outside, at least he wasn't getting much of a view. For the first time in a long while, I felt very angry towards him. Winter's little side tour had opened my eyes to what the Order did for society; he wouldn't have had to show me if Tarquin hadn't ripped my future away from me.

Tarquin looked up as we walked through, flashing us a broad

smile. It might have been directed at Winter rather than me but it still got my hackles up.

'Don't let him get to you,' Winter told me in an undertone.

'Am I being that obvious?'

'When you're pissed off, the tips of your ears turn red.' I stared at him. He shrugged. 'It's rather adorable.'

Unable to help myself, I grinned. 'I bet you never thought you'd call me that when we first met.'

'Oh,' he murmured, 'there are many things I've changed my mind about where you're concerned, Ivy.'

Something about the way he said my name made me feel very warm and very happy. At this rate, I'd be licking the soles of his feet and begging to be taken to the gym to lift weights and half kill myself. What a horrific thought.

We were almost at the corner of the room marked 'Records' when the door to Adeptus Price's office opened and the man himself appeared. He seemed even scrawnier than last time. He shambled over to us as if he had all the time in the world. 'Adeptus Exemptus Winter,' he said, waving his arms expansively. 'And … companion. Ms…' He paused. Considering that he was the head of HR and I was the subject of a meeting he had attended three days ago where he was blamed for my recruitment, I expected him to remember my name.

'Ivy Wilde,' I offered helpfully. I stuck out my hand. For a moment Price eyed it as if it contained germs then he shook it with a limp-wristed grip. He'd be reaching for the hand sanitizer or wiping his palm on his robe any second now.

Price released me and focused on Winter. 'What can we do for you?'

'We're looking for a personnel file,' Winter said. 'Oscar Marsh. He works in Geomancy.'

If Price was intrigued by the request, he didn't show it. 'Of course, of course.' He clapped his hands and pointed to Tarquin on the other side of the room, who was pretending to look busy.

'Villeneuve!' he barked. 'Get the file on a…' He looked back at Winter.

'Oscar Marsh.'

'Marsh,' Price repeated. 'From Geomancy.'

Tarquin got to his feet. 'Certainly, Adeptus,' he murmured. 'I'm happy to help.' He walked purposefully to the filing cabinets, as if he were delighted by this mundane task. I was delighted to see him acting like a general dogsbody but I'm kind of petty that way.

'Tell me, Adeptus Price,' Winter murmured, in a tone that suggested hidden steel and would have sent many a lesser witch scurrying for the hills, 'why were you visiting Adeptus Diall earlier this week? Apparently you were rather anxious to speak to him.'

Price jumped but he recovered quickly. 'Adeptus Diall helped me out from time to time.' He sighed, although it seemed calculated for sympathy rather than a genuine sound of despair. 'I've been having some difficulties with my staff and I was looking for guidance on how to deal with them. Some people don't have the respect for their elders that they used to.'

'Perhaps because respect needs to be earned,' Winter said.

Price stared at him. 'Quite.'

Winter switched tack. 'Do you keep all the personnel files here? I wouldn't have thought you have the space.'

Price chuckled. 'Well we are Human Resources. It makes sense that all the personnel files are kept here. They used to be all over the place but I have centralized the system. Between you and me, there was a terrible incident over in Amulets where they misplaced twelve files. It caused some consternation, I can tell you.' His smile dropped. 'Although not as much consternation as recent events. It's simply terrible what happened to Adeptus Diall. And the Cypher Man—'

'Thank you, Adeptus Price,' Winter said loudly.

The witch seemed to realise his error in broadcasting what

was supposed to be a secret, classified matter. He coughed to cover his mistake. 'Can we get you any refreshments while you wait?'

'Tea, please,' I chirped. I could do with a cuppa.

Winter frowned. 'Just the file.' The man had no true understanding of what it meant to be British.

'Fair enough. No rest for the wicked in Arcane Branch!' Price grinned and looked at me. 'So, Ms Wilde,' he enquired. 'How are you settling into your new role?'

Ha! So he did remember me after all. 'Oh, it's fabulous,' I enthused. 'But there aren't enough tea breaks.'

Price laughed, although it was obviously forced. 'Indeed. Indeed.' He licked his lips. 'I am sorry about the mix-up, you know. It was simple human error that can happen to us all.' He glanced anxiously at Winter. 'No one's perfect. And I do have some incredibly difficult people in my Department who…'

Tarquin cleared his throat. 'Adeptus Price? Could you come over here, please, sir?'

Fleeting annoyance flashed across Price's face. 'Excuse me,' he muttered, turning away to help Tarquin with the difficult task of opening a filing cabinet.

'I feel a bit sorry for him,' I whispered to Winter. 'He's clearly out of his depth here. And he did apologise.'

Winter glowered. 'Then in the same breath he blamed his Department for the cock-up. He's the one in charge. He should take full responsibility.'

I kept my voice low to avoid being overheard. 'By his own admission, he doesn't get a lot of respect from his team. Is he another person who benefited from Diall's work? It would make sense, given he was looking for him for help.'

'You mean was Price promoted despite being ill-equipped to manage the job?' Winter watched the witch put his hands on his hips and glare ferociously at Tarquin. 'It's certainly possible. He's only Adeptus Major. But not many witches are keen to run HR. It's not exactly a glamorous position.'

I'd say. 'We should ask him for his own personnel file too,' I suggested.

Winter quirked up an eyebrow. 'We should request the personnel file of the Head of HR from the Head of HR?'

I shrugged. 'Yeah.' My mouth twitched. 'You are Arcane Branch, right?' I teased.

'We,' he said. '*We* are Arcane Branch, Ivy.'

'So you're saying *I* should ask for it?'

Price began walking back to us. 'You will keep your mouth shut,' Winter told me. Contradictory plonker.

Price stopped in front of Winter, looking worried. 'There is a slight problem,' he said.

'What's that?'

'Oscar Marsh's file isn't here.'

'Then,' Winter said, his voice dropping dangerously, 'where is it?'

'Geomancy must have checked it out.' He looked over his shoulder to Tarquin who was still standing, looking bored. 'Have you got the logbook there?'

Tarquin held up a battered-looking notebook. 'Yes.' He scurried over, handing it not to Price but to Winter. Price glared and tried to snatch it out of Winter's hands; when that didn't work, he pushed me out of the way so he could peer over Winter's shoulder. If that bothered Winter, he didn't let it show. He flipped through the pages, using his finger to track down the columns.

'Ha! There!' Price crowed. 'Marsh's file was logged out last week.' He paused. 'I can't read that signature. Honestly, some people have appalling handwriting.'

Winter snapped the book shut and handed it back to Price. 'Thank you for your time.' He turned away then paused, as if a thought had suddenly occurred to him. 'Where were you yesterday morning, Adeptus Price?'

He blinked rapidly. 'Er…' He looked to Tarquin for help.

'You were at that meeting. With Practicus Lee. It was on your calendar.'

Price nodded. 'Ah, yes. Of course.' He smiled. 'Despite being a witch, Practicus Lee knows a fair bit about computers. We've been looking into ways of putting our records online. Not here, you understand,' he added hastily. 'Offsite where they won't affect anyone's magic.'

Winter grunted then glanced at me. 'I know who took the file. Let's go.' He half smiled, half grimaced at Price. 'Thank you again.'

'Adeptus Exemptus Winter!' Tarquin called. 'I can come with you if you wish. I know exactly what the personnel files look like, so I'm sure I can help.'

Winter's blue eyes were cold. 'I think Ms Wilde and I can manage,' he said. 'She's incredibly talented.' He took my elbow and gently propelled me away.

'I love you,' I whispered.

Winter grinned.

ONCE WE WERE BACK OUTSIDE, I nudged Winter. 'Could you really read that handwriting? Do you know who has Marsh's file or were you just trying to escape?'

'I recognised the writing,' he said grimly. 'Tobias Worth-Jones. He works over at Runic Magic.'

I whistled. Only the best of the best finagle their way into that department. 'Friend of yours?' I asked.

'Not really.'

'Do you have any friends?'

'Ivy,' Winter sighed.

I shrugged. 'Just asking. But I don't think we need to find your double-barrelled acquaintance.'

'I have a feeling I'm going to regret asking this. Why not?'

'Price did it.'

Winter turned to me. 'How did you come to that conclusion?'

'He was shifty and nervous. There's no way he got that job without Diall's help. And,' I added, 'he was wearing slip-on shoes. Never trust a man wearing slip-on shoes.'

Winter started walking again. 'And here was me thinking you were going to offer something insightful.'

'I did!'

Winter harrumphed, actually harrumphed. I didn't know people did that any more. 'Let me know if you find any real evidence.'

I remained earnest. 'People always think it's the big muscly guys you need to be afraid of. It's not. It's the weedy ones who have a point to prove.'

'Go on then,' Winter said, folding his arms. 'Why did he murder Diall?'

I thought about it. 'They were secret lovers. Diall stole the Manuscript in order to become more powerful and Price got worried that he'd be left behind.'

'So he killed the love of his life?'

'Okay, I'll admit my theory needs work.' I jabbed Winter in the arm. 'But that guy is definitely shifty.'

'I'll take that under advisement,' Winter said drily. With that, we both lapsed into silence.

IT WAS QUITE a trek to the building where Runic Magic was housed. Along the way, forgetting that I'd never got round to having my shoes re-soled, I stepped in a puddle. Soon I was walking along with a sodden sock and chilly toes, which didn't exactly put me in a good frame of mind.

The Runic witches didn't appear fazed by the weather. As soon as we rounded the corner and their grand old building came into view, I spotted several of them out on the grass in front.

Winter hissed in irritation. 'They've been told time and time again not to do that.'

'Do what?' The words were barely out of my mouth when the group separated: five witches on one side of the lawn and five on the other. A few others peeled off to the edges including, I noted, my old mate Anthea. Well, well, well. She might be in Tarquin's pocket but she was certainly doing well for herself if she'd been assigned to this department. I was proud of her; whether Anthea had avoided me for the last eight years or not, and regardless of her tattle-tales to Tarquin about my sudden reappearance, I still remembered our friendship.

I focused on the others. Winter was still bristling by my side; I had the feeling that he was about to put a halt to these proceedings, whatever they were. I placed a hand on his arm. 'Can we just watch? Pretty please? You don't need to enforce every rule. People will like you more if you loosen up a bit.'

'I don't need people to like me.' He sounded irritated but even so he relaxed slightly. I rubbed my palms together; whatever was about to happen, I reckoned it would be a whole lot of fun. And at least I wouldn't be expected to do anything for a few minutes. I'd take my moments of blissful inactivity wherever I could find them.

A tall, gangly witch on the right stepped forward. He tossed a coin in the air, caught it deftly and flipped it onto the back of his hand.

'Heads,' called out a witch from the opposing team.

The first guy looked down and grinned. 'Tails. We go first.' The other four witches with him pulled back their shoulders, a movement so synchronised that they must have practised it. They began drawing runes.

'They're attacking,' I breathed, finally understanding.

Winter rolled his eyes. 'Yes. They're idiots.'

Each witch apparently had a different speciality. One cast a rune for wind, sending a gust out towards their competitors. Another conjured up a swirl of leaves, seemingly from nowhere. It blocked the other team's vision long enough for a third and fourth witch to work together and draw twin runes to open up a long fissure in the ground.

The other team worked on defensive manoeuvres, casting runes to counter-balance the aggression and keep themselves safe. One almost tipped into the gaping magic sinkhole but another drew a rune quickly enough to snare his arm with a lasso and pull him back. It wasn't enough, though; the final witch on the attacking side cast his rune, a clever spell designed to momentarily alter the very physiology of living creatures. The other witches realised what he was doing and tried to counter it but they couldn't. Within moments, all their legs had turned to jelly and they'd fallen to the ground, yelling.

The winning side cheered while all the runes were undone. The sinkhole sealed up again and the losers staggered to their feet, their bones returning to normal. I wasn't impressed. They'd tried to defend themselves by blocking the spell; what they should have done was mirror it. It's an easier rune to draw so they'd have had more time to reverse it and win the day.

Winter folded his arms and glared icily at them all. 'The infirmary has to deal with the aftermath of these kinds of things far too often,' he muttered. 'And affecting the ground in this area can weaken the foundations of the buildings. It's completely irresponsible.'

'Spoilsport. No one was hurt.' I paused. 'Not permanently. The environment is back to normal. It's a waste of energy, sure, but don't witches have to practise?'

'In safe warded places. Not here.'

'It's harmless,' I told him.

'It's foolhardy.'

Winter was still in snort mode when Anthea finally spotted me and jogged over. Her eyes were shining. 'Ivy! Isn't this great?'

'It seems like a good way to burn off excess energy,' I agreed. Not that that was a problem I suffered from.

She arched an eyebrow in my direction. 'It'd be fun to see a match between you two. Two partners, squaring off against each other, one on one…'

Winter snorted impatiently. 'We don't have time for this.'

'We had time for your detour,' I pointed out. 'What's another five minutes?' I knew this was a safe bet: Winter was never going to agree. Unfortunately, it appeared that Anthea was well aware of that too.

'Well,' she said, 'in that case you and I should take a turn, Ivy. For old times' sake. I'd love to show you what I've learned. You can show off as well. I'm sure you've been doing some magic over the years.'

The tone of her voice suggested that I'd been out in a barren wilderness instead of suburban Oxford. 'Adeptus Exemptus Winter is probably right,' I said, using his formal title to remind her that he was supposed to be the one in charge. 'We really should get going.'

'What's another five minutes?' she asked, throwing my words back at me. Darn it. 'You should let Ivy off the leash, Adeptus Winter.'

I felt his sudden tension. 'She is her own person,' he said stiffly.

Anthea clapped her hands in delight. 'Brilliant. I'll take the right.' She skipped away.

'Bloody hell, Winter,' I muttered. 'You were supposed to put your foot down and refuse her.'

He gave me a blank look. 'How on earth was I supposed to

know that?' His jaw tightened. 'And for the record, you're not on a leash.'

'Apart from the magical binding one.'

He growled, 'That one's not my fault. It doesn't count.'

'Come on, Ivy!' Anthea called.

I sighed. I should have made up more excuses and wriggled away but it was probably faster to do as she wanted.

I shuffled over to the left-hand side. The witches who'd already competed had formed a half circle round us and more were wandering over out of curiosity. As a non-Order witch, I was an object of some fascination.

'The goal is to bring the other person to the ground.' Anthea bopped around, still brimming with enthusiasm. 'Only runes are allowed and there's to be no physical contact.' Humour flashed across her face and she wagged her index finger at me. 'And no sudden death spells or serious dismemberment. Whatever you do has to be immediately reversible when the combat ends.'

Combat? This was all getting a bit too serious. I eyed her then glanced at the audience. Whether I was attacking or defending, I knew deep down I'd have no difficulty in besting her. It wasn't ego. Anthea put her stock in rote-learned runes that had been taught by the Order for decades; I'd gone guerrilla. She wouldn't expect anything that I threw at her. But if I let my pride get in the way and showed what I was really capable of, I reckoned some of the other witches would clamour for more action. Not just today, either; it was possible I'd be here at the Order for some time. I dreaded to think what it would be avoiding potential challengers for the next ninety-six days. If I proved to be the weakling they expected, I'd be left in peace. There was really no contest.

The witch from the first fight stepped forward, tossed his glinting coin and caught it. He addressed me. 'Heads or tails?'

I shrugged. 'Tails.'

He revealed heads. Even better.

'If you're still standing after I've attacked,' Anthea said, 'we swap places. We're allowed to cast one rune each.'

I nodded to show I understood and banked down the temptation to check Winter's glowering face. Don't worry, I tried to project silently, this won't take long.

'Ready?' Anthea called. 'I'll go easy on you, I promise.'

I smiled. She grinned back and started her first rune. Her movements were slow, at least compared to someone like Winter, and I knew before she was halfway through what she was preparing to do. The magic she was using was barely Neophyte level. As her fingers drew upwards in a sweeping motion, it was clear that she was conjuring up a ball to fling at my shins to knock my feet out from under me. To stop it, all I had to do was cast a simple wall. It would take barely a breath. I pasted on a dull expression and waited.

Anthea's ball appeared five metres to my side. She had indeed progressed a great deal since we were teenagers; around double the size of a typical bowling ball, it was hurtling towards me with incredible speed. I furrowed my brow and concentrated. I had to get this just right.

Using jerky movements, I cast my defensive rune. There was a whistling sound as the air drew in around me. I slammed out the heel of my palm at the last second, pushing out a gust of air to knock the ball off course. Given the ball's velocity, however, the energy I put into it wasn't nearly enough. I half turned and it crashed into the side of my calf. Even if I'd wanted to stay upright, I doubt I'd have managed it. I just avoided sprawling face first by bracing my palms against the damp grass. There were a few huffs from the crowd; I was certain I caught at least one witch mutter, 'I told you so.'

Limping slightly because it bloody hurt, I pulled myself upright and grimaced in Anthea's direction. She looked appalled. 'I'm so sorry! Are you alright?'

'Yeah, I'm fine. You're just the better witch.'

'We can go again. You can cast first.'

I managed a half smile. 'No, I think I've suffered enough humiliation for one day.' I shrugged helplessly. 'There's not much a layman like me can do against the might of the Order.' I winced, walked over and shook her hand. 'Thanks, though. That was … not fun.'

'I'm sorry,' she said again.

'Don't apologise. That was the game.'

Anthea bit her lip. 'I told Tarquin you were here.'

'I figured.' I patted her on the shoulder. 'Don't worry about it.' Before I had to listen to any more apologies, I turned away and rejoined an unsmiling Winter. 'There we go,' I said with forced cheerfulness. 'I reckon that was enough delay to stop anyone being suspicious about what we're up to. If we were rushing around like mad things, someone might suspect something was up. Like, say, one of the Cypher Manuscripts being stolen.'

He just looked at me. 'Did you let her win?'

Something about his tone made me think that regardless of how much he disliked these sorts of magic challenges, he despised the idea of throwing a match even more.

'Alas no,' I said. 'Do you think I'd deliberately injure myself?' I pointed at my throbbing leg. 'I think I might have fractured something.'

He frowned and looked down. 'It's just bruised.'

Damn; I'd really have to get him to teach me how to do that some time. 'I guess I'm just not that great in a fight.'

Winter's eyes narrowed suspiciously. 'Then how did you beat two witches on your own and in a confined space?'

For a moment, I didn't have the faintest idea what he was talking about then I remembered Bell End and Alice. The latter was a Second Level witch with a reputation for highly aggressive skills. Oops. 'They didn't know I was a witch when they met me. I caught them off guard.' I pursed my lips. 'If I had more time to prepare, I might be able to best Anthea. Shall I go back and try again? I don't want you to be ashamed to be seen with me now that it's clear I'm not that skilled at magic when I'm under pressure.' I did my best to look worried.

This was getting ridiculous; I should just tell him the truth. It was what I'd normally do but, for some reason, I didn't want Winter to think badly of me for not putting in more effort to win. Better to be considered a magic weakling, I supposed, than just a weakling.

I wasn't sure whether he believed me or not; he could be darned difficult to read when he wanted to be. In the end, however, our mission won out. He checked his watch and muttered, 'Let's get a move on. We still aren't any closer to finding Volume 9.'

I bobbed my head and breathed out. 'Yep,' I said. 'Let's go.'

CHAPTER NINETEEN

It was lucky that Tobias Worth-Jones was as much of a stickler for work as Winter. Even though it was lunchtime, he was at his desk munching on a sandwich while trying to read through some magically enhanced papers. *And people wonder why I'm happy not to work at the Order.*

When he caught sight of us, Tobias's eyes widened and he stood up. He still had a mouthful of bread but that didn't stop him talking. 'Adeptus Exemptus Winter! What brings you over this way?'

With every word, I was sprayed haphazardly with particles of food mixed with saliva. I didn't try and save his dignity by pretending it didn't happen; instead I made a show of wiping my face and looking disgusted. Unfortunately the effort was lost on Worth-Jones; as per usual, it was Winter who got the message.

He got straight to the point. 'Your signature is on a personnel file that has been removed from HR,' he barked. 'We need it. And we need to know why you took it in the first place.'

Tobias appeared unconcerned. 'I have no idea what you're talking about.'

'Oscar Marsh,' I interjected helpfully. 'You logged out Oscar Marsh's file.'

'No, I didn't.'

'It's definitely your writing, Tobias,' Winter said. 'I'd recognise that scrawl anywhere.'

'When was this?'

'March tenth.'

Worth-Jones rubbed his chin thoughtfully. 'I did go to HR then,' he said slowly, 'and I did check out a file but it wasn't Oscar Marsh. It was for one of my own witches.' He pulled a face. 'A disciplinary matter, alas. Although I can see why there would be a mix-up, given it's Marsh's file that you're here about.'

Winter stilled. 'Why? What do you know about Oscar Marsh?'

Tobias blinked. 'Oh, Diall complained about him vociferously.'

I tried to think when I'd ever used the word 'vociferously'. Nope. Couldn't do it.

'What exactly did Adeptus Diall say?' Winter demanded.

'Oh, that Marsh was frequently late and had turned up drunk on one or two occasions.' He chuckled. 'Although who amongst us hasn't done that?'

I put up my hand. 'Me,' I said. 'I've never done that.'

Worth-Jones still didn't look at me. I brought my hand down and examined it. No, I wasn't invisible.

He continued. 'I think the biggest issue is that Marsh is incredibly weak at magic. He shouldn't even have been admitted to the Order in first place. Plenty of people with smatterings of magic manage without actually becoming witches.' He shrugged. 'Marsh is still Adeptus Minor though. How he managed to gain that position, I'll never know.'

Diall's grubby fingers were over everything. Winter didn't say anything like that to Tobias, however. He remained strictly on point. 'Do you know anyone who knew Marsh personally? We need to find his address.'

'Trumpton Avenue.' Tobias thought for a second. 'Number two, I believe.'

Winter stared. 'How on earth do you know that?'

'Because Diall had to go there on more than one occasion to pick up Marsh. He made a little ditty about it. Now how did it go?' He scratched his head. 'Ah, yes. "Twenty-two Trumpton Avenue houses the witch who hasn't a clue. Vodka, rum, Bacardi and…" No, wait. "Rum, vodka, gin…".' He frowned. 'No. Hang on. I'll have it in a minute.'

'I think we'll manage without it,' Winter said drily. 'Thanks for your time.'

Tobias was still mumbling and humming to himself as we walked away.

'He's the culprit,' I said as soon as we were at the end of the corridor. 'Tobias Worth-Jones is the guilty one for sure.'

Winter sighed. 'Why?'

'First of all,' I said, ticking off my fingers, 'he's eating lunch at his desk. He doesn't have enough time to take a break because he's spending all his free time reading Volume 9. Secondly, he knew Diall well enough to get all the gossip about him, so he definitely knew him well enough to be invited into his home where he murdered him. Thirdly, his tie has yellow stripes. Never trust someone wearing yellow.'

'What's wrong with yellow? It's the colour of sunshine.'

'It makes me look sallow and washed-out.' Winter took a deep breath and I grinned. 'Are you counting to ten?'

'Your theories are quite extraordinary, Ivy. Besides, I thought you were convinced that Price did it.'

'I changed my mind. It's a lady's prerogative.'

Winter halted abruptly. Slowly, he turned towards me. 'You … you're a lady?'

Ha. Ha. Ha.

TRUMPTON AVENUE SOUNDED CONSIDERABLY MORE upmarket than it actually was. Instead of a leafy road with pretty Victorian houses, which is what I'd imagined, Winter and I found ourselves in Oxford's version of hell. Although I'm sure that the council serves this area in the same way as the rest of the city, the road was strewn with rubbish ranging from old beer cans to cigarette ends.

On one side of the street, a shabby man mumbled to himself as he shuffled along. When he saw us he yelled a warning about two-headed sheep then shook himself and continued on his way. A scrawny cat, thankfully ginger rather than black, crossed our path and gave a defiant hiss in Winter's direction. The houses were small, often with boarded-up windows. They were also covered in a layer of grime which archaeologists would probably find fascinating.

'I bet they don't put this place in the tourist brochures,' I said.

Winter didn't answer though he appeared horrified. It didn't help when we discovered that number two wasn't before house numbers four and six, as you might expect. No, that would have been too easy. Instead, it was wedged in a terrace further down, as if the town planner had been having some fun and decided to rewrite the laws of basic arithmetic.

Winter gently nudged me out of the way so that he was the only person on the doorstep when he rang the bell. I picked some dirt out of my fingernails. If he was so keen to do all the work, let him get on with it. My mouth was parched and my sock was still wet. At this rate, I wouldn't have to feign illness; I'd end up in hospital with pneumonia. Or some kind of terrible bacterial infection.

Winter wasn't in the mood for waiting. When no one answered the doorbell, he knocked loudly. When that didn't work, he shouted, 'Oscar Marsh! This is Arcane Branch! Open up!' He knocked some more, the force of his fist making the flimsy door rattle and shake in its frame.

'You could try turning the doorknob,' I suggested. 'It would take a lot less effort.'

Winter wasn't ready to take the easy route. He knocked some more, with increased vigour. Without a warrant, he probably couldn't enter a property unless he had the owner's permission. I could fix that. I didn't want to stand here all day.

Taking a step backwards, I focused on the rusty doorknob. Like the rest of the house, and indeed this street, it had seen better days. It didn't matter what it looked like; the rune I'd developed was to avoid having to root around in the bottom of my bag for my keys. That might not sound like a particularly arduous task but, given the amount of crap I carry around with me, it could take some time to find what I needed. With this little magic rune, I didn't have to worry about losing my house keys – and Winter and I wouldn't have to stand out here until his knuckles were bloody.

With his back towards me, it was easy for me to sketch out the rune without him noticing. I added a little pinkie flick at the end as a flourish, which had precisely the desired effect. The doorknob turned and the door creaked open. Not by much but enough to reveal the dank and musty corridor beyond.

'Hey,' I said cheerfully. 'He must have heard you. Let's go.' Before Winter could argue, I nipped past him and went in, although the reek inside almost made me wish I hadn't.

Irritated, Winter stepped over the threshold and joined me. He looked at me suspiciously, as if he were sure that I'd had something to do with the door's miraculous opening. The whiff that reached his nose and made it wrinkle gave me the chance to forestall any pointed questions. 'Smelly, huh?' I said.

Winter shook his head. 'I've never smelt anything like it before.'

I stared at him; he had to be kidding. 'Chips and curry sauce,' I said. I lifted my nose and sniffed. 'And, if I'm not mistaken, just the faintest tinge of three-day-old doner kebab.'

Now it was Winter's turn to look astonished. 'People actually eat doner kebabs?'

'What else would they do with them? You can't beat a good kebab.' I smacked my lips. 'Especially with slatherings of chilli sauce.' I grinned. 'Let me guess: you're a vegetarian?'

'No, I'm not. But I don't eat garbage like that.'

I hadn't seen him eat anything yet; so far, he'd seemed to exist on air and a furrowed brow. My stomach gurgled to remind me that it was some time since I'd eaten anything substantial myself.

'I made dinner last night,' Winter said. 'I even went shopping. You'd have noticed if you hadn't crammed a chocolate bar into your mouth then fallen fast asleep.'

He'd cooked? Before I could ask what he'd made, there was a loud groan from a room nearby. Winter stiffened and shot me a warning glance as if I needed telling to keep quiet. I tutted softly.

We edged further in. Someone was definitely in the house; there was the sound of soft snoring. It was a wonder that they'd not woken up when Winter bellowed at the entrance. I nodded in satisfaction; that sort of dedication to sleep always impresses me.

Treading lightly, Winter walked in front of me and paused at the end of the gloomy corridor. He knocked on the door. The snoring continued. Nudging the door with his foot, he pushed it open. Inside there was a dimly lit room with large sash windows, draped with heavy velvet curtains. They would have looked rather grand but they were hanging off the rail in several places and looked as if they'd been flung up rather than carefully dressed. There was a flickering television screen in one corner and my gaze took in an extraordinary pornographic video involving several naked people and orifices I had no desire to think about. Winter hastily grabbed the remote control from the floor and switched it off.

The only other thing in the room, apart from empty bottles and squashed cans, was a sofa with a large lump on it. When the lump let out another snore, I decided that this had to be Oscar

Marsh. For all that Adeptus Diall had seemed to be an unpleasant fellow prior to his untimely death, he appeared to have hit the nail on the head as far as Marsh was concerned. I doubted this was an Order witch of whom the Ipsissimus was particularly proud.

I wondered if it troubled Winter that he spent his time around less than noble witches when the Order did so much good for the world. I suppose it was the nature of his job – of our job.

Winter cleared his throat. If he thought that was going to wake Sleeping Beauty, he was deluded. Marsh was face down with his arse sticking up in the air and one arm dangling over the sofa's edge. Considering what Winter had done to force me out of bed, I was surprised that he was being so delicate. 'Throw a bucket of water over him,' I said sourly. 'It worked with me.'

Winter grimaced. 'That was because I knew you weren't likely to spring up and start attacking me. This guy is another matter.'

I frowned. 'First of all, this guy is virtually comatose. Even when he wakes up, he's hardly going to be in a position to attack. Alcohol is seeping out of his pores, Winter. He's more likely to throw up and clutch his head than throw something at your head. And how did you know I wouldn't attack you? I might have.'

'You're not the type,' Winter dismissed, without explaining properly. 'If this Marsh killed Adeptus Diall, not to mention stole the Cypher Manuscript, then he's far more dangerous than he looks.'

I cast a doubtful look at the slumbering witch. There was no chance this was our man. Winter seemed to read my thoughts. 'Appearances can be deceptive, Ivy. Perhaps he's sleeping off a hangover because his guilt turned him to drink.'

'There's no evidence—' I began.

'I said perhaps. And you've accused everyone else we've met so far. Why not him?'

I shrugged; it just didn't seem very likely. In any case, Oscar

Marsh clearly wasn't going to wake up without further help. I glanced round the room. Unless I was going to chuck the dregs of flat beer into his face, there wasn't much that would help. Frankly, the man already smelled badly enough.

'I'll find the kitchen and get some water,' I said gruffly. I turned on my heel.

There was a small galley kitchen towards the front door. It was surprisingly clean but Oscar Marsh probably didn't do much cooking if he lived on a liquid diet. I was beginning to feel irritated. The Order obviously knew he had problems; there were plenty of things they could have done to help him.

I opened cupboards until I found a cup, took it to the sink and turned on the tap. Winter was shouting at Marsh in the other room. I paused and listened. It still didn't seem like the man had woken up.

Glancing down, I reached over to turn off the tap. That was when I spotted the small, charred fragment of paper caught in the plughole. I set the cup to one side and carefully pulled it out. It was little more than a few inches wide and had obviously been burnt but there were still a few words visible.

I squinted at them and my veins ran ice cold. I guess I'd been wrong about Marsh. Leaving the water where it was, I went back to Winter. He was crouched down by Marsh's head, poking him. 'Winter,' I whispered. He didn't react. I tried again. 'Rafe!'

The urgency in my voice reached him. He turned round and glanced at me. Grimly, I held out the tiny piece of paper. 'I probably should have worn gloves,' I said apologetically, realising that I had probably contaminated the evidence.

Winter stood up and took the paper. It took less than a second for its meaning to sink in. His face shuttered and something indefinable flashed in his eyes. Without another word he spun round, marched back to Marsh and hauled him upwards by the scruff of his neck.

Even Winter's violent tug didn't immediately wake up the

witch. He emitted a groan. When Winter shook him, he finally opened his eyes, bleary confusion in their murky brown depths.

'Wh – what?' Marsh gabbled.

'Philosophus Oscar Marsh, you are under arrest by proclamation of the Hallowed Order of Magical Enlightenment,' Winter spat, using official Order language. 'Any attempt to use magic to provoke, conceal or avoid taking responsibility for your actions will be held against you, regardless of your guilt or innocence. You are entitled to legal representation and to apply to the non-magical courts for consideration.'

Marsh still didn't seem to understand what was going on. I didn't blame him: one minute he was comatose in a puddle of his own spit and the next he had a furious Adeptus yelling at him. Then my gaze drifted downwards and I noticed that among the other stains on his grubby T-shirt there was definitely blood. My sympathy vanished in an instant.

'What have I done?' He blinked rapidly as if trying to remember.

'You stole the Ipsissimus's sceptre and Volume 9 of the Cypher Manuscript. Finally,' Winter hissed, 'you murdered Adeptus Exemptus Diall.'

Marsh just gaped at him. 'I don't think…' He moaned. 'I have a really sore head. Could we do this some other time?'

Winter laughed coldly in his face. 'Not likely. Your time is up.'

CHAPTER TWENTY

BY THE TIME WE FINALLY LEFT WITH THE HAPLESS MARSH IN TOW, his house was swarming with witches. I had to resist the temptation to point out gleefully to Winter that I'd been right about the smell; the poor Arcane Branch pair who'd been tasked with sorting through Marsh's rubbish had already found the remnants of a kebab and some half-eaten chips smothered in now-rancid curry sauce.

I was sitting with our charge in the back of the Order van as he was driven back to headquarters. There was a peculiar odour in the air; I'd have said it was Marsh but the only things he smelled of were stale chilli sauce, alcohol and sour sweat. Nobody said a word during the journey. It wasn't until we ended up in a small room in the Arcane Branch building that it seemed appropriate to speak.

We took our seats opposite a pale and sweating Marsh who was now dressed in a paper jumpsuit. 'Do you know,' I said to Winter, 'this is the first time I've been here? I've been working for you for weeks and I've never stepped into this building.'

Winter look at me strangely. 'It's only been a few days. It's hardly been weeks.'

'It feels like weeks.'

He rolled his eyes.

Oscar Marsh paid us very little attention. I cleared my throat and leant forward. 'Oscar,' I said. 'Have you been here before?'

The question didn't seem to register initially. 'Wh – what?'

'Have you been to Arcane Branch before?'

'Uh,' he scratched his head as if trying to remember. 'Yeah, a few times.'

'Why don't you tell us about them?' I prodded. If Marsh had priors, I wanted to know about them. Given the luck we'd had so far in procuring any files, I didn't rate our chances of finding out the information from the Order itself.

'Uh,' he said again. It appeared to be a favourite word of his. 'There was that time I fell into the lake.'

I shot Winter a confused look. He nodded. 'Do you mean the duck pond round the back of Geomancy?' he asked.

'Yeah, yeah,' Marsh said. 'No ducks, though. Just lots of green stuff.'

I sat back in my chair. 'That seems a bit unfair, getting questioned by Arcane Branch simply for a little stumble.'

Marsh's nose twitched. 'I turned the water into vodka. I was trying to drink it when I fell in.'

I raised my eyebrows. No wonder there weren't any ducks around. I didn't think paddling around in a lake of alcohol would be the favourite pastime of a bird – although it didn't sound all that bad to me. 'You don't like wine?' I asked.

'Huh?'

'Never mind.' I kept my eyes on him. 'When else?'

He twitched again. 'When else what?'

Either the man had the memory of a goldfish or he was good at avoiding answering questions. 'When else did you visit Arcane Branch?'

'There was the time I lost the building specs for Windsor

Castle,' he said. 'I don't know what all the fuss was about. They turned up.'

Intrigued, I drummed my fingers against the table top. 'Where were they?'

He shrugged. 'In a drawer. I'd forgotten I'd put them there.'

'A drawer where?' Winter asked.

'At home.'

Winter sat up even straighter than normal. 'You took important documents home with you and lost them?'

'It was only the one time,' Marsh grumbled. He rubbed at his face. 'Is this going to take long? I really don't feel very well at all. I think I might be sick.'

Winter picked up a small bin. 'Here you go,' he said without a trace of a smile. 'Be sick into this.'

Marsh took the bin and hugged it to his chest. I really hoped he held onto the contents of his stomach; I rarely did well with other people's vomit.

'So,' Winter said, all but rubbing his palms together. 'You have experience of taking documents which don't belong to you. Why don't you tell us what you did with Volume 9?'

'Volume 9?' Marsh whispered. 'You mean of the Cypher Manuscripts? You mentioned that before.'

'Yes.' Winter folded his arms. 'I did. Where is it? We know you've burnt at least one page. Where is the rest?'

Marsh swallowed. 'I don't know anything about it. I've never been near the Cypher Manuscripts. I've never even looked at them in the library.'

Winter scratched a note to himself; it should be easy to check whether Marsh was telling the truth or not.

The witch continued. 'I wouldn't take them. I wouldn't even know how to take them. Aren't they warded?'

Winter's lip curled. 'Usually, yes.' His jaw tightened. 'But you found a way round that, didn't you? You circumvented the systems, almost killing Ms Wilde and me in the process. What is it you're really after, Marsh? Is it power? You might as well tell us. The Manuscript will do you no good in prison.'

'I don't know what you're talking about! I've never touched it! I told you!'

'Then why did we find clear evidence that you had it in your home?'

'I don't know!'

Winter exhaled then abruptly changed tack, softening his voice. 'What happened with Adeptus Diall? Did he threaten you? Is that why you killed him? We know it wasn't premeditated, Oscar. Was it self-defence? We can help you if it was. We understand that Diall could be difficult.'

'Diall's a prick,' Marsh grunted. Then he paused and looked up. 'He's dead?' He snorted. 'Good riddance.'

There was a knock at the door and we all jumped, even Winter. He got to his feet and opened it. There was a low murmur before he beckoned me. 'You should hear this too, Ivy.'

I stood up. 'Don't go anywhere,' I told Marsh.

He glared and rattled the chain linking his ankles together. 'Unlikely.'

I padded over to Winter. He nudged me into the corridor and closed the door. A fresh-faced woman was standing there. 'We've had the preliminary reports, Adeptus,' she said. 'The fragment you found is definitely from the Cyphers. We need to double check but it looks like one of the earlier pages.'

That was something; the further on you went in each Volume, the more power and magic there was. Maybe Marsh had only read the first section or two. He certainly didn't seem to have much power or authority right now – unless he was waiting for the right moment to use the magic against us.

'Thanks. And the rest?'

'Adeptus Leith has been in touch. There's very little they can decipher from Philosophus Marsh's home. He has some effective wards in place that prevent us from casting a spell to see what he's been up to.'

Winter nodded, unsurprised. I, on the other hand, felt differently. 'But if he's a Philosophus, then he's First Level. You've said that only Second Level witches know how to put those kinds of wards in place.'

'He stole an entire volume of the Cypher Manuscript, Ivy, and almost drowned us both in a sewer,' Winter said. 'I think we can safely assume that he has magical abilities beyond his supposed level.'

I thought of the man on the other side of the door with his bloodshot eyes and broken veins on his cheeks and nose. He didn't strike me as someone with fabulous magical abilities but Winter was supposed to be the expert. All the same, it niggled me. This didn't feel right.

'The blood?' Winter asked the woman briskly. 'Do we have a match yet for Diall?'

She shook her head. 'Preliminary testing tells us it's definitely not Marsh's own blood and it's the same type as Diall's, but we can't say anything for sure yet.' She looked troubled. 'We've turned over his house and there's no sign of the missing Cypher Manuscript. People are starting to panic.'

The cat was well and truly out of the bag. 'So it's common knowledge what we're looking for?'

She nodded uneasily. Winter hissed in irritation. 'In that case,' he muttered, 'we'd better find it quickly before all hell breaks loose and there are pointed fingers and harsh whispers in every corner.'

The witch's mouth tightened. 'I'll do what I can to keep people calm. We'll send out a statement as soon as possible.' She turned and sprinted away. People around here certainly liked conducting everything at breakneck speed.

'You're expecting a large number of honourable Order witches to take advantage of this situation and start blaming their colleagues,' I said to Winter.

He was silent for a long moment. 'As you have stated on many occasions, Ivy, the Order is filled with ambition. Regardless of your opinion, ambition is a good thing. Everyone should want to better themselves and, yes, I do believe that the majority of the witches here are honourable in their ambitions. But they are also under great pressure to succeed. If a few can cast suspicion on others, they may have the opportunity to advance themselves.'

'That's why you need more people like me around.' I wasn't joking. 'People who are content with their lot in life.'

He regarded me thoughtfully. 'So you're admitting that you're glad to be here?'

I held up my palms. 'Whoa! I didn't say that. Besides, it's clear you don't really need me. What ever happened to good cop, bad cop? You're the one asking all the questions in there. I wanted to be the tough guy while you played all sweet and nice.'

'I've been trained,' he pointed out gently. 'It is probably better if I take the lead. Although it was a good idea of yours to probe Marsh about his other indiscretions.'

I wasn't sure that describing murder as an indiscretion was appropriate but I wisely kept my mouth shut.

'We'll have to check out Marsh's desk,' Winter mused. 'And it would be helpful to find his personnel file.' He glanced at me sideways. 'Perhaps you could put some pressure on that old boyfriend of yours.'

'Tarquin?' My lip curled. 'He's more likely to jump to your bidding than mine.'

The corner of Winter's mouth lifted. 'Just use some of that bubbly charm, Ivy. He'll be eating out of your hand like everyone else in no time.' Winter turned on his heel and went back into the interrogation room, leaving me with my jaw hanging open. Was

Winter eating out of my hand, then? I smoothed back my curls and blinked. Well, well, well.

I AMBLED over to Human Resources, taking advantage of the time on my own to shuffle instead of march like a soldier. There was no need to rush; Tarquin wasn't going anywhere. When I arrived, the frowny receptionist seemed keen to put me off now that I wasn't with Winter until I brandished his name around, together with insubstantial but dire threats about the might of Arcane Branch, and she let me pass.

Adeptus Price's door was open. I peered inside but he didn't seem to be there. I made a beeline for Tarquin's desk. His floppy hair was bobbing around as he tapped furiously at his keyboard. He was probably playing Candy Crush – that's what I would have been doing.

He didn't notice I was there until I was standing right over him. It wasn't Candy Crush; he was filling an application for Arcane Branch. I smirked. Too late.

'Hey, traitor,' I said chattily.

Tarquin grimaced, the expression giving his normally handsome face an ugly slant. 'What do you want?'

I perched on the edge of his desk, making myself at home. There was a bag of mint humbugs next to the computer screen so I helped myself to one. It was a mistake because the sweet immediately attached itself to the underside of several of my teeth, making it difficult to talk. 'I want Oscar Marsh's file,' I said. My words were indistinct but I thought he got the gist.

A sneer crossed Tarquin's face. 'Ah, yes. It's all over the campus, you know. Why on earth would Marsh, of all people, want the Cypher Manuscripts? He couldn't read even the simplest volumes.'

'Just hand over the damn file,' I said, unwilling to gossip with Tarquin.

'We've been through this. His file was checked out. Your partner didn't want to say who took it. It's your problem, not ours.'

'Let me see the logbook again,' I demanded.

Tarquin grinned. 'Make me.'

I shrugged. 'Okay.' I pulled back my shoulders and raised my voice, ensuring that everyone in the HR office could hear me. 'I am here from Arcane Branch, investigating the most serious matter that the Order has experienced for decades.' That was probably true; I couldn't say for sure. Whatever: it sounded impressive. 'If you continue to obstruct this grave investigation, I shall have no option but to arrest you and assume that you...'

'Fine!' Tarquin snapped.

I smiled. Winter might think I could charm the pants off Tarquin but all that was actually needed was the threat of public humiliation.

He pushed back his chair, sending it flying into the poor woman sitting behind him, and stomped over to the Records section. I tailed behind him so closely that I stepped on his heels. He glowered but didn't say anything. Ha! He was learning.

Tarquin grabbed the logbook and thrust it at me. 'Here.'

I took it and found the page that Price had shown us earlier. I tracked my finger along the line: it was definitely Oscar Marsh's file that was noted and the signature, which was almost illegible, could belong to Tobias Worth-Jones. It would be possible to alter the logbook using magic but I had the feeling that such a spell would be more trouble than it was worth. The logbook was probably warded against such magic. Worth-Jones's signature didn't look as if it would be easy to replicate free hand and Winter didn't seem to think there was anything untoward about his casual denial of involvement.

I adjusted my grip on the book while Tarquin looked on,

amused. The darn thing was bloody heavy. As I moved my thumb, I realised that the page opposite was indented from the writing on the other side. I flipped back, then forward, then back again. No magic at all: Worth-Jones had been implicated through an action that even a child could manage.

'What is it?' Tarquin asked.

'You lot are incompetent,' I said. 'Don't you pay any attention to who wanders in and takes files out?'

'That's Rebecca's job,' he answered, gesturing irritably at the receptionist.

Always passing the buck, that was how people like Tarquin worked. Everything was someone else's fault. I sighed and pointed to the previous page. 'Look. Here is Tobias Worth-Jones checking out the file for someone in his department. See?'

Tarquin reluctantly looked over my shoulder. 'Yeah? So?'

He was a plonker. I turned back to Marsh's entry. It matched perfectly. 'Someone went over his signature, pressing down so that it would appear on the next page. Then they traced over it and made it look like Worth-Jones had taken away Marsh's file. It was probably a bonus that his handwriting is so appalling.'

Tarquin's eyes took in the evidence. 'That's … that's … preposterous,' he said, his eyes darting to and fro as if I were accusing him of doing it.

'What's preposterous,' I said, 'is using the word "preposterous". Say it several times. It's a daft word.'

'Look, Ivy,' Tarquin said through gritted teeth. 'I don't know what you're trying to say but I can assure you that Human Resources takes its duties very seriously. We do not let just anybody waltz in here and mess around with the logbook. These files are private, they're not given out to anyone who simply shows up.'

'And yet,' I told him softly, 'the evidence that they are is right here.' I paused. 'I still need the file.'

'I don't know where it is.' He lowered his voice. 'I know I did you wrong all those years ago but I wouldn't do this.'

I arched an eyebrow. 'At no point have I suggested this was your doing but you're protesting quite…' I paused '…vociferously.' I grinned, very pleased with myself.

Tarquin waved a hand at the rows of filing cabinets. 'You are welcome to look through them.' His manner was stiff and unyielding. 'But on Adeptus Price's orders, I've already searched all of them in case the file was returned to the wrong place.'

That was interesting. Why would Price ask Tarquin to do that if he thought that someone else had checked out the file?

Tarquin wasn't finished. 'What are you doing here anyway? You don't want to be in the Order, Ivy. When you left eight years ago, you swore you'd never be back.'

'I didn't leave,' I reminded him. 'I was kicked out. Because of you.'

'All the same, this isn't your kind of thing. Even back then you never wanted to be in Arcane Branch. Why now? Why not leave and let someone else do your job? There are plenty of people who want it.'

'Oh, we all know it's you who wants it, Tarquin,' I responded. 'But you can't have it. I'm magically bound to work with Winter, whether I want to or not. So there's not a damn thing you can do about it.'

'It can't be that strong a binding,' he retorted. 'You're here and he's not. How does that work?'

I opened my mouth to answer then I realised he was right. The terms of the binding were that Winter and I worked in tandem, not just remain within five miles of each other; it had seemed that we were supposed to stay together while investigations were actively under way. But this time when we were apart, I hadn't experienced any strange prickling along my skin like before. Maybe it was because the spell was somehow aware I was here doing Winter's bidding. Or maybe it was for another reason.

'You're not much of a magic expert, are you, Tarquin?' I said dismissively. 'No wonder you had to cheat to get where you are.' He glared at me and I smiled in return. 'Oh, if only looks could kill.' I patted him on the shoulder. 'But they can't. So I'll have to get on with the vital business of the Arcane Branch and you can get back to your personnel files.'

And with that, I swiftly made my exit.

CHAPTER TWENTY-ONE

Arcane Branch was bustling. There was a buzz in the air that I'd not noticed when I came in with Winter the first time and there were many happy and relieved faces. I clocked two red robes slapping each other on the back and pursed my lips. Something was up.

I went back to the interrogation room. As soon as I entered, I saw Winter cuffing Oscar Marsh. 'What's going on?' I asked.

'The missing Manuscript has been found,' Winter told me.

I blinked in surprise. 'Really?'

'Apart from the one burnt page we already know about, it's intact.' He gave Marsh a little jab. 'It's just as well.'

I found my voice. 'Where was it?'

Winter smiled grimly. 'Here. It was at the Order all along.'

I looked from Winter to Marsh and back again. I had a feeling I already knew the answer but I asked anyway. 'Where exactly?'

'In Oscar's desk drawer.'

No shit. 'Was it locked? Warded? Was it difficult to get hold of?'

'None of the above.'

I licked my lips. 'Isn't that a little strange?'

'I don't know what it was doing there!' Marsh shouted. 'I'm being set up!' The effort of making this outburst seemed to affect him adversely; he'd only just finished speaking when his skin turned a faint shade of green. I hoped Winter was going to keep that bin handy in case Marsh threw up.

'Shut up,' Winter said, although his tone was mild. He looked at me. 'Did you get hold of his personnel file?'

'Nope.'

Winter's mouth tightened but otherwise he didn't react.

Another two red robes entered. The disgust in their eyes when they looked at Marsh was obvious. Winter passed him over into their custody then turned to me. 'All's well that ends well,' he said.

I considered this. 'Unless you're dead like Adeptus Diall. Isn't Marsh just a little too convenient? Isn't this all a bit too easy?'

Winter raised an eyebrow. 'I thought you liked the easy way out.'

I did and I was experienced at seeking it out, which was why Marsh's guilt was too straightforward. The man seemed barely capable of holding a conversation, let alone masterminding this kind of crime. Winter, however, didn't appear to give my concerns a second thought.

I pressed ahead. 'Does the blood on Marsh's shirt match Diall's?' I asked.

'We're still waiting on the lab results.' Winter smiled briefly. 'Come on. I'll take you home and you can sprawl out and snooze away the rest of the day.'

I stared at him. 'You do realise what time it is? The day is already over.'

He chuckled and patted me on the shoulder then headed out, leaving me to follow. I gazed at his back in confusion. Since when was Adeptus Exemptus Raphael Winter the chuckling type?

WINTER DROPPED me outside my block of flats; apparently he no longer felt the need to stay around me. When I'd suggested now would be a good time to release Bell End and Alice into the welcoming hands of either the Order or the police, he had demurred, telling me to wait until tomorrow. That wasn't like him either. I stood on the pavement as he took off, wondering what I was missing.

I went inside and checked on my trussed-up pair. Feeling a bit sorry for them, I gave them a chance to stretch out their limbs. Both appeared too dejected to try to escape; whether that was as a result of Diall's death or their prolonged incarceration, I had no idea.

Harold, for his part, seemed perfectly content. As I was leaving, he wedged himself next to Alice with a throbbing purr. Fickle creature, although not as fickle as Princess Parma Periwinkle. She was nowhere in sight. She was probably like her owner and had gone off to hunt for her own food because getting it out of a packet or a tin was too easy. Or she'd decided she didn't like it here and had headed off home. Whatever.

I took a long hot shower. When I emerged, Brutus was staring at me. 'Food.'

'Yeah, yeah.' I reached down and scratched under his chin. He nipped my fingers with his teeth.

'Food.'

The phone started to ring. Offering him a helpless smile, I went to answer it. 'This is Ivy.'

'Ivy! Thank goodness you answered! I've been trying to get hold of you but you never seem to be in.'

We were both well aware of how out of character this was. 'Hi, Eve. Things are … good. Harold is fine. I'm fine. More to the point, how are you?'

'Brilliant!' I could hear the joy in her voice. 'We're just about finished up here. I thought I'd screwed things up because the

Order sent two other witches but they've been a great help so I'll be home tomorrow. I can't wait to see my little munchkin.'

I hoped she was referring to Harold rather than me. 'That's great news.' I hesitated. 'Did these other two witches say anything about what was happening back in Oxford?' What I really wanted to know was whether she knew that I'd taken her coveted spot.

'No, not much,' she answered cheerfully.

I breathed a sigh of relief. Obviously she'd find out what had happened sooner or later but it was the sort of news I'd prefer to break in person. 'What time do you think you'll be back?' I asked

'Mid-afternoon, I reckon. Are you sure everything's okay?'

'Yes, yes. Just … come and see me before you do anything else, will you?'

Her voice immediately filled with suspicion. 'Why?'

'Nothing serious.' It wasn't life threatening anyway. 'I just want a quick chat.'

She let out a gasp. 'You want to talk to me about coming running, don't you?'

Er… 'Yeah,' I said unconvincingly. 'That's it.' I couldn't believe she really thought that but I'd go with it if allayed her fears until I could speak to her.

'Foooooooood!' Brutus howled, patently pissed off at the length of our chat.

'I'd better go,' I said. 'Brutus is getting annoyed.'

Eve laughed. 'So I hear. See you soon!'

I winced and put down the phone. Eve was a good person. I hoped she wouldn't be too hurt when she found out what had been happening.

I gave Brutus some of his favourite tuna and shuffled over to the sofa, plonking myself down with a happy sigh. 'Hello, my old friend,' I said aloud. 'It's been too long.' I was almost convinced that the sofa groaned in delighted response.

Laying down my head and stretching out, I closed my eyes.

Then I opened them again. I grimaced and turned onto my side, reaching for the remote. I flicked on the television and scanned through my recordings for the latest episode of *Enchantment*. The familiar theme music filled the room. I muted it and sat up straight.

Brutus sauntered in the room, licking his lips. 'Hey bitch.'

'Something's not right,' I told him. He jumped onto my lap and I stroked his ears. 'I should leave well enough alone. That would be the smart thing.' I glanced down at him. 'Right?'

'Where man?' Brutus enquired, obviously referring to Winter.

Where man, indeed. I chewed my bottom lip then reached for the phone once more. 'Hi, Iqbal,' I said, when he picked up.

'Ivy! How's tricks? Do you have that ossombe root yet? I'm looking forward to my karaoke session.'

My mind flashed to Diall's little jar secreted in my bathroom cabinet. 'That's not why I'm calling,' I prevaricated. For whatever reason, I still wasn't quite ready to separate myself from Winter. 'I want to know about that other way around the binding.' I thought of the strange smell that I suspected had been clinging to Winter, not Oscar Marsh. 'Herbal methods. You mentioned some kind of temporary hold last time we spoke.'

'Yeah, yeah. You're getting that desperate, are you? Winter must be a right bastard to work with.'

'Mmm. He's not so bad.'

Iqbal laughed. 'Damned by faint praise.'

I screwed up my nose. I hadn't meant it like that. 'The temporary thing?' I prodded.

'Yeah, hang on a minute. I've got it written down here somewhere.' I heard Iqbal shuffling some papers and then he came back on the line. 'Here we go. Culver's root. It's traditionally used in purification spells but I came across several references that suggested it would work on your binding too. It won't last long though, and the effects wear down quickly as the binding reacts against it.'

At least this was a herb I'd heard of, even if only vaguely. 'What does it smell like?' I asked.

'It's musty and fairly odorous,' he replied. 'I suppose it's similar to dried moss.'

I didn't know what dried moss smelled like but I bet that it was similar to the whiff I'd caught when I was in the van with Marsh and close to Winter. I felt an odd tightening in my chest. I was supposed to be the one who was straining against the bonds of the binding, not Winter. Why was he so keen to keep me away? Actually, I had a fairly good idea why but, for once, I'd take Winter's own advice and wait until I had more evidence.

'Thanks, Iq,' I said distantly. He murmured a response and I hung up.

Brutus had started clawing my thighs with sharp little jabs. 'There's no point getting comfortable,' I told him.

His ears twitched and he swung his head round towards me. 'Out?' he enquired. 'Again?'

I sighed. 'Again.' Goodness only knew why; I should be doing as I'd been told and vegging out on my sofa. But Winter might need my help, whether he wanted it or not. 'If you thought that someone was being set up, where would you look for proof that they were innocent?' I asked.

Brutus blinked at me. I gently nudged him off my lap and stood up. 'Yeah,' I said. 'That's what I was thinking too.'

CHAPTER TWENTY-TWO

By the time I got back to the Order, the sun had gone down. I left my taxi on a double yellow line – it was close to where I wanted to be and I was unlikely to block anyone in at this time of night – and picked my way through the shadows and between the dark buildings. I tried to remain hidden; I didn't want to bump into Winter until I was ready. I was so intent on looking for him that I almost collided with another group of witches walking in the opposite direction.

'Hey, it's Ivy Wilde!'

I smiled at Weathers, the receptionist from Geomancy, and glanced at his other two companions, Bethany the tea lady and Rebecca, the unfriendly receptionist from HR. 'How's it going?'

Weathers was grinning from ear to ear. 'Brilliant! How about you? I hear you've charged someone with stealing one of the Cypher Manuscript volumes.' He shook his head. 'I can't believe someone would be so audacious as to nick one.'

'Who is it?' Bethany asked, peering at me through the dim light. 'Who's the culprit? I can't believe someone would dare to steal such power. It had to be a Second Level witch, right? Other-wise it's just not plausible.'

'I wouldn't believe everything you hear,' I said. 'Gossip is unreliable.'

Weathers' expression dimmed slightly. 'They're not Second Level?'

I wagged my finger at him. 'I didn't say that, now did I?'

Rebecca flashed me an unexpected smile. It was the first time I'd seen her look happy. 'You're funny,' she burbled. 'The truth always comes out in the end. He'll finally get what's coming to him.'

I wondered how much she actually knew. How did she know it was a man who was in custody? All the same, I had better things to do than shoot the breeze. 'Indeed.' I smiled at them to indicate that I needed to move on. They understood, sidestepping out of my way and murmuring farewells. I breathed out. I probably ought to watch where I was going.

I continued until I reached the now-familiar squat structure of Human Resources. A few lights were still on inside and some red robes were visible through the windows. I wandered round, trying to not be too conspicuous but probably failing miserably. A few of the faces inside were familiar but I didn't know them well. Even brown-nosing Tarquin appeared to have disappeared for the evening.

'Well, Ivy,' I muttered to myself, 'this was a really smart idea. You could be snuggled up at home. Instead, you're lurking behind a tree in the dark.' Winter might not be here. For all I knew, he had a hot date and didn't want me to know about it. Except, I reminded myself, he wouldn't have needed a block on the binding if he were just going out for dinner.

It didn't look as if the last remaining HR witches were leaving for home any time soon and I wasn't going to hang around all night. I had to find a way to get rid of the lot of them without arousing suspicion. I considered and discarded several ideas. I needed all of them out of the building – and to ensure that no one came back. I could spring a leak and use water to drive them out but they'd probably send for maintenance to repair it before the morning. I'd avoid the sappy HR witches and run into burlier ones. I could call up, pretend to be from another department and invite them all out for a drink and a pizza but unless the food and drink materialised – and all the HR plonkers appreciated being sociable and fell for such a ploy – that wouldn't work either.

A fat droplet of rain fell from the sky and landed on the tip of my nose. Great. Now I was going to get soaked. Again. I cast my gaze upwards, eyeing the ominous clouds that were obscuring the sliver of moon. As I did so, I caught sight of the library, towering above the other buildings. I smiled to myself. I had just the thing.

Whistling, I put my hands in my pockets and strolled towards it. It would be open for a few hours yet. Maidmont had told me that they didn't shut until ten so getting in wouldn't be a problem.

I didn't want to spend time and energy of my own so, instead of sneaking around when I entered the library, I made a beeline for a librarian re-shelving books in the far corner of the ground floor.

'Hey, Phil!'

He jumped half a foot in the air; he'd been so preoccupied with his task that he hadn't heard me approach. 'Ms … Ms Wilde,' he stammered. 'Good to see you.' He looked over my shoulder as if expecting Winter to materialise. I hastily grabbed his attention before there were any awkward questions that I wouldn't be able to answer.

'We need your help,' I said briskly.

The librarian's eyes widened and I saw a flash of glee that his services were still required. Perhaps he had a secret ambition to be a spy. I could use that. 'But I thought the missing Manuscript had been recovered,' he said.

'Oh, it has.' I leant in closer and lowered my voice to indicate that we were co-conspirators. 'But we don't think that the real culprit has been identified yet.'

Maidmont bit his bottom lip. 'I checked the Cypher logbooks,' he murmured in a hushed tone to match my own. 'Oscar Marsh has never once been in to view the Cypher Manuscripts.' He raised his eyebrows meaningfully. 'Not once.'

I tapped the side of my nose. Maidmont immediately understood. 'I won't say a word,' he promised. 'What can I do?'

'There's a missing personnel file,' I told him. 'Oscar Marsh's.'

Maidmont looked even more excited. 'Isn't it at HR?'

'Well,' I whispered, 'that's just the thing.' A couple of young witches walked by. I stopped talking and took Maidmont's elbow, steering him away to a quieter corner. 'The file should be at HR but HR promise it's not there. In fact, they're not being very helpful *at all*. I need to get in there and see if they're telling the truth.'

He was horrified. 'You think an entire department is working against you?'

'No, it's probably just one or two people. But,' I added ominously, 'you can never know for sure.'

'How can I help?' he breathed.

'Time is of the essence.' Because I didn't want to wait around in the cold all night until the building was vacated. 'We're talking about an innocent man being in custody.'

Maidmont nodded vigorously. 'Yes, yes.'

'I need ' I paused and backtracked '...we need to gain imme-diate access to the HR building. We can't wait until every single witch leaves. We need a way to get them out of there so we can search it properly. The only way to do that is—' I held my breath before finishing my sentence for dramatic effect. It worked.

'What?' Maidmont asked. 'What? Tell me!'

'A fire,' I finished. 'A fire at the library.'

I could probably have asked for just about anything and Philip Maidmont would have given it to me but fire in his beloved library was a step too far. He drew back and gazed at me, horrified. 'Never,' he whispered. 'It's not worth it.'

Darn it. 'You don't understand,' I said quickly. 'I'm not asking for anything to be put in danger. All you need is a small fire for the magical wards to be engaged, right?'

He agreed warily. 'Right.'

'There's a basement below us. Clear a space in the middle and set one or two old bits of cardboard alight. Everyone who's left in any of the Order buildings will come running. The fire will already be out by the time they get here but they won't know that.'

Maidmont was appeased – but only just. 'What's to stop them from returning to their own buildings when they realise it's nothing serious?' he asked.

'You,' I said simply. 'You're going to have to put on the show of your life, Philip. We're counting on you. You tell them that, with the events of the last few days, you're too nervous to leave the library unattended. You need all the remaining witches to stay overnight to make sure all these precious books and manuscripts and documents are safe.'

'They'll never fall for that.'

I put my hand on his shoulder. 'They will if you're convincing enough. They've just learned that we almost lost an entire Volume of the Cyphers, Phil. No-one will want to be the only witch not dedicated enough to keep watch all night. It wouldn't look good on their CVs.'

'But…'

'Trust me.' I smiled. 'This will work.'

I'D BARELY MADE it back to the shadows around the HR building when the screeching began. Watching the witches inside, I noted a moment of frozen shock before they all sprinted for the door, hurling themselves at the library. I gave myself a pat on the back then I waited a little bit longer. For once, my patience was rewarded.

Not long after everyone had gone, robes flapping in breeze, a dark figure peeled away from the corner of the building. I'd have recognised that straight-backed march anywhere. Winter strode forward, pausing once to glance towards the library. I held my breath and hoped he'd realise that there were more than enough bodies heading in that direction to deal with whatever might – or might not – be happening, and that he'd stay on course. When he continued towards the front doors of HR, I knew he'd made the right decision. I gave a little jig. He thought he could pull the wool over my eyes but he was wrong. No one outsmarted me unless I wanted them to. Apart from Brutus. And maybe the Ipsissimus. Okay, and several others. Tonight, however, I was in charge.

I counted to twenty, giving Winter time to get to the spot he wanted. Then I followed on my tippy-toes. I wanted to see him jump with shock when I confronted him.

Pushing open the door as quietly as possible, I headed inside the HR building. I was getting to know the layout after the number of times I'd been here in the last few days. I veered round Rebecca the receptionist's desk and into the large office space. Now that it was almost entirely empty, there was a rather tragic air about it.

A small light wavered above Winter's head from the far corner. Records. Aha. Treading lightly, I went towards him. He was busy opening drawers so I was able to get right up behind him. When I was less than a foot away, I stopped and grinned. I was hoping for a small scream when I announced my presence.

'Don't just stand there, Ivy,' Winter snapped. 'Come and help me search.'

I jerked several inches upwards. The plonker. The absolute plonker. 'You knew I was here? All along?'

'Of course.' He still didn't turn around, intent as he was on pulling out files, examining the names and dropping them again. 'Who else would be impatient enough to set a fire in the library because they didn't want to wait for everyone to finish work?'

I bristled slightly. 'I didn't set the fire. Maidmont did.'

Winter finally glanced at me. 'You drew that poor librarian into your scheming?'

I drew myself up. 'Scheming? Scheming? You're the one who's been scheming, mister!'

He looked exasperated. 'I didn't want you here, that's true,' he admitted. 'But when I saw you loitering around outside, I knew you'd end up with me so the entire venture to exclude you was pointless.'

I tried to banish the small knot of hurt in my chest and put my hands on my hips. 'You found a way round the binding.'

'Don't get excited,' he growled. 'It's only temporary.'

'Why?'

'So I could come here and investigate without any nasty side-effects.'

'Is that what I am?' I spat. 'A nasty side-effect?'

His sapphire-blue eyes blinked in surprise. 'I was referring to the binding's side-effects, not you.' Winter sighed. 'I don't believe that Oscar Marsh is the witch we're looking for, despite the evidence to the contrary. If I'm right, the real culprit is not only clever but also very dangerous. You let a First Level witch beat you with a spell that wouldn't have fooled a Neophyte earlier today. I didn't want to risk you getting hurt, so it seemed prudent to make use of the temporary block on the binding.' His expression grew rueful. 'I should have known better than to think you'd be fooled. I suppose I hoped that you'd take advantage of the opportunity to loll around at home in peace and quiet.'

'I threw that damn fight,' I snapped. 'That would have been obvious if you knew anything about me. I didn't want to spend the next hundred days fighting off challengers.'

'How was I supposed to know that? Why didn't you tell me that you lost deliberately?'

I looked down. 'I didn't want you to think badly of me. I mean, I know you think I'm a lazy arse.' I paused. 'I *am* a lazy arse but I didn't want you to think I was like that. Even if I am.'

Winter's gaze softened. 'You're not as lazy as you think you are. You're here, after all.'

'You're not as stuck-up and strait-laced as I thought you were,' I said grudgingly.

'I'm stuck-up and strait-laced enough not to set the library on fire just to gain a few extra hours.'

'Oh, shut up. Maidmont has things under control.' I grinned. 'Besides, it's just as well I'm here. You're looking in the wrong place. Tarquin's already been through these files with a fine tooth-comb.'

Winter's eyebrows shot up. 'And you believe him?' he asked.

'In this, I do. He wants to give off the appearance of being a good little boy witch. If Marsh's file was discovered later down the back of one of these cabinets, Tarquin would feel the heat. He won't want any more fingers pointing in his direction. He's on shaky ground as it is, given what he did to Eve.'

Winter cocked his head. 'What did he do to Eve?'

I'd forgotten that he didn't know that little titbit. 'Never mind,' I said. 'It's not relevant to this.'

He let it go. 'If Marsh's file isn't here and it's not at Diall's house, I have no idea where it could be. It may contain vital information. If we can work out why Marsh was used as the patsy for the theft and the murder, we have a good chance of finding the real bastard who did all this.'

'It's obvious why Marsh was fingered,' I argued. 'He's in no position to fight back. He's clearly not doing very well for himself and there aren't many people who'll vouch for him, given his many indiscretions. Whoever took Volume 9 has returned it

229

because either they can't access the magic or they've got what they wanted from it.'

'That's as may be,' Winter responded. 'But it doesn't help us get any closer to the truth. It can't be a coincidence that Marsh's file has gone missing. Whoever has it is our prime suspect but that doesn't necessarily help us right now.'

I met his eyes and I had a sudden epiphany: Winter had all the answers. He just wanted me to come to the same conclusion. I didn't have the evidence that he was so fond of but maybe he realised that evidence wasn't all it was cracked up to be. Not when Oscar Marsh was currently languishing on the basis of theoretically concrete evidence.

'We're in HR for a reason,' I said softly. 'While we can reasonably believe that it was Diall who used his magic to steal the sceptre and then the Cypher Manuscript, because he would have enough magic ability for both, he's not the worst witch in this scenario. Someone murdered him and took the Manuscript for themselves. We know that Diall often helped to elevate witches to high positions for which they were not always suited. Maybe one of those particular witches took against him. Perhaps Diall was laying on too much pressure to do his bidding.' I shrugged. 'Perhaps they just didn't like him.'

Winter drew out a neatly folded piece of paper from his pocket. 'It took some time,' he said, 'but here are the names of everyone who was promoted with Diall's vote. There are twenty-three names.'

I whistled. 'That's quite a lot. Not an insurmountable number to investigate but it will still take time.'

'Indeed. And if the Manuscript *has* turned up because our culprit has already absorbed all the magic, then we need to hurry before they make their move.'

'This is too easy.'

Amusement flashed across Winter's features. 'Is it?'

I rolled my eyes. 'I told you from the start: Adeptus Price is the bastard we're looking for.'

'Actually, your first suggestion was the Ipsissimus. And your reasoning for Price was that he wore slip-on shoes.'

'I didn't directly accuse the Ipsissimus,' I pointed out. 'Not really. And I had other reasons for naming Price. It's clearer now. Whoever murdered Diall knew where he lived and what wards he had in place at his home. As Head of HR, Price would have had access to that information. He's clearly not very good at his job either. His staff despise him. So chances are, he's one of those witches on your list.'

Winter neither denied nor acknowledged my theory. I ploughed on. 'Tarquin gave him an alibi when we visited by saying that he'd been with Practicus Lee. But Tarquin probably just saw it on his calendar. He wouldn't have been at the meeting with them. Price could have cancelled it without anyone knowing. And with his knowledge of the witches in the Order, Price would also have been aware of Marsh's shortcomings. He was probably on the disciplinary board after Marsh's other misdemeanours. Price knew that Oscar Marsh would make the perfect scapegoat.'

'There's no proof,' Winter said. 'If Price took Volume 9, he doesn't have it now. We do. And if he killed Diall, there won't necessarily be a trail of blood proving it.'

I held up my hand. 'But,' I said softly, 'if he has Oscar Marsh's personnel file we're halfway there. We just need to find it.' I waited for a beat. 'Or hang around and wait until Price uses his new magic skills to take over the world and become our ruler.'

Winter smiled. 'Let's not do that, then.'

'Good idea.' I straightened. 'And you don't need to shut me out or try and protect me, Rafe. I can look after myself. I reckon I'm more of a help to you than a hindrance.'

His smile dropped and he regarded me seriously. 'You're right – on both counts.' He leant towards me until I could feel his breath on my skin. 'Price's name is on the list. And I didn't take him seriously as a suspect until you mentioned him the first time around.'

I grinned smugly into his blue eyes. 'See?' I said. 'Slip-on shoes.'

CHAPTER TWENTY-THREE

WE ABANDONED THE FRUITLESS SEARCH OF THE FILING CABINETS and headed for Price's office. While it was unlikely that there would be anything there, given its public nature and how often Price was out of the office, it seemed prudent to run a close eye over everything he had squirrelled away.

Although I'd been in here once before, my focus on that occasion was Tarquin and the poor woman he was currently stringing along. This time I paid more attention to my surroundings. There wasn't a whole lot to look at: Price wasn't exactly a clutter-bug. His desk had an empty tray, a single sharp-nibbed pencil and a notepad lying on the top. There wasn't even a photo of any loved ones. Every drawer was locked.

I picked up the notepad and grinned. 'I've always wanted to do this.' I grabbed the pencil and shaded over the first white page. 'Wait for it,' I said. 'Wait for it…' I peered at the faint letters that had revealed themselves. 'Ah ha!'

Winter leant across me to take a look, affording me another whiff of the culver's root he had secreted about his person. 'You know, you can lose the magic herbs now.'

'I'll keep them for a while. I like knowing you're here of your own volition,' he said in my ear.

A small thrill went through me. What was wrong with me these days? The Order was clearly rubbing off in ways that were most uncharacteristic. I quickly pointed at the paper. 'He's written a note to himself. Look.'

Winter looked more closely. 'Milk. Bread. Washing-up liquid. Hardly the magic bullet we're looking for.'

'Yeah, but it worked! Without using any magic at all, I can now read exactly what's going on in his life. It's like I'm Nancy Drew.'

'Go you,' he murmured. He moved away and crouched down by the desk. 'Warded. If I can get the right herbs to open this…'

I sketched out my old reliable spell for him and all three drawers popped open. 'There you go.' I curtsied. 'You're welcome.'

Winter turned and stared at me. 'You just opened that.'

Well, duh. 'Yeah.'

'But it's warded.'

Puzzled, I put my hands on my hips. 'Not very strongly.'

'Show me that rune.'

His tone brooked no argument. I shrugged; it was no skin off my nose. I re-sketched the rune, this time aiming for the final locked drawer on the other side of the desk. It burst open, banging into Winter's leg. He didn't move, however; he just watched my hands. 'That's not a known rune.'

'You know all the runes?'

'I have an almost eidetic memory, Ivy. I've trained myself to remember. That is not a rune I've ever seen before.'

This line of questioning was becoming uncomfortable. 'So? I developed it on my own.'

He took a step towards me. "Do you have any idea how unusual that is?'

I sighed. 'Only because the Order sticks to tradition and traditional runes.'

'No. They stick to traditional runes because it's incredibly difficult to create new ones. There's an entire research and development department dedicated to the art and even they only manage a new rune once every few months.' Something indefinable glinted in his eyes. 'I think I'm beginning to understand you properly now.'

I didn't have the faintest idea what he was talking about. 'I'm not a thief,' I began. 'I don't go around breaking and entering. It's just a rune I developed to help me in case I lose my house keys.'

He held up his hands. 'Don't get all defensive.'

'Don't get all enigmatic. What do you mean, you understand me now?'

'You could have fought harder against your expulsion. Yes, your boyfriend has friends in high places but if you'd shouted louder, people would have listened. You didn't though. You wanted to be expelled.'

My mouth dropped open. 'What? At the time I bloody didn't.'

He was watching me like a hawk. 'Maybe not consciously.' He dropped his voice. 'You were bored.'

I was beginning to get irritated. 'So? Being a Neophyte isn't exactly exciting. I'm sure you remember that with your specially trained memory.'

'I loved every minute.' He still hadn't taken his eyes off of me. 'It's lazy-genius syndrome.'

'Huh?'

'You're unpredictable. Life doesn't stimulate you enough so you all but give up on it. The Order moves too slowly for someone of your abilities so it was probably a relief when they kicked you out. It's more common than you realise; lots of clever people end up checking out. It's a defined psychological syndrome.'

'Yeah,' I said sarcastically. 'I'm a genius. That's why I drive a taxi for a living.'

He came closer. 'You have a high need for cognitive stimulation. Others won't provide it for you. Most jobs won't either. So you fall back on the one person you can trust – yourself.' He smiled. 'But you're enjoying this job. You're stimulated now.'

I tilted my face up to his. 'Well,' I drawled, 'you are standing *very* close.'

'Joke all you like. I'm speaking the truth and you know it.' He moved back.

'If I were a genius,' I declared too loudly, 'I'd already have the smoking gun to put Adeptus Price away for life.'

'Well then, we should get on and find it.' Winter turned away and started rummaging through the top drawer.

I watched him for a moment, unwilling to acknowledge that he might be right with his daft theory, then I shrugged. Winter could analyse me all he wanted; it was a free country. I didn't have to pay him any attention when he did it.

I left him to rifle through Price's desk and turned to the filing cabinet. Perversely, it wasn't locked. Of course: it was vital to lock your desk and keep sticky fingers away from your pens and pencils but when it came to confidential files, anyone could nab them. I rolled my eyes. Price might be a murderer and thief but he wasn't the sharpest tool in the box.

I ran my finger along the files and whistled when I spotted one labelled 'Cypher'. Ah ha. I slid it out and flipped it open, just as Winter stepped back onto my toe. I yelped and dropped the file. 'Jeez!'

'Sorry.'

'I should think so,' I grumbled. 'Everyone knows muscle weighs more than fat and you weigh a ton.'

He smiled at my backhanded compliment. I knelt down to scoop up the file, angling my face upwards at Winter's body as I did so. Perhaps there was something to working out at the gym. Not for me, naturally. But for him. Definitely for him.

I grabbed a sheet of paper that had scooted under the desk, stretching my fingers to reach it. As I did so, my attention was caught by something. 'Winter,' I said slowly.

'I prefer it when you call me Rafe,' he murmured.

'Stop nattering,' I tutted. 'Come and look at this.' I pointed to the underside of the desk. He hunkered down beside me and followed my finger, exhaling loudly when he saw the file taped there. 'Do you think…' I began.

'Let's not rush to any conclusions.' He reached into his pocket and drew out a long set of tweezers. I shifted away to give him the room he needed and watched agog as he carefully prised the file away from the tape. He pulled it out with the delicate touch of a surgeon, stood up and placed it flat on the desk. I joined him.

It was Oscar Marsh's file. His name was scrawled across the front in a sweeping cursive script and, just in case there was any confusion, the tab at the side proclaimed the same name. I held my breath as Winter used the tweezers to flip it open.

All of Marsh's details were there: his address, his age, his position, his medical files. There were notes attached detailing his problems; apparently the Order hadn't abandoned him to his alcoholism as I'd suspected. In fact, he'd been instructed to attend several counselling sessions but hadn't turned up to a single one. I felt a wave of unexpected sympathy for him.

'Smoking gun,' I grinned.

'Not quite,' Winter answered. 'But we're getting close.'

I waved the Cypher file at him. 'There's this too.' I opened it up. There was nothing there other than the long catalogue list of available spells but it was another nail in Price's coffin, even if only a small, slightly crooked one.

'It's not enough,' Winter said. 'Given the nature of this investigation and who we are accusing, we need things to be watertight.'

I folded my arms. 'Price had Volume 9 in his possession for days,' I argued. 'We can't just leave him out there on the streets. He could already be putting his nefarious plans in place. We were looking for Marsh's file. We've found it. Bring Price in and get him to confess.'

Winter shook his head. 'He still has plausible deniability.'

'We can't leave him out there to do damage! The easiest way…'

'This isn't about the easy way, Ivy. This is about the right way.'

I glared at him. Good grief, he could be infuriating sometimes. 'So what's the right way?'

He met my eyes. 'We find Price and follow him,' he said grimly. 'Then we can discover exactly what he's up to.'

LESS THAN AN HOUR LATER, I pulled up my taxi as close to The Herboire as I could. It had only taken Winter a couple of phone calls to discover that most evenings Price hung out at this pretentious wine bar. I didn't even know that wine bars still existed.

Winter was already waiting outside, gazing up at the place as if he'd just discovered a new species. 'Welcome to the nineties!' I said, joining him.

He threw me a confused look. 'I'm not sure what you mean,' he said. 'And I still don't understand why we couldn't take my car.'

'I meant,' I said, 'that no self-respecting millennial would be found hanging around in a time warp like this. And I took my taxi so I don't have to traipse back to the Order headquarters.' I gave him a pointed glance. 'You could have come with me and left your car.'

Winter snorted. 'My car has all the equipment we need to make an arrest.'

My eyes widened. 'Handcuffs?'

He nodded. 'Amongst other things.'

'Whips? Chains?' I pushed myself onto my toes and examined his features. 'Do you spend your free time hanging out in S&M clubs?' Winter tsked. I smirked. This was fun. 'So what's the plan?'

'We wait until Price comes out then we follow him at a safe distance.'

I considered this. 'And what if he just goes home?'

'Then we stake out his house until he makes another move.'

'But that could be days.'

'If that's what it takes to bring this bastard down, Ivy, that's what we'll do.'

Winter might be happy to sit around waiting for Price to do something but I couldn't be arsed. Deciding I had a much better idea – and that it probably wouldn't appeal to my grumpy partner – I nodded my head. 'Well, I think I'll go grab a nap. I want to be fresh and alert for when he puts his newfound magic into action.' I pointed towards the wine bar. 'Unless he's already persuaded the poor owner of this dump to jump to his every whim and we're too late.'

Winter peered in through the windows. 'He's just having a drink. There's hardly anyone else in there. I think we're safe for now.' He said all this with a completely straight face, as if it were possible that Price was going to take over England by subjugating one wine bar at a time. He looked back at me. 'Do you seriously need to nap?'

'Oh yes.' I bobbed my head vigorously. 'We can take turns. You can rest later.' Before he could point out that this was a silly idea, I jogged back to my taxi and slid into the driver's seat. I slumped down as if getting comfortable, aware that Winter was still watching me. It was touch and go whether I'd get away with this but, when he marched across the road to take up position in an alleyway, I reckoned I'd succeeded. It was for the best. I didn't want to have to trail after Price for days. Or even hours. Winter would thank me later.

I didn't have long to wait. I was just getting comfortable, with my eyes drifting closed, when Price's weedy figure emerged from the bar. I sat bolt upright, hastily clipped on my seatbelt and flipped on my taxi-for-hire light. Price glanced one way up the street then the other, caught sight of me and raised his arm. I mentally high-fived myself.

'Ivy,' I whispered, 'Winter was right. You *are* a sodding genius.'

I put the taxi into gear and indicated, driving the short distance to where Price was waiting. With the dark night and my bright headlights, he wouldn't get the chance to see who I was until it was too late.

Price clambered in the back. 'Willowbrook Lane,' he grunted. 'And I know the route like the back of my hand so don't try the long way round.'

I waited a beat for him to recognise me. When all he did was settle into his seat and look out the window, my grin widened. 'Absolutely, sir,' I murmured. I caught sight of Winter's pale face as he stepped out from the shadows and stared as I drove off. I gave him a tiny nod. Work smarter, not harder. He'd learn.

It didn't appear that Price's little sojourn and tipple had done anything to relax him. The bruises under his eyes were even more pronounced and he kept twisting his fingers in his lap. He was acting like he had the weight of the world on his shoulders – or a very guilty conscience.

I was debating my next move when Price's phone rang. His expression contorted in a grimace but he still answered it. 'Yeah?'

I kept my eyes on the road but my focus was on Price. Was he speaking to an accomplice? Maybe I'd get all the evidence I needed without having to do more than drive around for a bit. I might even get lucky and he'd give me a tip.

'I can't do that, Mother,' Price hissed. 'I don't have time.'

He paused as whoever was speaking to him replied. Whatever they were saying, it didn't please him in the slightest. 'I've got people breathing down my neck in all directions. And no, not just the Ipsissimus. I've got a bunch of idiots working for me, all of whom make it very clear that they despise me. That Villeneuve fellow completely fucked up and sent some First Level to the back of beyond, causing no end of trouble that I got the blame for. It was hardly my fault that he messed up. No one under-stands the stress I'm under.'

His caller said something but, despite straining my ears, all I could hear was an indistinct murmur.

'Don't you think I've tried that?' Price half yelled, half whined. 'They won't listen to anything I say! I'm at my wits' end. Even the bloody receptionist throws daggers when she thinks I can't see. She's been letting almost anyone in through the door as if she doesn't care, and she laughed in my face when I tried to talk to her about it this morning. They're a bunch of lazy incompetents. I've had enough. I don't want this any more. I'm thinking of quitting.' There was a pause. 'I don't care if other witches don't quit! I've had enough!' He jabbed viciously at a button on the phone and tossed it down beside him.

I wrinkled my nose. Shrugging, I put plan B into action and indicated right when I should have gone left. Despite his earlier warning, it took Price a few moments to realise what I'd done. I was already down a darkened street and heading in the opposite direction out of town when it finally dawned on him that we weren't going to his home.

'Hey!' he protested, sitting forward. 'I told you, no funny busi-ness! Where are we?'

'Taking a short cut,' I said cheerfully, watching him in the mirror. On this road and at this time of night, it was unlikely I'd have to worry about oncoming traffic. I needed to keep my eyes on my new captive.

Price blinked. 'You're a woman?'

'You only just noticed?' Not that I should be surprised, given what I already knew of the man.

He stared at the back of my head then into the mirror at my reflection. 'I know you,' he said slowly.

'Yes. You do.' I smiled.

His eyes shifted and he started to reach into his pocket. Taking one hand off the steering wheel, I drew a rune that made his seatbelt tighten. It yanked him backwards, constricting his movements. 'What the hell do you think you're doing?' he screamed. 'Let me go!' He jerked wildly against the belt, panic guiding his movements. With his hands still free, he belatedly realised that he could still cast a spell against me. The fingers on his right hand began to draw, a sluggish rune designed to hurt. I responded by magicking up a barrier, which his spell fell against uselessly. His mouth dropped open. 'What the hell was that?'

'Something I've been working on for a while,' I told him. In truth, I hadn't been sure it would work against higher-level spells. Price really had been promoted beyond his abilities. My barrier wouldn't hold against another spell, though, regardless of how weak it was. He didn't need to know that. 'Try anything again,' I threatened, 'and you'll be sorry.'

Fear flared in his eyes and he did nothing to disguise it. 'Let me out! Stop this car and let me out, you bitch!'

'What is it with the word bitch?' I enquired.

Price was too busy screaming to hear me. 'Let me out! Let me out! Let me out!'

Good grief. Even Bell End and Alice were less annoying than this and they'd been trussed up for days. 'Are you scared?' I asked softly. 'Because you should be.'

I'd hardly done anything but Price's fear was increasing. I was more used to being an object of derision than creating terror these days. It worried me slightly that I enjoyed it.

Price started babbling away nonsensically to himself. To my surprise, he didn't attempt another spell; it was as if he'd already given up – and that was what disturbed me the most. I liked to think that if I were taken hostage I'd fight until my dying breath.

Other than his incessant mumbles, Price seemed no longer willing to try.

I'd just reached my destination when a new pair of headlights swung into the road behind me. I glanced at them in the rear-view mirror; I reckoned Winter had caught up to us. That gave me about thirty seconds. Okay dokey. I pulled up, turned off the engine and, ignoring Price's terrified whimper, got out of the car before hauling him out.

'You've been a sneaky little bastard,' I hissed in his face, keeping hold of his collar to stop him running away. It was lucky he was a scrawny fellow; I didn't fancy my chances of trying this on anyone my own size – or larger.

He moaned. 'Let me go. I've not done anything.'

I nearly laughed in his face. 'Oh yes, you have. I know everything. Poor Oscar. Why did you choose him to be the fall guy?' I asked. 'What did he ever do to you?'

Price's expression fell even further. 'Who … who's Oscar Marsh?'

I tutted. 'Marsh? Is that his last name? I didn't mention it.'

Too late, Price realised his mistake and did his best to back-track. 'Yes, you did!' he burst out. 'You were looking for his file the other day! You said his name then.' Darn it. He was right. Then he swallowed, his nervousness betraying him.

I lowered my voice until it was dangerously soft, mimicking Winter when he was truly pissed off. Hey, if it worked for him then I'd give it a shot. Besides, Winter was already pulling up and I was out of time. 'Why did you murder Diall? Was it so you could steal the Cypher Manuscript from him?'

Price swung his head towards Winter's car, obviously praying this was someone who would rescue him from the mad blonde witch who'd kidnapped him. Winter, however, merely got out of his car and crossed his arms over his broad chest. His headlights illuminated both Price and me. When he stepped forward into the light and Price realised who he was, his shoulders sagged in defeat. 'It was an accident,' he mumbled. 'I didn't mean to do it.'

Triumph coursed through me. 'Go on,' I said, keeping my voice even although it was difficult not to fist pump the air.

'I went to him to ask for help. I'd found the Cypher Manuscript in my drawer but I hadn't put it there, I swear! I'd never have taken it. But when I realised what it was, I knew no one would believe me. I begged Diall to do something. At first he told me he'd look into it but then nothing happened. He didn't do anything. You lot were crawling over everything and Diall had left me hanging. It was only a matter of time before I was fingered. So I went to see him again. He told me it was too late, I'd been an idiot and the smartest thing I could do was to come clean. All he worried about was himself and how this would reflect badly on him,' Price said helplessly. 'He said he'd made a mistake helping me to get this job, that I was going to screw it up after everything he'd done for me. He didn't want anyone looking into my files too closely because they'd incriminate him. He told me that I had to confess to taking the Manuscript to save everyone else. He never cared about me! He only ever cared about himself!'

I stared at Price. Everything he'd said sounded like the truth. He was too anxious and panicked and it seemed like he wanted to get it all off his chest. Had he really been set up from the start? If so, by whom?

'What did you do with the Manuscript?'

He dropped his head again, the picture of misery. 'I planted it in Oscar Marsh's desk. He's a drunk and an idiot. Diall had complained about him often enough so I knew he'd be perfect. If someone was going to blame me then I'd blame someone else. I burnt one page, went to his house and left a fragment there for someone to find.' He stared with wild, writhing eyes. 'It was only because I didn't have a choice! There was no other way out! You'd never have believed me if I'd told you the truth.'

'Did you kill Adeptus Exemptus Diall because you didn't have a choice?' Winter asked so quietly that it took a moment for his word to register.

Price gazed back at him. 'It was an accident! When I told him I wouldn't confess to something I hadn't done, he tried to arrest me! He was going to use a spell against me and turn me in so I grabbed his knife to try and hold him off. I didn't mean it to hurt him.'

'*It* didn't hurt him, Price,' Winter said. '*You* hurt him. *You* killed him.'

Price dropped to his knees and started to sob. 'I didn't mean to. I didn't mean to. Oh God, please help me.' His shoulders started to shake and he covered his face with his hands, unable to say another word.

Winter had no sympathy. He reached into his car and drew out a set of handcuffs. 'Adeptus Major Price,' he intoned. 'You are under arrest by proclamation of the Hallowed Order of Magical Enlightenment. Any attempt to use magic to provoke, conceal or avoid taking responsibility for your actions will be held against you, regardless of your guilt or innocence. You are entitled to legal representation and to apply to the non-magical courts for consideration.' He snapped the cuffs round Price's wrists and pulled him up to his feet. Then he glanced at me. I gave him a smug smile. Yeah, I'd solved Diall's murder.

In your face, Order Boy. In. Your. Face.

CHAPTER TWENTY-FOUR

Winter drove Price back to the Order headquarters in his car while I followed. It was probably just as well the poor murdering witch didn't have to travel with me because I turned up the music so it was blaring out deafeningly. Yeah, it was the middle of the night but so what? I'd just solved a murder. I deserved it. Of course, that didn't stop Winter glowering at me when we finally arrived back at the Arcane Branch building.

While Price was being processed and the police were informed, Winter drew me into a small room down a narrow corridor. I looked round. 'Is this your office?' I enquired. 'It's kind of pokey. You should try out for Human Resources. I hear there's an opening.'

He ignored my words. 'What did you think you were doing back there?' he enquired icily.

'Your job,' I said, hopping up onto his desk and swinging my legs. 'I'm kinda hungry now though. You got anything to eat?'

Winter gritted his teeth. 'You could have been hurt, Ivy. If Price had turned on you…'

'He tried and he failed. He was never going to get the better of me. And I never would have managed it if you'd not used culver root to try and get rid of me.'

'A cornered animal…'

'Yeah, yeah. My methods might have been unorthodox but I got results. Quit complaining.' I punched him lightly on the arm. 'All's well that ends well.'

'Is it?'

I looked at him. 'You believe that Price was telling the truth about the Cypher Manuscript,' I said. 'That it was deliberately left in his office by someone else and he just panicked when he found it.'

Winter didn't say anything.

'It's possible,' I admitted. 'He doesn't appear to have the intellectual power to put a plan like stealing Volume 9 into place and the way it was nicked was pretty damn intricate. It didn't take much to get him to confess, either. It was as if he wanted to tell me what he'd done. But if Diall took the Manuscript, he might have planted it in Price's desk because he wanted to get rid of him. His little protégé wasn't working out as well as he'd hoped and he wanted to get rid of the dead wood. Instead, he just ended up dead himself.'

Winter rubbed his chin. 'No. In that scenario Price would have given Diall up in a heartbeat. Don't forget that Price said that Diall didn't want to be incriminated if the HR files were looked at too closely. There must be details in there that prove that Diall used his position to get incompetents promoted beyond their station. The only way to avoid scrutiny of the files would have been for Price to give himself up. It wasn't the plan at the start, though. Price also said that Diall had promised to help him when he went to him the first time.'

I snapped my fingers. 'Because Diall thought he had the inside track on *you*. You wanted to investigate Diall, you told me that yourself. He must have known you were onto him and was already taking measures against you. He was afraid you were going after him. When Price went to him the first time, he'd already sent Bell End and Alice on their mission against Eve. They weren't there because of Volume 9, they were there because Diall was worried about you and what you were up to. But when Bell End and Alice didn't come back…'

Winter jumped in, warming to my theory. 'He must have known something was wrong. He didn't know about you but that didn't matter. He thought the gig was up. His only saving grace was that there was no sign of either Bellham or Fairclough so he couldn't know for sure what had happened to them. Maybe he thought he could blame Price for everything. If Price was charged with stealing Volume 9, anything could be laid at his door and the world would probably believe it. In any case, Diall would have wanted as much deniability as possible so he was prepared to walk away from Price and whatever deal they'd made. With his only ally abandoning him, Price would have been desperate. We know that he used the HR files to find Oscar Marsh. He was being set up and, unable to see any other way out, he set up someone else in the process.'

'But,' I pointed out, 'Price was being set up for stealing the Cypher Manuscript. If Diall didn't take Volume 9 and Price didn't take Volume 9, then who did?'

'Someone with a grudge against Price.' He paused. 'I spoke to Maidmont. He doesn't think that the Manuscript has been touched apart from the single page that was burnt. Maybe we've been going about this wrong way. We focused first on the idea that it had to be a higher-level witch who was the culprit and then that it was someone related to Diall who was tired of being used by him. But what if it's the opposite? What if it's someone lower down the scale who wanted to see a witch like Price get his comeuppance for being given a position they didn't deserve?'

I thought about it. 'Does it matter?' I asked. 'Whoever took it didn't kill anyone. They wouldn't have had time to read any of the spells before they planted it in Price's desk. No wonder his desk was the only thing that Price bothered to ward. He must have put the spell in place after he found the Manuscript there.'

'They might not have kept it for themselves but look at what happened as a result of their actions. Not to mention that whoever took the Manuscript tried to drown us, Ivy.'

Winter had a good point there. Yeah, it mattered. Even if I'd have to work that little bit harder to find them.

He continued. 'Of course, all this is mere speculation. There's no evidence.'

'Of course,' I responded drily. I looked at him. 'When was the first time Price's name came up?'

'When we went to see him about Oscar Marsh.'

'But we didn't just go to ask him about Marsh, did we? Bethany the tea lady had told us about Marsh but she also told us that Price had been round at Geomancy looking for Diall. In fact, she'd made a point of saying that he'd seemed frantic.'

Winter raised his eyebrows. 'What are you suggesting?'

I didn't answer him. Instead, I jumped off the desk and made a beeline for the main desk. Price was sitting slumped in a chair with several red-robed witches staring hard at him in case he dared to try anything. I pushed my way through. 'Price,' I said, 'listen to me.'

He didn't even lift his head. 'What?'

'When you went to see Diall the first time after you found the Manuscript, did you go to Geomancy?'

He looked up blearily. 'What? No, don't be stupid. I went to his house. Diall never liked it if I acknowledged him when other Order members were around. If I'd gone to Geomancy, he'd have bitten my head off.'

I whipped round to run back to Winter but he was already there. 'Bethany lied,' he said.

'She planted the first seed against Price. It was subtle, so as not to raise suspicion, but enough to make us wonder about him.'

Winter shook his head. 'What is she? Neophyte? Zelator? She wouldn't have the skills to pull off the theft.'

'Not on her own,' I said. 'But maybe she had help.' Winter gave me a questioning glance. 'I saw her,' I told him. 'Yesterday when I was on my way to HR.' I paused. 'You know, when you dumped me.'

He rolled his eyes. 'I didn't dump you.'

'Whatever. Anyway, she wasn't alone. She was with Weathers, the receptionist from Geomancy, and Rebecca, the receptionist from HR.'

'The one who never smiles?'

'Right. Except she was. Smiling, I mean.'

Winter was silent for a moment. 'We can't interrogate someone for smiling.'

'Nope.' I waited.

'But she would have good reason to be irritated with Price if she felt she was being held back in favour of others who were less skilled. And the other two would have the same reason to act against Diall.' He rubbed his chin thoughtfully. 'What if the note about the sceptre we found in Diall's home wasn't written by him? What if it was written *for* him? Maybe the trap in the sewers wasn't for us at all. Maybe it was for Diall.'

'And it was just our bad luck that we got there first,' I mused. I glanced at him wryly. 'All this from the man who doesn't believe in superstitions or fitting evidence to theories.'

Winter shrugged. 'At the very least we should find out where they all live and pay them a visit.'

I grinned. 'Now? It's the middle of the night. And we don't have any proof of anything apart from a little lie.'

Winter licked his lips. He felt the same glow that I did. We were on the right track; I knew it in my bones. 'You're right. But it's also time we finished this.'

I held up my palm for a high five. Winter stared at it as if it were a strange, alien thing he'd never seen before. I dropped my hand in disgust but I was still grinning. And this time so was Winter.

Weathers' little flat was still and silent and Bethany's was much the same. Winter's magic assured us that no one was inside either of them. That just left Rebecca. As we reached her house in a small suburb not too far from the city centre, I felt the adrenaline pumping round my body. The more I thought about it, the more Winter's theory seemed to be true.

'They're all together,' I breathed. 'And conspiring against the Order. It's the only thing that makes sense.'

'We still don't have a scrap of evidence, Ivy,' Winter cautioned.

'It fits. You know it does.'

He didn't answer. Instead, we both stared up at the red-brick house. There was a light on inside, just visible at the top of the closed curtains. 'Three people,' Winter grunted.

'See?' I crowed.

'Keep it down,' he whispered. 'And it's still not proof. Maybe they're just relaxing together after a long day at work. It makes sense that they know each other, they're of similar Levels and ages.'

'It must be gone two in the morning. That's not relaxing, Winter.' There was a sudden loud burst of laughter. 'That's a party.'

Winter ran a hand through his hair. For the first time, he looked rather tired. 'What worked with Price won't work here. They'll feed off each other. Unless we separate them, they'll never confess. And,' he reminded me harshly, 'without proof, we need a confession.'

I thought about it. 'If we can eavesdrop on them, we might get what we need.'

His brow furrowed. 'The house is warded against spells.'

'Even though they're all still First Level?'

'Bear in mind what we think they've done,' he answered.

True. If our theory was correct, they weren't the magical weaklings their Level suggested. 'Then we do this the old-fashioned way. I'll sneak in. You wait out here until I call you.'

Winter put his hands in his pockets and glared. 'No, I'll sneak in. You wait out here.'

I snorted. 'You just want all the glory for yourself.'

Winter looked astonished. 'I certainly do not. In fact…' His voice faltered when he saw that I was grinning. 'Fine,' he snapped. 'We'll sneak in together. But don't make a move until I do. We already know how dangerous these three can be.' He paused. 'And they might just be having a drink after work. They might be entirely innocent.'

'It might not be a drink, it might be an orgy. Well,' I amended, 'a threesome anyway.'

Winter looked faintly green. 'Let's hope not. Come on. There's probably a back door.'

Winter took the lead. There was a small path leading round to Rebecca's back garden; it was convenient but difficult to navigate silently, given that it was covered in pebbles. Winter flipped up the latch on the gate and went through it, stopping a few feet into the garden. I was hot on his heels.

'Well, well, well,' I murmured. 'The plot thickens.' I took in Rebecca's garden. Even under the shroud of darkness, it was clear to see how seriously she took herbology. There were all manner of carefully arranged plants taking up the entire space apart from a small path so she could gain access for weeding or snipping or whatever.

Winter knelt down, his fingers brushing against a small purple leaf. 'It's still—'

'Not evidence, I know,' I said with a sigh. 'But you have to admit it's starting to look more and more likely that she's involved in all this. What kind of First Level witch has a herb garden on this kind of scale?'

Winter didn't answer.

I rubbed my eye, feeling a vague itch. 'Eyelash,' I breathed. I put the tiny hair on the back of my hand and stared at it then I blew it gently over my shoulder and made a wish.

Winter rolled his eyes. 'That's not going to work.'

'We'll see,' I said smugly. I pointed to the back door leading into the house. 'Come on, then.'

He put a finger to his lips, unnecessarily indicating silence. With slow, deliberate movements, he twisted the doorknob. There was a faint squeak as it opened and I held my breath. When there was nothing more than the continued sound of raucous laughter from inside, I exhaled in relief.

Winter edged into Rebecca's kitchen. It was empty of people but there were several open bottles of wine on the counter. I peered round. Up ahead there was a glint of light from what I assumed was the living room.

'I'd have given anything to have seen Price's expression,' Weathers' familiar voice said, a gleeful chortle colouring every word.

'The man deserves everything that comes to him.' That was Rebecca.

I whipped my gaze towards Winter but he frowned and shook his head. He wanted more. I scowled. They were all congratulating themselves; it was obvious that we'd found what we were looking for.

'Tomorrow,' Weathers murmured, 'I am going to put in my application for Arcane Branch.'

'You won't get in.'

'You don't know that.'

'Oh come on,' Bethany said. 'No one knows what we've achieved. You're still First Level.'

'I have skills.' There was a pout in his voice.

'I know that, but no one else does. And until the dust settles, you're going to have to keep those skills to yourself. We need to lay low until we're sure this has worked.'

I jabbed Winter's arm triumphantly. He glared at me and shook his head again. Good grief; how much evidence did the guy need? He'd told me not to make a move until he did but if we did things his way, we'd be here all night. Yet again, I'd have to force our hand.

I gently nudged him out of the way. He reached out to grab my arm but, for once, I anticipated his move and remained free. Before he could do anything, I opened the door and grinned at the three hapless witches. 'Hello!'

There was an almost comical moment when they stared at me, unmoving, their expressions frozen in horror. Then Rebecca broke the sudden silence and leapt to her feet, reaching for a small pile of pre-mixed herbs on the coffee table.

'Don't!' I said, doing what I could to forestall Winter from joining me as well as trying to stop Rebecca attacking. 'I'm alone and I'm not here to cause problems.' I focused my attention on Weathers as he seemed the most likely to soften first. 'I'm on your side.' I held up my palms to indicate that I was coming in peace. 'I wasn't planning on confronting you all but when I saw the light, I knew I had to act. I had to speak to you about what you've done.' I schooled my face into a look of admiration; they had to believe me if this was going to work.

'Check the back,' Bethany said. Rebecca remained poised to fling the herbs and whatever nastiness they contained at me.

Weathers scooted past me, ducking his head into the kitchen and then out towards the back garden. I held my breath, hoping Winter had the sense to stay out of sight.

'No one's there,' Weathers said. 'Not that I can see.'

Bethany picked up a candlestick and brandished it in my direction. 'Start talking,' she spat. 'What do you think you're doing breaking in here?'

'Colonel Mustard in the library with the candlestick,' I said happily. 'Or rather you three in the library with the sceptre. You know what I mean.' I dropped into a chair and beamed. 'You guys are my heroes.'

'What are you on about?'

'Oh, come on, you know I don't want to be part of the Order. You're in HR. I bet you looked up my file. Price screwed up and that's why I've been forced to work with that plonker Winter. But anyone who's working from within to bring down those higher Level freaks is good in my book.' My eyes gleamed. 'I want to join you.'

Bethany folded her arms. 'What are you talking about?'

'You set up Price. You stole the Manuscript and planted it in his office.'

'Don't be ridiculous,' Weathers burst out. The panic in his expression belied his words.

I ignored his weak denial and leant back, trying to look relaxed. 'How on earth did you know the ward around the sceptre had degraded? It was a stroke of genius stealing that.'

'We didn't steal it!'

I shrugged. 'Borrowed it then. Hid it in the library sewer.' I gave the three of them a hard look. 'You know I almost died down there. That was what pissed me off and made me start looking for the real culprit. I realised the truth earlier tonight: it wasn't me you were trying to kill, it wasn't even Winter. You wanted to get Diall. It all makes sense.'

Rebecca stayed calm. 'We haven't done anything. You're crazy. And where the hell is your partner?'

I waved my hand dismissively. 'He got hold of some culver root and blocked me out.' I sniffed. 'Like I wanted to work with him. The man's a fool.'

Bethany looked at Rebecca. She nodded slowly. 'Culver root would do the job.' Then her eyes hardened again. 'Who else knows you're here?'

'No one. This was a spur of the moment thing.' I smiled. 'So what's the plan? Who are you bringing down next? Price is in chains. He's not getting out any time soon. Winter will see to that. And now that I'm in Arcane Branch, I think I've got a lot to offer you.' I clapped my hands. 'We can bring the entire Order down. That'll teach them.'

They exchanged glances. 'What led you to us?' Bethany asked, choosing her words carefully to avoid any suggestion of culpability.

I stuck to the truth as closely as I could. The more I lied, the more chance there was that I'd be found out. If I could get these three to believe I was with them in heart and spirit then I'd win.

'She was smiling,' I said, jerking my head towards Rebecca. 'When I saw you three earlier tonight. It seemed out of character.' Rebecca glowered harder. 'And,' I continued, 'you were the one who put me onto Price in the first place, weren't you, Bethany?' I shook my head as if in amazement. 'I didn't know for sure about anything but with the three of you here...' My expression dropped. 'Please don't tell me I'm wrong. I really want to work with you guys.'

Bethany sank back onto the sofa. 'We didn't plan on taking the sceptre. It was going to be a few old books.' She shrugged. 'Anything that would have involved the wards being reset would have been enough. But then Weathers realised the sceptre ward was weak and that we could break it.' She threw him an irritated glance. 'We almost didn't get the concealing spell up in time.'

'You guys have some awesome skills.'

'Yeah,' Rebecca said shortly. 'We do. All three of us should be Second Level. We have the magic, we've proved that. But because we don't suck up to the right people, we're stuck with menial jobs.' She glared at me. 'Let's get one thing clear, though. We're not trying to bring down the Order.'

I blinked. 'Oh.'

'Yeah,' Weathers said. 'Oh.'

'We love the Order,' Rebecca told me. 'That's why we did what we did. We want it to be as strong as possible. We want people to be treated with merit, to gain their Levels not because of politics but because they deserve them. So, yeah, we came up with a plan to destabilize Price and get rid of Diall.'

'You weren't supposed to get hurt in the sewer,' Weathers said. 'That was for Diall. We got lucky when Price killed him for us.' Lucky? Well, that was one way of discussing murder although it wouldn't be my choice.

'It would have been easier if you'd drowned though,' Bethany mused, 'Because then we wouldn't have to do this.'

Uh oh. 'Do what?'

Rebecca lifted up her hand, which still contained the herbal mixture. 'This.' She flung it at me.

I scrambled to put up a rune to protect myself but it was too late. All I could do was minimise the herbs' effects. I choked. My chest felt tight and it was difficult to breathe. 'What?' I gasped. 'Why?'

'You're not one of us,' Rebecca sneered, her face looming towards mine. 'Winter is a good guy. We need more witches like him and fewer witches like you, Diall and Price. You're the lazy ones. We're the ones who get things done.'

My hands clawed at my throat; it felt like my windpipe was closing up. What the hell was wrong with me? And why hadn't Winter burst in yet?

'The Order needs to be strong,' Weathers intoned with the zeal of a true convert. 'You're weak.'

My knees buckled underneath me and my vision swam. This was not good, it was not good at all.

'I'd watch your words,' I heard Winter say suddenly from the door. I closed my eyes in relief. Thank goodness – though I still couldn't breathe. 'Ivy's not weak. She is, however, remarkably reckless.'

And then all hell broke loose. Weathers leapt towards Winter and prepared to throw out a rune while Rebecca scrabbled for more herbs. I spluttered, able to make out little more than blurry shapes. My head was pounding and I was feeling distinctly nauseous. Something flew across the room but it was only when it smashed into the wall on the other side and fell down with a grunt that I realised it was Weathers. Winter sidestepped Rebecca's batch of flying herbs and muttered his own incantation under his breath. At the same time he took out his own herbs and threw them at her.

Bethany let out a battle cry and launched herself at him. There was a pained shriek as he drew a rune and she dropped to the floor in mid-flight. I collapsed sideways. Good for Winter, a little voice said in my head.

'You're an idiot.'

I forced my eyes open. I could just make out Winter's features. He hissed in irritation and reached into his pocket, taking out a small bag of herbs. He put the tiniest pinch under my nose and I gasped.

'I can breathe.' I started to cough. 'Oh, thank goodness.' I blinked rapidly and looked round the room. Weathers was still in the far corner, groaning loudly. Bethany and Rebecca were completely prone. I stared. 'Did you bring down three witches?' I asked, my voice thready and weak.

Winter sighed. 'Yes.'

'In about three seconds?'

'There might be three of them, Ivy, but they're only First Level. Knowing one or two Second Level spells doesn't make you Second Level. They're not as good as they think they are.'

Apparently, neither was I. I grabbed Winter's hand and struggled to my feet. '*You* really are that good, though.'

'Yeah,' he said simply and without a trace of ego. 'I really am.'

I considered this. There was something to be said for Order training after all. I pursed my lips. 'Thanks,' I muttered.

'No problem.' Winter hesitated. 'Thanks for getting these three to confess.'

I felt suddenly abashed. 'I guess we make a pretty good team.' I flicked a look at Weathers. 'You could have been part of that!' I called. 'There will be no Wilde Wintry Weathers now!'

Winter rolled his eyes. 'Next time, don't burst in through the door like that. At least not without discussing it with me first. You repeatedly prove that you have no regard for your own safety. You could have been seriously hurt.'

'I *was* seriously hurt! I'm going to require several weeks of convalescence. I almost died! Again! What took you so long anyway?'

'I was hiding in a cupboard and the vacuum cleaner got in my way.' He inclined his head towards mine. 'Don't tell anyone.'

I smirked. 'My lips are sealed. Honest. I wouldn't tell anyone that the big bad Adeptus Exemptus Raphael Winter almost got his partner killed and missed a fight because a household appliance got in his way.'

'Ivy…'

I grinned. 'What?'

CHAPTER TWENTY-FIVE

I GOT OUT OF THE CAR FEELING MORE KNACKERED THAN I'D EVER felt in my life. Even my bones were weary. It had been a long time since I'd returned home when the sun was shining. All the same, there was an odd buzz of euphoria running through my veins. We'd solved the crimes, Winter and me. I was starting to see why he liked his work so much. Only starting, mind; I wasn't a total convert. But if the Order brought in a three-day working week, I might be persuaded…

Winter climbed out from the other side of the car and we shared a glance of satisfaction. With his normally pristine clothes messed up, and with his top button undone and his tie askew, he looked rather adorable. I glanced down, taking in the state I was in. Well, at least one of us looked good.

'Out of curiosity,' he murmured, 'what did you wish for? With the eyelash?'

'A lie-in tomorrow,' I chirped.

'You're kidding me.'

'Nope.'

Winter sighed dramatically but I swear I spotted the ghost of a smile on his lips. As if to cover it, he knelt down and started tying his shoelace. From the other side of the road, there was the sound of a car door closing and a familiar voice.

'Ivy! I'm so glad I caught you!' Iqbal darted across, his face split into a wide grin.

I gave him a quick hug. 'Hey! Good to see you. What are doing here?'

His smile stretched even further. 'You're gonna love me,' he promised.

I bopped him on the arm. 'I already do, Iqqy pop.'

Iqbal took my hand and began to murmur. A strange itching sensation rose up my arm, then it turned to burning. Suddenly alarmed, I tried to yank my hand away. My heart began thumping against my chest and I could feel sweat breaking out across my brow. I stared at Iqbal in horror but he continued to smile, although his teeth were gritted at the same time as if he were concentrating very hard.

'What the…' I heard Winter exclaim from the other side of the car. He staggered upwards just as Iqbal finally released me.

The pain vanished almost immediately. Iqbal swept out a proud bow. 'You're welcome!' he beamed.

'The binding,' I said slowly.

He nodded vigorously and opened his palm to reveal what I knew was ossombe root. There was only a tiny quantity but it had been enough. The invisible magic thread that bound me to Winter was most definitely gone. I didn't need to test it to be sure, I just knew.

'After your phone call yesterday,' Iqbal chirruped happily, 'I knew things were getting desperate. I asked around and found an old professor of mine who happened to have some ossombe root lying around in his study. He agreed to give it to me if I gave him an outline of my thesis by the end of the month.' A faint furrow creased his forehead. 'So you really owe me now, Ivy. I deserve at least one ballad.'

My mouth was dry. I swallowed several times and looked

helplessly at Winter. His face was an implacable mask. 'We're free,' I whispered.

Winter pulled back his shoulders. 'It would appear so.'

Iqbal gave him a nervous glance. 'Hi, Adeptus Exemptus Winter. I didn't see you there until it was too late. I hope you don't mind that I took off the binding but I knew that Ivy was getting desperate.'

Winter didn't look at him; his eyes were trained on me. All I could do was shrug awkwardly. 'Yeah,' I said. 'Desperate.' Darn it.

A curious expression crossed Iqbal's face as he realised that I wasn't jigging around as ecstatically as I should be. He lifted his shoulders and gave me a funny look then, putting my lack of joy down to Winter's brooding presence, he clapped me on the shoulders. 'The Cauldron,' he said. 'Seven o'clock tonight. You can come too, Adeptus,' he called across to Winter. 'You've not lived until you've heard Ivy sing. I need to head off and start that outline but I expect you to be on time.' He waggled his fingers. 'You both owe me big time.'

My shoulders dropped. Arse.

With Winter by my side, I climbed the stairs up to my floor. I didn't even call for the lift; it just seemed like too much effort. Winter didn't say a word and neither did I. For once, I didn't know what to say.

Near the top, footsteps tripped up behind us. Thinking it was Iqbal again, I turned. My heart sank. Eve. Any euphoria I'd felt five minutes ago was now well and truly gone.

'Ivy!' Genuine delight crossed her face. 'It's so good to see you! Honestly, you wouldn't believe all that's happened to me. In fact…' Her voice faltered as she realised who was standing beside me. 'Adeptus Exemptus Winter. What are you doing here?'

Winter coughed and looked at me. I scratched my neck. 'Maybe we should go to my flat,' I suggested. 'You can make me a cup of tea and we can talk about it.'

'I'M BEING PROMOTED to Second Level?' Eve's eyes were saucer-wide and shining.

I fidgeted. 'Yeah. I'm sorry. The binding has been removed now so maybe you'll still get to work with Winter. I should have told you before but it didn't seem right to do it over the phone.'

Eve barely heard me. 'Second Level? I hoped, you know I hoped, but I thought I'd have to do the exams first. My parents will be thrilled! I'm thrilled! And Arcane Branch?' She glanced at Winter. 'Do you think I'll still have a chance of getting a spot?'

'A position has just opened up,' Winter said stiffly, not looking at me.

Eve jumped to her feet. 'This is just amazing,' she said, still shaking her head in disbelief. 'I have to go and tell Harold Fitzwilliam Duxworthy the Third.' She darted out of the room.

I twisted my fingers in my lap. 'That went better than I expected,' I said.

Winter murmured non-committally.

I took a deep breath. 'I didn't know Iqbal was going to do that,' I said in a rush. 'I didn't ask him to. Well, not really. In fact, I found some ossombe root a few days ago and stuffed it in my bathroom cabinet. The binding wasn't all that bad.'

Winter didn't say anything. Bloody hell, this was hard work.

There was a sudden thump from the bedroom. Relieved to have a distraction, I opened the door to investigate. My secret stash of catnip had been attacked and there was a trail leading from the smashed jar on the floor all the way to the bed. Both Brutus and Princess Parma Periwinkle were rolling around on the duvet with expressions of feline glee. Winter peered over my shoulder and grunted with disapproval.

'Ivy?'

From beyond the living room, Eve reappeared with her arms

by her sides and a confused expression on her face. 'Why are there two people tied up in the middle of my living-room floor?'

CHAPTER TWENTY-SIX

EPILOGUE

He stood outside, hands shoved in his pockets and a flat, grim line across his mouth. The pub was well lit and busy. Every time the door opened to welcome a new patron, the sound of appalling music drifted out. He half turned to leave. This was a pointless venture; the sensible thing would be to go home right now. There were reports to write and he knew that it wouldn't be long before he had another time-consuming assignment to occupy both his days and nights. Besides, she didn't want him there.

The door opened again and a group of friends fell out, giggling and stumbling towards him. From inside, the music faded away to a burbling voice. 'Our next victim is the fabulous Ivy Wilde who…' The door banged shut, muffling the words.

Winter sighed. Then his feet swerved round the happy group and into the pub's interior almost of their own volition.

Ivy's friend, if that's what he was, was pushing her up onto the small stage. She was laughing, her blonde curls bouncing and catching the light, but he could see the reluctance in her eyes even from this distance. She turned in his direction, her chin angling upwards and he hastily veered left towards the bar and caught the eye of the barman.

By the time he had a whisky in hand, Ivy was already onto the second verse. Her cheeks were rosy pink and there was a tremor to the fingers that were clutching the microphone. She wasn't a particularly bad singer but her lack of enthusiasm made her painful to watch. He wished that she wouldn't sway her hips like that. The movement only served to accentuate her curves and, despite the quality of the whisky, his mouth felt uncomfortably dry.

Regardless of her reluctance, the crowd seemed to appreciate her efforts. They were certainly whooping and cheering loudly enough. The more they yelled, the more confident Ivy grew with both her singing and her dancing, to the point where she replaced the microphone back on its stand and abandoned her sultry swaying for more energetic movements. What no one seemed to have noticed was that she also seemed to be inching closer and closer to the edge of the stage. It wasn't a long drop – probably less than a metre – but she'd no doubt had one or two drinks already and she could fall and hurt herself. That was what he told himself when he pushed his way through the crowd to get closer to her.

'Oi!' A fat man holding the dregs of a pint of beer glared at him. Winter glanced in the man's direction, which was enough to make him immediately subside. Winter nodded, satisfied.

He'd just reached the front of the stage when Ivy whipped round with alarming speed, as if attempting a pirouette. Her sparkling eyes fixed on him and widened. Unfortunately, her surprise was also her undoing: her feet kept moving but her body didn't follow and, almost in slow motion, she began to topple forward. Winter didn't pause. He braced himself, held out his arms and caught her as she fell.

'Oooomph!' Ivy coiled her arms round his neck and beamed

up at him. She smelled of honey and sunshine and just the tiniest smidge of ancient magic. He breathed in deeply. 'My hero!' she burbled.

Winter stared down at her, his expression inscrutable. 'Are you trying to maim yourself?' he inquired.

Her smile widened. 'I know, right? This is why I hate doing karaoke. It's far too energetic.'

'Ivy! Are you alright?' Her dark-haired friend appeared, concern on his face.

Ivy extricated herself from Winter. 'Apart from the horror of that song, Iqbal, I'm good.' She reached up and patted Winter's chest. 'My partner saved me.'

Winter's jaw clenched. 'We're not partners any more.'

For a moment a shadow crossed Ivy's face then she brightened again. 'You should count yourself lucky,' she grinned. 'I'm far too much like hard work.'

It was on the tip of Winter's tongue to tell her that she should know by now that he liked hard work. But someone else was bearing down on them, throwing shot glasses in their direction.

'Tequila!' Ivy smacked her lips. 'I really shouldn't.' She took one anyway and downed it.

Iqbal grabbed another glass and thrust it at Winter. 'Adeptus Exemptus, I think you deserve one for that catch.'

Under any other circumstances Winter would have refused but he knew that was what Iqbal was expecting, so he took the glass and tipped it back, wincing slightly as the fiery liquid burned down his throat.

'Good man!' Iqbal clapped him on the shoulder. 'Let's get another round!' He headed off to the bar.

'Come on.' Ivy tugged Winter's elbow. 'We've got a table in the corner.'

He allowed himself to be led through the crowd. Ivy plonked herself down on one of the chairs with a happy sigh. Winter debated for a moment then joined her. 'Who's your friend?' he asked, his tone harsher than he'd intended. 'You didn't introduce us earlier when he gave you the ossombe root.'

'Huh?' Ivy looked blank for a moment then realised who he was talking about. 'Oh, you mean Iqbal. We go way back.' She waved her hands around. 'He's a good guy. He just likes karaoke too much.' Her eyes fixed on him. 'What's going on back at the Order?'

'Do you really want to know?'

She pursed her lips. 'I risked life and limb, Winter. I think I deserve to know.'

'Rafe,' he found himself saying. 'You should call me Rafe.'

A softer smile curved round Ivy's mouth but before she could say anything Iqbal reappeared with another tray of shots. He placed it on the table. 'I got a selection!' he yelled over the music. 'I wasn't sure what you'd all like.'

Ivy beamed her approval and chose a glass at random. Winter watched as she took a delicate sniff then shrugged. 'Bottoms up.'

Winter picked up one of the little glasses without looking at it. He kept his eyes on Ivy, clinking his glass against hers before he drank.

Iqbal cleared his throat. 'So, Adeptus,' he said. 'What's going on back at the Order now that the truth has been revealed?'

'I just asked that!' Ivy said. 'Tell us!'

Winter shrugged. The news would be in the morning papers so there wasn't any point in staying quiet. 'The Ipsissimus is putting in an immediate review of all promotional procedures. Everyone who's achieved a position beyond First Level is going to be scrutinised. It'll take months but it'll be worth it.'

'What about Bell End and Alice?' Ivy asked. A curl had fallen across her forehead and Winter itched to brush it away. He put his hands under the table instead.

'Who?'

'Uh, Bellham. Matthew Bellham and Alice Fairclough. What's happened to them?'

'They've been released but they're on probation.' Ivy scowled. 'They were acting under orders.'

She snorted indelicately. 'That's no defence.' Privately, Winter agreed.

Ivy got clumsily up to her feet. Winter automatically stood too but she merely gave him a confused look. 'I'm off to the ladies' room,' she declared. 'I need a pee. Are you coming too?'

'I was being a gentleman,' he muttered. She didn't hear him – she was already bustling through the crowd.

Winter sat down and picked up another glass without thinking. Iqbal smiled. 'To the Order!'

'To the Order.' Winter gulped it down. He glanced behind him; there was no longer any sign of Ivy.

Iqbal leant across the table. 'What are your intentions?'

Winter blinked back at him. 'Excuse me?'

'With Ivy,' Iqbal said, a sudden sharp focus in his dark eyes. 'She likes you a lot, you know, but she's more vulnerable than she lets on.'

Winter's skin was beginning to itch. 'I like her too. She's an extraordinarily talented witch. It's a real shame she's not in the Order.'

Iqbal watched him. 'That wasn't what I meant.'

Winter looked at him. Ivy hadn't answered his question properly before. 'Are you and her…' he began.

'No. But she's a good friend.' Iqbal turned as someone shouted his name from the other side of the room. 'I should go. It was nice to meet you again, Adeptus Exemptus Winter. Be nice to Ivy.' He walked off, just as the woman in question returned. Winter saw him lean his head down towards her ear and murmur something. Ivy's cheeks turned an adorable shade of pink and Winter frowned.

She pushed her way back through the crowd to the table. 'I've done my duty and sung my songs,' she said. 'And now I want to go home and sleep for three days.' Her eyes twinkled. 'I think I deserve it.'

'I think you do,' he returned. 'I'll walk you out.'

It seemed far colder outside than it was when he'd arrived. The cool air hit him almost immediately and he realised that drinking on an empty stomach had affected him considerably. He wasn't the only one: Ivy swayed alarmingly and banged into him. He just managed to shoot out his arms and hold her upright. 'Be careful,' he said gruffly. 'You're drunk.'

Ivy gave a peal of laughter. 'So are you!' She tugged at the spot on her arm where the binding had been placed. 'We made a good team, you know. I'm almost sorry it's all over.'

He folded his arms. 'Almost?'

She didn't hear him. 'You're a good guy, Adeptus Exemptus Raphael Winter.' She peered at him. 'And you really do have the most amazing blue eyes. They're the colour of the Mediterranean on a sunny day.' She leant in closer. 'Or lapis lazuli.' She pushed herself up on her tiptoes to get an even closer look. 'You know, in Italy and Spain Prince Charming is known as the Blue Prince.'

He gazed down at her, a strange knot in his chest. 'You're too wonderfully stubborn to be Cinderella,' he told her. 'You're far more kick-ass than she is. No wicked stepmother would ever make you act like a servant.' He paused, aware that he was starting to babble. 'And you don't need a magical ballgown to be beautiful.'

Ivy smiled. 'I'd rather be Sleeping Beauty. I think she's more up my street.'

Winter laughed.

She arched an eyebrow at him. 'Not because she spends so long in bed but because of how she's rescued.' Slightly flummoxed, Winter stared at her. Ivy tutted. 'Maybe you're the one who needs rescuing.'

Then she kissed him.

'WINTER!' The voice penetrated the folds of his sleep. 'Winter!'

'Mmm.' He opened his eyes blearily. For a brief moment, he felt utterly content. Ivy was staring down at him, her hair mussed up and her lips faintly bruised. He didn't think he'd ever seen anything more beautiful. That was when he realised her expression was one of horrified alarm.

He shot bolt upright. Ivy clutched the duvet. 'Hi,' she said. She looked more awkward than he'd ever seen her – and that included in the gym on that first morning.

He frowned as a thought occurred to him. Didn't she remember last night? They'd both been tipsy. He stilled. Had he taken advantage of her? Ice ran through his veins.

Ivy peeked underneath the duvet at herself, then she peeked underneath the duvet at him. She tried to smile but it was obvious how shocked she was to find them both without a stitch of clothing.

'Hey,' he said. He cleared his throat. Damn it. 'Um.' This was not going well. 'So.'

Her tongue darted out to wet her lips. 'So.' She didn't look upset so much as incredibly uncomfortable. Winter realised with a sinking feeling that she was embarrassed.

Willing to do just about anything to make her feel better, he shifted slightly. 'We should probably never speak of this again.'

Ivy nodded vigorously. 'Absolutely!' she said, jumping on his words with an alacrity that dismayed him. 'It never happened.' She scooted to the edge of the bed. Winter dropped his gaze. He was a prize idiot.

Without warning, Ivy yanked hard on the duvet and wrapped it around herself then raced for the bathroom – to get away from him, he thought. She slammed the door shut behind her. Winter sighed and turned away. He should get his clothes and get out of here. Ivy was obviously filled with regret. He couldn't look at her face when he felt so very differently.

He reached down to grab his trousers. Brutus sauntered over and head butted his legs before sitting down and looking up at him with slitted eyes. 'The trouble,' the cat said, 'with consorting with partners of oppositional temperaments, is that next morning one can never be sure whether they are too giddy with delight to express their thoughts or too horrified.'

Then he winked.

ABOUT THE AUTHOR

After teaching English literature in the UK, Japan and Malaysia, Helen Harper left behind the world of education following the worldwide success of her Blood Destiny series of books. She is a professional member of the Alliance of Independent Authors and writes full time, thanking her lucky stars every day that's she lucky enough to do so!

Helen has always been a book lover, devouring science fiction and fantasy tales when she was a child growing up in Scotland.

She currently lives in Edinburgh in the UK with far too many cats – not to mention the dragons, fairies, demons, wizards and vampires that seem to keep appearing from nowhere.

You can find out more by visiting Helen's website: http://helenharper.co.uk

OTHER TITLES

The complete *FireBrand* series

A werewolf killer. A paranormal murder. How many times can Emma Bellamy cheat death?

I'm one placement away from becoming a fully fledged London detective. It's bad enough that my last assignment before I qualify is with Supernatural Squad. But that's nothing compared to what happens next.

Brutally murdered by an unknown assailant, I wake up twelve hours later in the morgue – and I'm very much alive. I don't know how or why it happened. I don't know who killed me. All I know is that they might try again.

Werewolves are disappearing right, left and centre.

A mysterious vampire seems intent on following me everywhere I go.

And I have to solve my own vicious killing. Preferably before death comes for me again.

A Charade of Magic complete series

The best way to live in the Mage ruled city of Glasgow is to keep your head down and your mouth closed.

That's not usually a problem for Mairi Wallace. By day she works at a small shop selling tartan and by night she studies to become an apothecary. She knows her place and her limitations. All that changes, however, when her old childhood friend sends her a desperate message seeking her help - and the Mages themselves cross Mairi's path. Suddenly, remaining unnoticed is no longer an option.

There's more to Mairi than she realises but, if she wants to fulfil her full potential, she's going to have to fight to stay alive - and only time will tell if she can beat the Mages at their own game.

From twisted wynds and tartan shops to a dangerous daemon and the magic infused City Chambers, the future of a nation might lie with one solitary woman.

Book One – Hummingbird

Book Two – Nightingale

Book Three – Red Hawk

The complete *Blood Destiny* series

"A spectacular and addictive series."

Mackenzie Smith has always known that she was different. Growing up as the only human in a pack of rural shapeshifters will do that to you, but then couple it with some mean fighting skills and a fiery temper and you end up with a woman that few will dare to cross. However, when the only father figure in her life is brutally murdered, and the dangerous Brethren with their predatory Lord Alpha come to investigate, Mack has to not only ensure the physical safety of her adopted family by hiding her apparent humanity, she also has to seek the blood-soaked vengeance that she craves.

Book One - Bloodfire

Book Two - Bloodmagic

Book Three - Bloodrage

Book Four - Blood Politics

Book Five - Bloodlust

Also

Corrigan Fire

Corrigan Magic

Corrigan Rage

Corrigan Politics

Corrigan Lust

The complete *Bo Blackman* series

A half-dead daemon, a massacre at her London based PI firm and evidence that suggests she's the main suspect for both ... Bo Blackman is having a very bad week.

She might be naive and inexperienced but she's determined to get to the bottom of the crimes, even if it means involving herself with one of London's most powerful vampire Families and their enigmatic leader.

It's pretty much going to be impossible for Bo to ever escape unscathed.

Book One - Dire Straits

Book Two - New Order

Book Three - High Stakes

Book Four - Red Angel

Book Five - Vigilante Vampire

Book Six - Dark Tomorrow

The complete *Highland Magic* series

Integrity Taylor walked away from the Sidhe when she was a child. Orphaned and bullied, she simply had no reason to stay, especially not when the sins of her father were going to remain on her shoulders. She found a new family - a group of thieves who proved that blood was less important than loyalty and love.

But the Sidhe aren't going to let Integrity stay away forever. They need her more than anyone realises - besides, there are prophecies to be fulfilled, people to be saved and hearts to be won over. If anyone can do it, Integrity can.

Book One - Gifted Thief

Book Two - Honour Bound

Book Three - Veiled Threat

Book Four - Last Wish

The complete *Dreamweaver* series

"I have special coping mechanisms for the times I need to open the front door. They're even often successful..."

Zoe Lydon knows there's often nothing logical or rational about fear. It doesn't change the fact that she's too terrified to step outside her own house, however.

What Zoe doesn't realise is that she's also a dreamweaver - able to access other people's subconscious minds. When she finds herself in the Dreamlands and up against its sinister Mayor, she'll need to use all of her wits - and overcome all of her fears - if she's ever going to come out alive.

Book One - Night Shade

Book Two - Night Terrors

Book Three - Night Lights

Stand alone novels

Eros

William Shakespeare once wrote that, "Cupid is a knavish lad, thus to make poor females mad." The trouble is that Cupid himself would probably agree…

As probably the last person in the world who'd appreciate hearts, flowers and romance, Coop is convinced that true love doesn't exist – which is rather unfortunate considering he's also known as Cupid, the God of Love. He'd rather spend his days drinking, womanising and generally having as much fun as he possible can. As far as he's concerned, shooting people with bolts of pure love is a waste of his time…but then his path crosses with that of shy and retiring Skye Sawyer and nothing will ever be quite the same again.

Wraith

Magic. Shadows. Adventure. Romance.

Saiya Buchanan is a wraith, able to detach her shadow from her body and send it off to do her bidding. But, unlike most of her kin, Saiya doesn't deal in death. Instead, she trades secrets - and in the goblin besieged city of Stirling in Scotland, they're a highly prized commodity. It might just be, however, that the goblins have been hiding the greatest secret of them all. When Gabriel de Florinville, a Dark Elf, is sent as royal envoy into Stirling and takes her prisoner, Saiya is not only going to uncover the sinister truth. She's also going to realise that sometimes the deepest secrets are the ones locked within your own heart.

The complete *Lazy Girl's Guide To Magic* series

Hard Work Will Pay Off Later. Laziness Pays Off Now.

Let's get one thing straight - Ivy Wilde is not a heroine. In fact, she's probably the last witch in the world who you'd call if you needed a magical helping hand. If it were down to Ivy, she'd spend all day every day on her sofa where she could watch TV, munch junk food and talk to her feline familiar to her heart's content.

However, when a bureaucratic disaster ends up with Ivy as the victim of a case of mistaken identity, she's yanked very unwillingly into Arcane Branch, the investigative department of the Hallowed Order of Magical Enlightenment. Her problems are quadrupled when a valuable object is stolen right from under the Order's noses.

It doesn't exactly help that she's been magically bound to Adeptus Exemptus Raphael Winter. He might have piercing sapphire eyes and a body which a cover model would be proud of but, as far as Ivy's concerned, he's a walking advertisement for the joyless perils of too much witch-work.

And if he makes her go to the gym again, she's definitely going to turn him into a frog.

Book One - Slouch Witch

Book Two - Star Witch

Book Three - Spirit Witch

Sparkle Witch (Christmas novella)

The complete *Fractured Faery* series

One corpse. Several bizarre looking attackers. Some very strange magical powers. And a severe bout of amnesia.

It's one thing to wake up outside in the middle of the night with a decapitated man for company. It's another to have no memory of how you got there - or who you are.

She might not know her own name but she knows that several people are out to get her. It could be because she has strange magical powers seemingly at her fingertips and is some kind of fabulous hero. But then why does she appear to inspire fear in so many? And who on earth is the sexy, green-eyed barman who apparently despises her? So many questions ... and so few answers.

At least one thing is for sure - the streets of Manchester have never met someone quite as mad as Madrona...

Book One - Box of Frogs

SHORTLISTED FOR THE KINDLE STORYTELLER AWARD 2018

Book Two - Quiver of Cobras

Book Three - Skulk of Foxes

The complete *City Of Magic* series

Charley is a cleaner by day and a professional gambler by night. She might be haunted by her tragic past but she's never thought of herself as anything or anyone special. Until, that is, things start to go terribly wrong all across the city of Manchester. Between plagues of rats, firestorms and the gleaming blue eyes of a sexy Scottish werewolf, she might just have landed herself in the middle of a magical apocalypse. She might also be the only person who has the ability to bring order to an utterly chaotic new world.

Book One - Shrill Dusk

Book Two - Brittle Midnight

Book Three - Furtive Dawn

Printed in Great Britain
by Amazon

41298166R00169

Rhyming ret.
of the Bard's ,

ALAS,
POOR
SHAKE
SPEARE

Denis O'Leary

ISBN 9798581978856

CONTENTS

ACKNOWLEDGEMENTS

I wish to thank:

Margaret, my wife, for her constant love and support.

My son, Paul, for the design of this book.

My son, David, for the illustrations.

My daughter, Catherine, for her advice and suggestions
for improvement.

My sister, Irene Nolan, for her meticulous proof-reading.

Professor Gustavo San Roman and, separately, Fr Michael Collins
for their comments and advice, and for putting me under pressure
to publish.

Jack Cleary, Eamonn Doyle, Liam Hartigan and Gerry O'Hara,
for their feedback.

FOREWORD

Foul murder, true love won and lost
And tragic heroes paying the cost,
Witty fools and cast-out Kings,
Weird witches, airy-fairy things;
Some Shakespeare plays I here rehearse
In humorous, light-hearted verse.

Shakespeare liked to intertwine
Sub-plots throughout the storyline.
Herein, though, I've excised a lot
To concentrate on the main plot.

And he has minor characters whose
Raison d'être's to amuse.
These, in my summaries, I eschew
Except for minor characters who
Sometimes, though not often, say
Something important in the play.

What the Bard put on the stage
Was written for a bygone age.
Some folk, today, find understanding
Ye olde English too demanding.
The language I have used to write
This homage to the master might
Seem, to some, to disrespect
The scholarship of Shakespeare's text.
But what that argument ignores
Is that in Tudor times playgoers
Heard what the playwright had to say
In the parlance of their day

And, whether literate or not,
They understood the drama's plot
In language that the hoi polloi
And erudite could all enjoy.

So, in that vein, I here present
Light-hearted and irreverent
Plot-summaries that give the gist
Of works by the great dramatist
Where wit and culture are allied
And bawdiness and taste collide.

Puck, an impish fairy sprite,
In mischief-making takes delight.
By using spells and magic skill he
Loves to make folk look real silly.

A
MIDSUMMER
NIGHT'S DREAM

Who's Who:

THESEUS, *Duke of Athens.*

HIPPOLYTA, *Queen of the Amazons, betrothed to Theseus.*

EGEUS, *Hermia's father.*

HERMIA, *Egeus's daughter, in love with Lysander.*

LYSANDER,
DEMETRIUS, } *young gentlemen in love with Hermia.*

HELENA, *in love with Demetrius.*

QUINCE, *a Carpenter.*
BOTTOM, *a Weaver.* } *Producing a play to celebrate the Duke's wedding.*

OBERON, *King of the Fairies.*

TITANIA, *Queen of the Fairies.*

PUCK, *a mischievous Sprite.*

The Duke of Athens lovingly
Wooed Hippolyta who will be,
In four days time and then for life,
Theseus's wedded wife.

Theseus is the Duke of Athens.

Hippolyta is the Queen of the Amazons.

Egeus is an Athenean gentleman.

A citizen whose name's Egeus
Has brought a problem to Theseus.
He has a stroppy daughter who
Won't wed the guy he wants her to.
She says she doesn't love him and her

Lysander is a young Athenean gentleman.

Heart belongs to young Lysander.
Her Dad's insisting that she wed

Demetrius is another young Athenean gentleman.

Demetrius, his choice, instead.
Theseus says she must comply
Or else he'll sentence her to die,
Or to lifelong virginity
In some god-forsaken nunnery.
Lysander wants them all to see
Demetrius lacks constancy
And, therefore, is unworthy of

Hermia is Egeus's daughter.

Helena is a young Athenian lady.

Hermia, his own true love.
He tells how beautiful Helena
And Demetrius had been a
Loving couple and that they
Had been each other's fiancé.
But then, when Hermia he espied,
Demetrius's ardour died.
He dumped Helena and departed
Which left the poor girl broken-hearted.
And now, though she still loves him dearly,
His love-interest's elsewhere, clearly.

Lysander and Hermia hope
That they can secretly elope,
Be wed and with his aunt reside
On her estate so far outside
The Duke of Athens' jurisdiction
That Hermia needn't fear conviction.
They tell Helena what they plan.

And she thinks that perhaps she can
Persuade Demetrius to follow
Them into the woods tomorrow.
His love for Hermia might wane
And she might win him back again.
Helena, though that hope is slight
Will tag along, tomorrow night.

* * *

Peter Quince thinks 'twould be great
For artisans to celebrate
Duke Theseus's wedding day
By putting on a special play.
To each one he assigns a part
And tells them learn their lines by heart.
In Palace Wood, tomorrow night
They will rehearse 'neath pale moonlight.

Quince is one of the group preparing a play to celebrate the Duke's wedding.

* * *

Throughout these woods the fairies roam;
This is the place that they call home.
But, sadly, their royal family now
Is having a domestic row.
The King of Fairies, Oberon,
Thinks that the little orphan son
Born to Titania's close friend
Who came to an untimely end,
Ought to be his to rear and train.
But she insists the lad remain
With her, until such time as he
Has reached his full maturity.

Titania is the Queen of the Fairies.

Puck, an impish, fairy Sprite,
In mischief-making, takes delight.

Puck uses his magic powers to carry out many of Oberon's wishes.

By using spells and magic skill, he
Loves to make folk look real silly.

Oberon tells Puck he must
Find, and to him alone entrust
A very special, purple flower
The juice of which has wondrous power;
If, when a person takes a nap,
A tincture of this flower's sap
Is placed upon the eyelids, then
When that person wakes again,
With the first living thing they see
They'll fall in love, most ardently.

Meanwhile, young Demetrius
Thinks Helena's being a wuss.
Her constant declarations of
Undying, though unwanted, love
Are driving him around the bend
So much so, that if they don't end,
He'll do some mischief to her, so
He tells her she must let him go.
Oberon, unseen, o'erhears
Demetrius's hurtful sneers;
He thinks 'twould be a lovely move
To turn that heartlessness to love.
And so, the next time that they meet,
He asks Puck to perform this feat:
To find the rude Athenian guy
And, as he sleeps, with care apply,
To both his eyes, the magic lotion
That will inspire love and devotion.

The King finds where Titania sleeps
And, over to her, quietly creeps
And very carefully applies
The magic lotion to her eyes.
He's hoping that, when she awakes,
Some ugly beast her fancy takes
So that all her love will be
For some vile beast exclusively.

Puck's looking for the guy from Athens
And thinks he's found him when he happens
On Lysander who's reposing
While Hermia too, close by, is dozing.
When he has juiced Lysander's eyes
Puck's job is done and off he flies.

Following Demetrius,
Helena finds, is strenuous
And so considers 'twould be best
To sit awhile and take a rest.
But she has sat down right beside
Lysander, whose eyes open wide,
So she becomes the object of
Her best friend's boyfriend's boundless love.
Lysander, straight away, avers
She's won his heart and he's now hers.
Hermia's really, really miffed
And blames Helena for the rift.

*   *   *

The artisans have found a glade
That, for rehearsal, 's ready made.
The Fairy Queen, Titania, lies
Nearby, unseen by human eyes.

Puck's looking on and he can tell
Rehearsal's not going very well.
The actors feel they have to make
Some changes, for propriety's sake.
The windbag, Bottom, is the one
Who tells them all what must be done
But some of his proposals are,
To say the least, peculiar.
Bottom speaks his lines and makes
An exit and Puck undertakes
Some magic mischief-making that
Leaves Bottom looking like a prat.
He's given him an ass's head
Which fills his mates with so much dread
That they forget about their play
And, in a panic, run away.
And that is when the Fairy Queen
Wakes up and falls for this strange being.

As Puck is telling Oberon
About these funny goings on,
They quickly come to realise
That there are *two* Athenian guys.

Oberon has come across
Demetrius, sleeping on the moss
And puts the lotion on his eyes.
Through the Palace Wood, Puck flies
To fetch Helena here so she's
The one Demetrius first sees
When he, from slumber, wakes and then
He'll fall in love with her again.

The trouble is Helena now
Has got two love-sick gents in tow.
Lysander and Demetrius
Are both with love delirious.
And misconstruing what they've said
She thinks they're messing with her head.
And she becomes quite paranoid
And with both men is quite annoyed.
If she's the butt of their cruel fun
She won't respond to either one,
And, wishing to be on her own
Turns on her heel and heads for home.
At this the lads are clearly stunned
And blame each other for being shunned.
With insults and name-calling each
Inflames the other till they reach
The stage where they are full of ire
And, at each other, spitting fire.
They're running out of angry words;
They'll have to settle this with swords.
So they start looking for a space
Wherein their duel can take place.
Puck uses his ability
And skill at human mimicry
To make each think that he can hear
The other fellow coming near,
While all the time this Sprite, so smart,
Is really keeping them apart.

Lysander's walked mile after mile
And now must sit and rest a while.
As weariness up on him creeps
His eyelids droop and then he sleeps.

Then very gently Puck applies
The magic lotion to his eyes
And, when he wakes, he will espy
The lovely Hermia nearby.
Not far away Demetrius
Rests in the arms of Morpheus
And that's the place Helena thinks
She'll lie down for forty winks.

*   *   *

Titania seems to be in thrall
To Bottom, who's enjoying all
The love and care that she devotes
To pleasing him on whom she dotes.
What, up till a few days ago
Was of concern, 's no longer so.
Her page, her dead friend's orphan son,
She now gives up to Oberon.
He's glad that she has seen the light;
This proves she knows that he was right.
To show he's grateful he'll surprise her;
He gives them the spell-neutraliser.
Then she and Bottom, instantly
Return to their normality.

*   *   *

Hippolyta and Theseus,
With Hermia's father, Egeus,
While taking some fresh morning air
Have come into the woods, and there,
Just off their path, they see a number
Of young folk in peaceful slumber.
When they see who the youngsters are
They think that this is so bizarre.

Lysander wakes up to the sight
Of Hermia in the morning light
And heartfully assures her of
His ardent, never-ending love.
An' Demetrius regrets the day
He dumped his lovely fiancé
And he is sorry that he's been a
Disappointment to Helena,
And, if she'll take him back, he's sure
That, this time, his love will endure.
The Duke and Co are glad to see
No signs of animosity,
And wonder how it's come to pass
That these two lads who loved one lass
In Palace Wood have, overnight,
Made peace and sorted things out right.
The young folk tell of strange events;
Their recent shared experience.
Incredibly, to them, it seems
As though they've shared each others dreams.
But, thankfully for all involved
Their differences have been resolved.
No love-triangle now survives;
They now live unencumbered lives.
The Duke's so pleased that he invites
Them to perform their marriage rites
With Hippolyta an' him, an' they,
To celebrate, will see a play.

*   *   *

In Athens, back at Quince's place,
The actors can't find any trace
Of Bottom, who they really need
If, with the play, they're to proceed.

'Cause no one else can play his part
There's not a chance the play can start.
But gladly, Bottom then comes back
and everything's once more on track.

Although the drama they present
Shows them to be incompetent,
And though the script's somewhat confused
The audience is quite amused.
And, now relaxed, the newly-weds
Contentedly, head for their beds.

*Now that Helena's got his ring
and Bertram's child is carrying
his Ts and Cs have been fulfilled.*

ALL'S WELL
THAT ENDS WELL

Who's Who:

COUNTESS OF ROUSILLON, *Bertram's mother.*
HELENA, *the Countess's ward, in love with Bertram.*
BERTRAM, *Count of Rousillon.*
LAFEU, *an elderly lord.*
STEWARD *to the Countess of Rousillon.*
KING OF FRANCE.
A WIDOW OF FLORENCE, *owner of The Pilgrim's Rest boarding house.*
DIANA, *the Widow's daughter whom Bertram tries to seduce.*

Gerard de Narbon, the physician,   *France's foremost*
When he was dying, did petition   *medical expert*
The Count and Countess Rousillon
To give his only child a home.   *Count Bertram's parents*
[To her he left the recipes
For all his cures and remedies].

The Countess loves the child and she
Treats her just like family.
She has a son, a handsome lad;
Helena fancies him, like mad,   *Helena is the daughter of*
                                                    Gerard de Narbon.

But she is very meek and shy
Which, probably's the reason why
She keeps her love for Bertram hidden,
Suspecting that 'twould be forbidden.

*Bertram is the son of
the Count and Countess
Rousillon.*

The old Count's died, but life goes on,
Now Bertram's Count of Rousillon,
And Lord Lafeu's come from the King
With orders that he is to bring
The Count to Paris so that he
Can swear unswerving loyalty.

*Lord Lafeu is an old
friend of the King of
France.*

Alone, Helena lets tears flow
Because her status is so low
And Bertram's standing is so high
That she can't hope to qualify
To be his soulmate although she
Loves him to bits, clandestinely.
Though not expressed, her love is true,
But Bertram hasn't got a clue;
Self-centred, haughty, upper class
He treats her like a servant lass.
Helena knows not where to start
To catch his eye and win his heart.
She speaks aloud her dreams and fears;
She's not aware the Steward o'erhears.
And having heard away he goes
And tells the Countess what he knows.

*The Steward was the
senior member of the
household staff.*

The Countess and Helena chat.
That's when Helena finds out that
The Countess would be pleased to see
Her ward involved romantic'ly
With Bertram, who has gone to stay
At Court, in Paris, far away.

If he's in Paris and she's not
She'll lose whatever chance she's got.
It's crystal clear what she must do,
So she goes off to Paris, too.

Alas, the King's health is so poor
His doctors think he's at death's door.

She asks the King's old friend, Lafeu,
To organise an interview
So she can see the King herself
And diagnose his state of health.
His own physicians have assured
Him that his illness can't be cured,
So he's not overly excited
When this wee lass says he must fight it,
Insisting she can make him better
If he will just agree to let her
Use her father's remedy
For this specific malady.

That there's some hope of health again
The King's convinced, especially when
She lays her life upon the line
If he's not cured in two days' time.
So he's persuaded to give in
And try her Daddy's medicine.

The deal the King and she agree
Is, if by then, he's illness-free
Her life's not forfeit and moreover
He'll help her find and wed her lover.
[In France, the King has got the power
To force a noble bachelor

To wed whoever he should choose].
Helena asks the King to use
This power to let her pick her man.
And she will choose young Count Bertram.

The potion works, the King feels good
And he's so full of gratitude,
He gives Helena her reward:
She'll be allowed to choose the lord
With whom she wants to share her life
And be an ever-loving wife.

The King calls all his noblemen;
Explains what's happening to them
And why, for him, it's such an honour
To bestow this gift upon her.
From all the lords the King brings on
She chooses Bertram Rousillon.
But Bertram doesn't want to wed
A girl who is so lowly bred.
The King insists that Bertram do
What he, his Sovereign, tells him to.

Now Bertram is infuriated;
And he feels humiliated.
The King thinks he is being compliant
But, in his heart, he's still defiant.

He tells Helena to go home
And take a letter to his Mum.
He says that he has things to do;
He'll join her in a day or two.
She sees her duty's to obey.
But Bertram plans to run away

To Florence, where he'll go to war,
And see Helena never more.

His Mum peruses Bertram's letter.
Its contents really do upset her:
While his wife stays, there's not a chance
He'll ever come back home to France.

Helena, too, receives a letter
Saying they can never be together
'Less she acquires the ring he's wearing
And a child of theirs is rearing;
Unlikely, as they've separated
Before their union's consummated.

*   *   *

Then, as a pilgrim to Saint Jacques,
Helena leaves — she won't come back,
So that the Count of Rousillon
Can give up war and come back home.

The pilgrimage to Santiago in Spain. Known as the Camino, there were many different routes, but none would have taken a French pilgrim through Florence.

She visits Florence, on the way,
As fate would have it, the same day
That Bertram comes back, glorious;
In war he's been victorious.
Throughout the city, he's being feted
As his victory's celebrated.

A widow and her daughter run
The Pilgrim's Rest to which she's shown,
And as they watch Bertram's parade
She learns of the attempts he's made
To woo the daughter, but Diane
Won't entertain a married man.

The Pilgrim's Rest is a boarding house.

Diana is the daughter of the widow who owns The Pilgrim's Rest.

Helena tells that they'd been wed
But Bertram, full of anger, fled
Saying they can't be together till
His Ts & Cs she can fulfil.

Diana feels naught but disgust
That she's the object of his lust
And readily agrees a plan
To help Helena get her man.

The girls decide on what to do:
The next time Bertram comes to woo
Diana smiles and leads him on
And makes him think her heart's been won.
Bertram's lust-befuddled brain
Believes no woman can sustain
Resistance to his manly charms.
He's not surprised Diana warms
To him at last, and now she's said
Tonight she wants him in her bed.

But first, to prove his love he must,
That ring he wears, to her entrust,
And, in exchange, tonight she'll bring,
And give to him, her special ring.
And Bertram's happy to concede
That there's an overwhelming need
To keep their tryst a secret so
Her mother doesn't come to know
And end the game they plan to play
Before their fun gets under way.
So, when he comes at twelve at night
They make no noise; there is no light.

*   *   *

With great success, Helena's tried
To sow the rumour that she died.
Through France and Florence word has spread;
Friends and relations think she's dead.
The Count decides to take a chance,
And packs his bags and heads for France.

*   *   *

Back at his Mum's, to his frustration
The King is there on visitation.
Bertram's brought before the King
Who notices Helena's ring,
[The ring he gave her when she cured him,
And, as she put it on, assured him
She'd wear it always and forever
And take it from her finger never,
Unless, in bed, she placed it on
The finger of Count Rousillon].

When asked, the Count tells porky pies,
That 'tis Helena's, he denies.
He says, one day, as he went out
In Florence for a walk-about,
A lady threw it from above
Wrapped in a note declaring love
'Cause she believed that he was free
To hook up matrimonially.
When he revealed his married state
Her discomposure was so great
And her discomfort caused such pain
She didn't want the ring again.

Diana and her Mum arrive
And Bertram's fortunes take a dive.
Diana claims, as his wife's dead,
The Count must marry her instead
'Cause he had promised that he'd do so
When she'd allowed him to seduce her.
To prove the truth of what she says,
The ring he gave her, she displays,
[The Countess sees that it's the one
Worn by the Counts of Rousillon
And passed down through the generations.]
And then against all expectations
Claims, as a token of her caring,
She gave the Count the ring he's wearing.
Confusion reigns 'cause that ring is
The one the King is sure was his.
Diana's Mum goes for the jeweller
Who'll testify he gave it to her.

But when, into the room, they come
[The jeweller and Diana's Mum]
Everybody there's amazed.
The 'jeweller' upon whom they gaze
Is Bertram's wife, alive and well.
Helena then proceeds to tell
How she had managed to persuade
Diana and her Mum to aid
Her put in train the clever plan
That got her pregnant by Bertram,
When, in the darkness he thought he
Was, with Diana, making free.

And now that she has Bertram's ring
And Bertram's child is carrying,
His Ts & Cs have been fulfilled.
And Bertram says that he is thrilled,
And that he's sorry he betrayed
Helena's love and that he'd made
Her so unhappy for so long.
And he's convinced that they belong
Together now, and from now on
She'll be the Countess Rousillon.

And, just as Shakespeare said it would
All's well that ends well, and that's good.

One day they meet the love-sick poet
And notice, dangling at his throat,
The golden chain that Rosalind had
Given to the handsome lad
Who'd won her heart when he'd knocked out
The champion in that wrestling bout.

AS YOU LIKE IT

Who's who:

OLIVER DE BOYS, *Orlando's older brother who inherited their father's estate.*

ORLANDO, *Oliver de Boys' youngest brother, in love with Rosalind.*

CHARLES, *a Wrestler.*

DUKE FREDERICK, *has usurped his brother's title and dominions.*

ROSALIND, *the banished Duke's daughter, in love with Orlando.*

CELIA, *Duke Frederick's daughter.*

GANYMEDE, *Rosalind disguised as a country boy.*

ALIENA, *Celia disguised as Ganymede's sister.*

ADAM, *Oliver de Boys' servant.*

A SHEPHERD.

THE BANISHED DUKE, *Rosalind's father, living in exile.*

JACQUES DE BOYS, *Orlando's other brother.*

This Shakespeare play is a Romance
That's set somewhere in rural France.
Sir Rowland, ere his life was spent,   *Sir Rowland de Boys was*
In his Last Will and Testament   *a gentleman, owner of a*
Instructed his son, Oliver,   *large estate.*
His first-born and the de Boys heir,
To educate his brothers, then
To set them up as gentlemen.

Orlando, who's the youngest son
Is mad 'cause Oliver's not done
For him what their Dad specified
In his Last Will before he died.
No chance to be a gent has he,
'Cause Ollie's kept his legacy.
With naught to lose, he thinks he might
Stand half a chance if he should fight

Charles is a professional wrestler.

The wrestler, Charles, who's known to break
Opponents' bones and even take
The lives of some who've shown more pluck
Than sense or strength or skill or luck.

Duke Frederick usurped the Dukedom and sent his brother, the rightful Duke, into exile.

Duke Frederick just loves to watch
A vicious, close-fought wrestling match
But thinks this contest makes no sense
[Orlando lacks experience].
So, thinking he might not enjoy
Seeing Charles, the champion, break this boy
In body and in spirit, tells
His daughter and his niece — young girls
The headstrong, stubborn youth might heed —
To fake concern for him and plead,
And see if feminine charms can make
The lad withdraw, for pity's sake.

Rosalind is the daughter of the banished Duke.

Celia, Rosalind's cousin, is Duke Frederick's daughter.

But Rosalind and Celia find
They cannot make him change his mind.
Their interest's spurred him on to show
He'll bravely, into danger, go.

All gather 'round to watch the slaughter,
But things don't go the way they ought to:
Like David slew Goliath, long 'go,
Orlando wins with one great throw.

And now it looks like Rosalind might
Have fallen for him at first sight.
A chain from 'round her neck she takes,
And bids him wear it for her sake.

Then Fredrick spoils the atmosphere;
Tells Rosalind, 'Get out of here'.
His daughter, Celia, pleads with him
But his mind's set; he won't give in,
So she decides that she'll go too.
The girls start planning what they'll do.

Two well-dressed, rich young ladies are
Bound to be mugged, ere they get far,
So they decide, for safety's sake,
There are precautions they must take.

They'll be disguised so they can pass
For country folk, a lad and lass.
Tall Rosalind is sure that she'd
Pass for a boy named Ganymede,
And Celia thinks she'd pass as being a
Country lass known as Aliena.
For Arden forest they'll set out
'Cause Rosalind's Dad is there, no doubt.
They gather up their jewels and cash
And hit the road, with some panache.

*   *   *

Orlando's going home again,
Back to his family's demesne.
But, just in sight of his abode,
He meets old Adam on the road.

*Adam is one of Oliver's
servants.*

33

His brother's servant lets him know
That home's the last place he should go,
'Cause Oliver, it seems, has said
He wants to see Orlando dead.

Orlando an' Adam both agree,
From these parts, they had better flee.

* * *

Frederick is broken-hearted
That Celia, with his niece, departed.
'Cause Rosalind fancied Orlando,
He thinks to the de Boys' they'd go.
So Oliver is brought to Court
In order for him to report
To Frederick [who's really riled]
Where he can find his only child.
Oliver's not got a clue
And claims there's nothing he can do.
But he is told to concentrate
All of his efforts to locate
The fugitives so Celia might,
With her dear Daddy, re-unite,
Else Frederick says he'll confiscate
Oliver's entire estate.

* * *

The girls are tired and weary when
They reach the Forest of Arden.
They need to eat and sleep and rest
Before proceeding with their quest
To [still disguised in rough attire]
Find the Duke who's Rosalind's Sire.

They ask a shepherd that they meet
To help them find something to eat
And maybe, someplace they can stay,
For which they have the cash to pay.
The man for whom this guy tends stock
Is trying to sell his farm and flock,
And so, the girls acquire his place
And humble rustic life, embrace.

*   *   *

Meanwhile, Orlando an' Adam too
Reach Arden, wondering what to do,
'Cause, weak from hunger and footsore,
Old Adam can go on no more.
They reckon that Orlando should
Leave Adam, and go search for food.

Orlando comes across a bunch
Of guys preparing to eat lunch,
He draws his sword, says he must steal
Their food for his and Adam's meal.
Their leader tells him sheath his sword,
That they're both welcome at this board.
Orlando says he's sorry for
His bandit-like behaviour.

As they're partaking of their meal
The stories that they tell reveal
That, in the past, the leader had
Been friendly with Orlando's Dad;
That he'd once been the rightful Duke
Ere Frederick, his brother, took
His Dukedom from him and had sent
The real Duke into banishment.

*   *   *

Aliena and young Ganymede
Enjoy the simple life they lead.
And tryin' to locate Rosalind's Dad
Has not the urgency it had.

Sometimes they see, attached to trees,
Love poems fluttering in the breeze.
These verses rustling in the wind
Are all in praise of Rosalind.
One day, they meet the love-sick poet
And notice, dangling at his throat,
The golden chain that Rosalind had
Given to the handsome lad
Who'd won her heart when he'd knocked out
The champion in that wrestling bout.

When Ganymede decides that 'he'
Will tease him 'bout his poetry
Orlando doesn't realise
That 'he' is Rosalind in disguise.

She tells him she can cure him of
His 'totally irrational' love.
The cure requires him to pretend
That Ganymede is Rosalind,
And he must visit every day
And say to 'him' the things he'd say
To Rosalind as if 'twere she
Was listening, in reality.

Alas, all that this treatment does
Is give them both a lovely buzz.
Their courtship's getting more intense
Until the ultimate pretence

When they'll exchange mock-marriage vows.
But first Orlando, the mock-spouse
Has to abandon his mock-bride
To go and eat at the Duke's side.
He promises, within the hour,
He'll come back to his 'bride' once more.

Orlando was on his way back,
When he espied, just off the track,
A venomous and dangerous snake
Poised, ready and about to take
The life of some guy on the ground,
Spread-eagled, sleeping very sound.
But, seeing Orlando coming hither
The snake slid off with rapid slither.

But then he spied another danger —
A lion was eyeing up the stranger.
Orlando, with sword drawn, advanced
To fight the beast. He quickly glanced
Down at the man, saw 'twas none other
Than Oliver, his nasty brother.
Though tempted, then, away to steal
And let the lion enjoy his meal,
His conscience bade him stay to fight
The hungry cat and do what's right.
The racket from this fierce affray
Roused Oliver who straight away
Knew that by then he'd be deceased
Had not Orlando fought this beast.

Oliver then underwent
A change of heart; wished to repent
The things he'd done to, and denied
Orlando since their father died.
So, with the brother he'd reviled,
Orlando now's been reconciled.

* * *

Orlando has sent Oliver
With an important message for
Young Ganymede saying how ill-fate
Has forced him to postpone their date.
When with his claw the lion slashed,
Orlando's arm was deeply gashed
And Oliver, as proof, has brought
A saturated blood-soaked cloth.

And strangely, that's how Oliver
Meets Aliena an' falls for her
And she for him. They quickly plan
To marry as soon as they can.
As there's no reason to delay,
They plan to marry the next day.
Then with Aliena as his wife,
He'll stay and lead a simple life,
So to Orlando he donates
All of their family's estates.

Orlando thinks it is a shame
That his romance is but a game,
And can't continue to pretend
That Ganymede is Rosalind.
He tells the 'lad' he needs to feel
That his love-life is truly real.

Ganymede then claims that 'he'
Can make things happen magic'ly
That if tomorrow he returns
The lass for whom Orlando yearns
Will come to him as his sweetheart
And promise him they'll never part
[The Duke has met his daughter and
Approves the marriage she has planned.]

Next day all gather 'round to see
The sylvan marriage ceremony.
But first there are a few surprises.
The girls no longer wear disguises.
As Rosalind and Celia they
Have come, their marriage vows to say.

And then, to add to all their joys,
Onto the scene, comes Jacques de Boys
With news about Duke Frederick who
Was coming with an army to
Destroy his brother and ensure
The power he'd stolen would endure.
A holy man, along the way,
Persuaded him, his hand to stay.
And now he's got religion and
Returned the usurped wealth and land.
Rosalind's Dad is Duke once more.
All's as it was in days of yore.

*Jacques de Boys is
Orlando's other brother.*

Pisanio knows, that the next day,
The General will pass this way ....
He's certain Lucius will engage
'Fidele' in the role of page.

CYMBELINE

Who's Who:

CYMBELINE, *King of Britain.*
IMOGEN, *Cymbeline's daughter by his first wife.*
POSTHUMUS, *Cymbeline's ward who marries Imogen.*
THE QUEEN, *Cymbeline's second wife.*
CLOTEN, *the Queen's son by a former husband.*
PISANIO, *Posthumus's loyal servant.*
IACHIMO, *a Roman acquaintance of Posthumus; a false 'friend'.*
LUCIUS, *a General, leader of the Roman army.*
FIDELE, *Imogen disguised as a boy.*
MORGAN, *living the life of a hunter, he is actually*
BELARIUS, *a banished lord who, many years ago, kidnapped Cymbeline's
    infant sons.*
POLYDORE & CADWAL, *reared as Morgan's sons. They are really*
GUIDERIUS & ARVIRAGUS, *Cymbeline's sons.*

It seems misfortune's always been
Companion to King Cymbeline.
His first wife died when they were young —
They'd not been married very long.
For him, his Queen had left behind
A daughter and two sons to mind.
One day, when in their nursery
[the older boy was only three]
The King's two sons were stol'n away —
Ne'er seen again since that sad day.

*Cymbeline is King
of Britain.*

He then adopted Posthumus,
The orphan of Sicilius,
A soldier who had loyally served.
The King thought that the boy deserved
A shot at life, so brought him home
And raised him like he was his own.

*Imogen is Cymbeline's
daughter.*

Thereafter Imogen and he
Were reared in close proximity.
As they grew up, they closer got
Till they agreed to tie the knot.
They did it in a secret way
Afraid of what her Dad might say.

Now he's found out and Cymbeline
Has lost his head and vents his spleen
On Imogen, his only daughter,
Because he says she hadn't sought her
Dad's approval to get wed
But married secretly, instead.

The Queen is Imogen's step-mother,
The Queen's son, Cloten's her step-brother.
The King and Queen wished them to be
United matrimonially.
That's why the King tells Imogen
She'll not see Posthumus again
Because he's banished and is banned
From e'er returning to this land,
And Imogen, with him's not goin'.
Her Dad insists she stays at home.

The loving couple promise to,
Though forced apart, be ever true.
Her long-dead mother's diamond ring
['Tis Imogen's most precious thing]
She gives to Posthumus, and he
Gifts her a bracelet. They agree
These symbols of their faithful love
They'll always wear, and ne'er remove.

Then Posthumus sets off for Rome
And Imogen remains at home.

*   *   *

Now Posthumus's serving man,
Pisanio, whene'er he can
Lauds Posthumus, and that is why
The Queen decides that he must die.
She thinks he undermines her son
Who's hoping to ascend the throne.
She asks the court physician for
Strong poison to administer
To deadly vermin she says should
Be totally wiped out for good.
The doctor though, fears that she may
Intend it for some human prey.
The 'poison' that he gives her will
Appear to, but won't really, kill.
She hands Pisanio the stuff
And tells him, when he's feeling rough,
When he's too knackered to do more,
It will his energy restore.

Pisanio is very loyal to Posthumus.

*   *   *

When Posthumus tells friends in Rome
About the wife he's left at home;
That chastity and faithfulness
Are virtues that she does possess
To such a high degree that he
Fears not for her fidelity,

Iachimo is sneaky and dishonest, and not a true friend.

A nasty 'friend' named Iachimo
Says off to Britain he will go,
And wagers, ere he's back again,
He will have bedded Imogen.
Being certain Imogen won't stray
Posthumus agrees to lay
That ring he wears upon his hand,
A bet 'gainst Iachimo's ten grand.

As soon as e'er he reaches Britain
The cocky Roman starts to hit on
Imogen, but always fails
Because her constancy prevails.
Faced with embarrassing defeat,
Iachimo decides to cheat.
He creeps into, at dead of night,
Her bedroom, where she's sleeping tight,
And, careful not to raise alarm,
Removes the bracelet from her arm.

With such clear evidence he does
Quite easily fool Posthumus
Who hands to Iachimo his ring
[In his eyes now a worthless thing].

Now Posthumus conceives a plan;
He writes home to his serving-man
Pisanio, instructing him
To take the life of Imogen,

Because it's only just that she
Should die for her adultery.

To Imogen he writes to say
His banishment he'll disobey.
He'll come to Britain on a boat
And land somewhere that's so remote
That they, in secrecy, can meet
And if they're totally discreet
The King won't know he's misbehavin'.
If she'll sneak down to Milford-Haven
Together they will have the chance
To re-kindle their romance.

[There, no-one knowing where she is,
Pisanio can do the biz.]

Pisanio just cannot do
What Posthumus has told him to;
But writes back to his master, and
Says everything has gone as planned,
And then tells Imogen about
Her husband's plan to wipe her out.

* * *

Some years past, Britain did agree
To pay the Romans annually
A tribute to avert invasion
Quite imminent on that occasion.
But this year, Britain's failed to pay
And Lucius has come to say
That such refusal will ensure
That Rome, on Britain, will wage war.

Lucius is a General in the Roman army.

Pisanio knows that the next day
The General will pass this way.
If Imogen will wear men's clothes,
[His other doublet and spare hose]
She'll have no problem, and in truth
Will pass for Fidele, a youth.
If e'er her stamina should wane,
So that her strength she can regain,
He gives her her step-mum's elixir
Saying that 'tis guaranteed 'twill fix her.
He's certain Lucius will engage
Fidele in the role of page.
And that is how they plan she's goin'
To meet with Posthumus in Rome;
She needs to hear his explanation
For planning her assassination.

When seeking Lucius, next day
Fidele, though, has gone astray,
And after hours of roaming 'round
Comes to a cave and there lies down.

Morgan is a hunter.

Morgan and his sons live here
And now return from hunting deer.
Fidele gives an explanation
For why 'he's' in this situation:
To Milford-Haven 'he' was going,
But being a stranger and not knowing
The route, 'he' went astray somewhere,
And that's why 'he' is here, not there.
Morgan and his sons agree
They like Fidele's company
And, hospitably suggest
'He' stay with them and be their guest.

One day Fidele's not too well
And Polydore and Cadwal tell
'Him' rest at home will do 'him' good
While they go out and hunt for food.
Fidele thinks 'he' needs a fixer
And takes Pisanio's elixir
Which slows 'his' metabolic rate
And leaves 'him' in a death-like state.
When they return the hunters see
Fidele — dead apparently.
Outside, they place the body down
And scatter flowers all around.

*Polydore and Cadwal are
Morgan's sons.*

*　　　*　　　*

Lucius has gone back home
To raise a fighting force for Rome,
And Posthumus, though he's a Brit,
'S conscripted to be part of it,
And as a Roman soldier's made
Prepare, his homeland to invade.
But that's not on, so he decides
First chance he gets he's switching sides.

Soon as his feet hit British soil
He slips away and goes AWOL.
[His Roman uniform has gone
And British clothing he's put on].

The Romans have reached Britain and
While Lucius scouts out the land
He comes across Fidele when
The 'youth' has 'come to life' again.
'He' asks if Lucius will employ
'Him' as his personal page-boy.

*　　　*　　　*

47

Morgan's sons are really keen
To go and fight for Cymbeline.
They and their Dad, with shields and swords,
Set off to meet the Roman hordes.
But when they reach the battlefield
It looks like Britain's fate's been sealed.
Cymbeline's been captured and
The Romans have the upper hand
Till Morgan and his sons attack
To free the King and bring him back.
Then Posthumus comes on the scene
And helps them rescue Cymbeline.

Their leader's back and straight away
The Brits take heart and win the day.

But Posthumus is full of woe
For having told Pisanio
To take sweet Imogen, his wife,
Away to Wales and take her life.
He hates himself and that is why
He feels he now deserves to die.

In Roman uniform again
He plans to die for Imogen.

Cymbeline, as head of state,
His victory must celebrate.
'Cause with the win he is delighted,
Morgan and his boys are knighted,
But there is neither hide nor hair
Of the fourth guy who was there.

The prisoners of war all wait
To hear the King decide their fate.
And Posthumus is with them there
Dressed as a Roman Legionaire,
And Iachimo, the guy that cheated,
Is also one of the defeated.

Lucius makes a heartfelt plea;
Asks that Fidele be set free.
The 'lad' is young and British so
The King agrees to let 'him' go,
And having been with victory blessed
He'll grant Fidele one request.

Fidele turns to Iachimo
Saying what 'he' really wants to know
Is where he got that diamond ring.
The scoundrel admits everything:
To win a bet he'd claimed he'd bedded
The wife that Posthumus had wedded.
Then Posthumus lets fly a blow
Intended to floor Iachimo
But strikes Fidele and that's when
The truth's revealed —'tis Imogen.

Then up speaks Morgan saying he must
Confess that he's Belarius
Who, banished twenty years ago,
Risked royal wrath and didn't go.
The King's two sons, heirs to the throne,
He'd kidnapped and reared as his own.
So Polydore and young Cadwal
Are really not his sons at all.

When Belarius had kidnapped them he had changed their names to Polydore and Cadwal and reared them as his own.

Midst sheer delight and lots of fuss
Guiderius and Arviragus
The two sons Cymbeline had sired
Have princely status re-acquired.
And Cymbeline is so delighted,
Because his family's re-united,
That he now pardons everyone
For doing whatever they have done.

He sends the Roman soldiers home
And he agrees to pay to Rome
The tribute he'd refused to pay
[that was the cause of the affray].
The King's decision's wise indeed —
Now future peace is guaranteed.

And happily, all's well again
With Posthumus and Imogen.

He'll organise a fencing match
So that the courtiers can watch
The Prince and Laertes fence and see
Which has the more ability.

HAMLET,
PRINCE OF DENMARK

Who's Who:

HAMLET, *Prince of Denmark, son of the late King.*

GERTRUDE, *Hamlet's mother, married Claudius shortly after the death of Hamlet's father.*

FORTINBRAS, *Prince of Norway.*

HORATIO, *Hamlet's true and trusted friend.*

CLAUDIUS, *became King following the death of his brother.*

OPHELIA, *Polonius's daughter, Hamlet's girlfriend.*

POLONIUS, *Lord Chamberlain.*

LAERTES, *Polonius's son.*

ROSECRANTZ, GUILDENSTERN & OSRIC, *Courtiers.*

It is now many centuries since
Of Denmark, Hamlet was the Prince.
William Shakespeare tells the story;
It starts off sad and ends up gory.

Hamlet's father used to be
The King, but died quite suddenly.
His widow, Gertrude, doesn't tarry;
With haste, indecent, does re-marry.

*Gertrude is
Hamlet's mother.*

The Prince cannot forgive his mother
For marrying his father's brother.
From head to toe in black he's dressed
Perhaps to show that he's depressed.

Prince Fortinbras of Norway plans
To win from Denmark all the lands
Lost in the war his uncle had
'Gainst Denmark, led by Hamlet's Dad.
'Cause of the threat that this presents
The sentries man the battlements
And they're disturbed a little when
A ghost, in armour, comes to them.
The Prince's friend, Horatio
Believes that Hamlet ought to know
Because he's certain sure... almost...
This spectre's Hamlet's father's ghost.

So, to eliminate all doubt,
The Prince decides to check it out.
The ghost appears and tells his son

Claudius replaced Hamlet's father as King of Denmark.

What Claudius, the King, has done —
Just how he took his brother's life
And then went on to take his wife.

The Prince swears to avenge his Dad.
He reckons, if he feigns being mad,
King Claudius won't have a clue
About what he intends to do.

*   *   *

The threat of war that Denmark feared
Now happily has disappeared.
Prince Fortinbras has set new goals
And now he wants to fight the Poles.
And Claudius allows he may
March through Denmark on the way.

*　　*　　*

Hamlet's acting very strange
Ophelia's sure he is deranged.
Polonius thinks there's every chance it's
'Cause she's rejecting his advances.
Queen Gertrude thinks that that maybe
Explains her son's insanity.
The King, who harbours some concern,
Asks Rosencrantz and Guildenstern
To speak with him, see can they find
If Hamlet's really lost his mind.

Ophelia is Hamlet's girlfriend.
Polonius, Ophelia's father, is the Lord Chancellor.

Rosencrantz and Guildenstern are supposedly friends of Hamlet but are really loyal to the King.

The Prince has written a wee sketch
About a horrible old wretch,
And hires an acting troupe to play
The drama for the Court, one day.
The villain of the piece, it's clear,
Pours poison in his victim's ear
And then, soon as her husband's dead,
He moves into the widow's bed.

The King is spooked and troubled too
'Cause he'd been sure that no one knew
He'd murdered Hamlet's Dad allowin'
Him be the King and wear the crown.
That Hamlet knows is obvious
And that's a threat to Claudius.

Polonius tells Hamlet that
His mother wants to have a chat.
And then he sees a chance for him
To hide nearby and listen in
Intending to tell everything
He hears to Claudius, the King.

The conversation, very sadly,
From the start goes really badly.
The Prince gets in his mother's face —
He tells her she's a pure disgrace,
And he's ashamed that she's his mother
'Cause she has married his Dad's brother.
He is with so much anger filled
That Gertrude fears she might be killed.
Polonius, behind a screen
Hears Hamlet's Mum, in panic, scream.
He's worried for her safety, an'
He yells for help, loud as he can.
Believing it's the King that's there
Prince Hamlet draws his rapier

An arras is a screen or And through the arras makes one thrust
wall-hanging made from And poor Polonius bites the dust.
tapestry.

Because the Prince is popular
The King fears that to use the law
Might lead to uproar and unrest
And so he thinks it will be best
Not to go public, but instead
To quietly inter the dead.

Because he sees him as a threat
He's planning the young Prince's death.

That's why the murderous King Claude
Sends Hamlet to spend time abroad,
And Guildenstern and Rosencrantz
To kill him, when they get the chance.
Efficient killers, they are not.
The Prince evades the murderous plot,
And then heads back to Denmark's shore
To sort things out in Elsinore.

*Elsinore is the Royal
Palace.*

Ophelia's brother, Laertes

Laertes is Polonius's son.

Comes home, with anger all ablaze.
He wants revenge for his dead Dad
And for his sister who's gone mad.
The King speaks to him, and convinces
Him the blame is all the Prince's.

Claudius has a cunning scheme
That will fulfil the young man's dream.
He'll organise a fencing match
So that the courtiers can watch
The Prince and Laertes fence, and see
Which has the more ability.
The contest, though, will not be fair
For Laertes's sword will bear
No button on its point, and will
Be a weapon that can kill.
And, just so nothing's left to chance
Its lethal powers they will enhance;
They'll smear the blade with a concoction
Of powerful and fast-acting toxin.

In case this plan does not succeed,
Claudius reckons they might need
A back-up plan that will contrive

T'ensure the Prince does not survive —
He'll make a drink with poison laced
That close to Hamlet will be placed,
Which, if the Prince feels dehydrated
He'll drink, and thus be terminated.

Ophelia, Hamlet's fiancé,
Finds life more bitter, day by day,
And now, her boyfriend's raving mad
And only gone and killed her Dad.
With funeral rites obscenely hurried,
Polonius was quietly buried.
The Lord Chamberlain, one would expect,
Should have been shown much more respect.
It's not surprising the poor kid
Eventually flips her lid,
And, 'neath a willow in a stream,
She drowns, by suicide, 'twould seem.
Back home, the Prince observes the maid
Ophelia, in her grave being laid.
His heart is rent with bitter grief
From which he can find no relief.

Osric is a courtier.   Osric tells the Prince he brings
A message for him from the King
Saying that he's organised a bout
To let all at the Court find out
If Laertes or Hamlet will
Prove to have the greater skill
In swordsmanship, at which they both
Are quite adept and good and know it.

Just before this fencing treat
Begins, the two contestants meet
And Hamlet tries to sympathise
With Laertes, and apologise
For all the troubles and the woes
That he has caused while in the throes
Of madness, and which never would
Have happened had his health been good.
Though Laertes, half-heartedly,
Seems to accept th'apology
He still wants the satisfaction
Of putting the plan into action.

As the contest opens it's
The Prince who makes the first few hits.
To celebrate, the Queen picks up,
And takes a slug from, Hamlet's cup.

Next, Laertes thrusts, hits and draws blood —
For Hamlet now things don't look good.
Then somehow in the heat of play
Both drop their weapons and when they
Recover them an error's made:
Each guy picks up the other's blade.
Hamlet's next attack gets through;
And Laertes is wounded too.
Now each of them's been stabbed and gored
With Laertes's poisoned sword.

Horatio and Osric see
Each swordsman's bloody injury.
They wonder how this came about
In a friendly fencing bout.

Just then the Queen, who hovers near,
Staggers and cries out in fear
[as to the floor she starts to sink]
That she's been poisoned by her drink.

The Prince suspects some villainy.
Laertes confesses it was he —
And he admits he bared the point
And with poison did anoint
His fencing foil, and by its power
They'll both be dead in half an hour.

He did this 'cause of his desire
To get revenge for his dead Sire.
Repenting with his final breath,
Tells 'twas the King planned Hamlet's death.
So Hamlet runs King Claudius through.
Then, from his wounds, the Prince dies too.

*   *   *

Prince Fortinbras, has won his war,
And going home via Elsinore
Finds all these bodies lying about —
The Danes have wiped each other out.
'Cause of this Royal Family row
The throne of Denmark's vacant now
And, as no closer heir is found,
He's offered and accepts the crown.

Then with their daggers, one by one,
They stab him till the deed is done.

JULIUS CAESAR

Who's Who:

JULIUS CAESAR.

A SOOTHSAYER.

MARK ANTONY, *Caesar's friend.*

CASSIUS, *Organiser of the conspiracy to assassinate Caesar.*

BRUTUS, *An honourable, highly respected Roman.*

CASCA,

TREBONIUS,

DECIUS BRUTUS,

METALLUS CIMBER,

} *Conspirators against Julius Caesar.*

CALPURNIA, *Caesar's wife.*

OCTAVIUS CAESAR, *Caesar's nephew and adopted son.*

LEPIDUS, *a close ally of Caesar.*

PORTIA, *Brutus's wife.*

TITINIUS, *a friend of Brutus and Cassius.*

STRATO, *Brutus's servant.*

PINDARUS, *Cassius's servant.*

In triumph, Caesar has returned;
All work and trade has been adjourned
As working plebs decide that they
Will take a Roman holiday.
His victory has given rise
To him being lauded to the skies.

Julius Caesar is a successful Roman General and Politician.

There is a psychic in the crowd
With powers of prophecy endowed
And Caesar's told by this soothsayer
He should the Ides of March beware.
But Caesar and his friends proceed
And to the warning pay no heed.

The great man's popularity

Mark Antony is a close friend of Caesar.

Grows greater when Mark Antony
Three times offers him the crown
And three times Caesar turns it down.

Some nobles, though, are not too sure
That his intentions are so pure,
And they believe that Caesar plans
To take Rome's power into his hands.
They fear that the Republic's dead
And Empire is what lies ahead.

Cassius is the ringleader of the conspiracy to assassinate Caesar.

Cassius determines that
He'll overthrow this autocrat;
Sets out to see if he can find
Some other Romans of like mind.

Brutus is a friend of Caesar's who joins in the conspiracy.

Of all the men that he approaches
Brutus proves to be most cautious.
He needs some time to think if he
Should join in this conspiracy.
Cassius wants him on his side
Because he's honoured far and wide
And being most respectable
He'd make their cause acceptable.

Cassius feels there's not much time
For Brutus to make up his mind.
He knows that Brutus will come round
If lots of citizens are found
To say that they don't want to be
The subjects of a monarchy.
He sends him letters that purport
To come from Romans who support
The notion that the Senate must
Not into Caesar's hands entrust
The government and power of Rome
To let him rule all on his own.

So Cassius's little group
Now has Brutus in the loop
With Casca, Cinna, Decius
And Cimber and Trebonius.

These men are all members of the conspiracy.

Then this conspiratorial crew
Meets to consider what to do.
First, they reckon they will slay
Caesar later on that day.
Cassius thinks that they should send
Mark Antony off with his friend;
That he too should be put to death
But Brutus says he's not a threat.

Lest Caesar plans this day that he
Will stay at home with family,
Decius says that he can lure
Him from his home and will ensure
That Julius Caesar keeps his date
With those who wish to seal his fate.

*Calpurnia is
Caesar's wife.*

Calpurnia, in a vivid dream,
Her husband's murder has foreseen.
As well as that, the Augurers say
That he should stay at home this day.
But Decius says he must come out
Because the Senate is about,
[Because of Caesar's great renown],
To give to him the Roman Crown.

Then Cassius and Company
Arrive, saying that they wish to be
With Caesar as he leaves his home
To walk the crowded streets of Rome
To take his Senate scat where he
Hopes to be honoured presently.

As Caesar's entourage gets close
To the stately Senate House,
That's when Trebonius makes his play
And draws Mark Antony away.

Metallus Cimber, on his knees
In front of Caesar, makes a plea
Requesting Caesar to relent
And lift his brother's banishment.
His friends around about him muster
Encircling Caesar in a cluster.
Then with their daggers, one by one
They stab him till the deed is done.

Then Brutus makes a speech to tell
The citizens that all is well;
That though he loved him as a friend
Caesar's life just had to end,

And that he was assassinated
'Cause his ambition was inflated;
His lust for power was such that he
Threatened all their liberty.
He says his honour he will stake
That what they did was for Rome's sake.
The plebs accept this explanation
For Julius C's assassination.

Brutus says he will agree
That Caesar's friend, Mark Antony,
May now the citizens address
 So long as he does not express
Words that criticise or blame,
Or in any way defame,
The men who cut great Caesar down
For wanting to accept the Crown.

Mark Antony's use of rhetoric
Is powerful and does the trick.
His words arouse the populace;
Their mood goes rapidly volte face
'Cause Caesar, in his will, said they're
Each, of his wealth, to get a share.
Mark Antony has done his job
And Caesar's heirs become a mob.
He's turned them into predators
Who'll seek out the conspirators.
As hunters through the city roam
Caesar's killers flee from Rome.

*   *   *

*Octavius Caesar is
Caesar's adopted son.*

Octavius has come to Rome
And now resides in Caesar's home.

*Lepidus is a friend of
Caesar's. He, Octavius
and Mark Antony are the
Triumvirate that now
rules Rome.*

Mark Antony, Lepidus and he
Hold a meeting and agree
That they're the guys who're clearly meant
To hold the reins of government
And straightaway decide they must
Kill everyone they do not trust.

*   *   *

Cassius and Brutus are
Preparing for the coming war.
They've raised a force of well-trained men
In hopes of taking Rome again.
But, sadly, they are not agreed
How, tactically, they should proceed.
Cassius thinks they should hold back
And force the enemy to attack.
But 'cause they've been so discommoded
The locals' goodwill's been eroded
And Brutus thinks that there's a chance
They'll join their foes as they advance
And he tells Cassius that is why

*Philippi, in Macedonia,
was where the final battle
between the army of the
Triumvirate and the
forces of Caesar's assassins
took place.*

They have to march to Philippi.

Brutus has been told his wife
Portia's taken her own life.
And, later on that night, he's most
Surprised to meet with Caesar's ghost
Who troubles and upsets him sayin'
At Philippi they'll meet again.

So Philippi then, is the place
The armies will come face to face.
As they come closer, Brutus sees
A weakness in his enemies.
Before his swift and fierce attack
Octavius is forced right back.
Alas, though, Cassius has found
That his adversary's making ground;
His army's being encircled and
Mark Antony's got the upper hand.

'Way in the distance there's a fuss
And Cassius sends Titinius
To find out which side's troops are they
And let him know the state of play.
And then he sends Pindarus too
To higher ground, with better view.
Alas! Alack! It turns out he's
In error about what he sees.
He says Titinius is taken.
That leaves Cassius badly shaken
And leads him quickly to decide
To organise his suicide.

Titinius is a friend of Brutus and Cassius.

Pindarus is Cassius's servant.

In fact Titinius survives
And back with good news now arrives.
'Cause Brutus made a fierce attack
And forced Octavius to pull back.
This news however comes too late:
Cassius already's met his fate.
He'd got his servant, Pindarus, to
Take his sword and run him through.

But now that Cassius has departed
Brutus fights on broken-hearted.
And as the battle rages on
His hope of winning is soon gone.
His close associates are slain;
His will to win is on the wane.
His army's under pressure and
His foes now gain the upper hand.
His chance of victory fades away
And Antony will win the day.
He bids all of his friends goodbye
As he prepares himself to die.
Afraid that if he's captured he'll
Be tied onto a chariot-wheel
And in that manner, be displayed
In the victory parade,

Strato is Brutus's servant.　He asks his servant, Strato, to
Help him to do what he must do;
To take his sword; hold it so high
While he runs onto it to die.

Mark Antony and Octavius
In victory are generous.
Recognising Brutus stood,
And acted, for the people's good
The victors in this war elect
To treat his body with respect.
They take his body and display it,
Arrange for it to lie in state,
Honouring, with this protocol,
'The noblest Roman of them all'.

Lear's self-esteem is badly battered;
His status and his pride are shattered.
And feeling totally forlorn,
Walks off — into a violent storm.

KING LEAR

Who's Who:

DUKE OF BURGANDY $\Big\}$ *seeking Cordelia's hand in marriage*
KING OF FRANCE

LEAR, *King of Britain.*

GONERIL, *Lear's eldest daughter.*

DUKE OF ALBANY, *Goneril's husband.*

REGAN, *Lear's second daughter.*

DUKE OF CORNWALL, *Regan's husband.*

CORDELIA, *Lear's youngest daughter.*

EARL OF KENT, *King Lear's advisor.*

FOOL.

EARL OF GLOUCESTER, *a loyal follower of King Lear.*

EDMUND, *Gloucester's bastard son.*

EDGAR, *Gloucester's legitimate son.*

TWO suitors from abroad have come
[The Duke of Burgundy is one,
The other is the King of France].
Each hopes that he will get the chance
To prove that he's the one who ought to
Get to marry King Lear's daughter.   *Lear is King of Britain.*

King Lear, who's reached a ripe old age,
Decides he wants to disengage
From wielding power, but sad to say
He didn't find some other way.

His kingdom will, Old Lear's decided,
Between his daughters, be divided.
Each daughter's love for him will merit
The portion that she will inherit.

Goneril, eldest of the three,
Wed to the Duke of Albany,
Knowing what he wants to hear,
Unbounded love declares for Lear.
And Regan [married to Cornwall],
Lear's second daughter, has the gall
To claim it is her greatest pleasure
To love her Dad beyond all measure.
With bloated ego Lear can't see
The depth of their hypocrisy.

Though she's the apple of his eye,
Cordelia will not tell a lie.
She tells her Dad she can profess
A daughter's love, no more, no less.

Lear rants and raves and blows his top,
Decides at once he's going to drop
Cordelia from his list of heirs.
His loving daughters, he declares
Will each get half his realm and power. He
Says Cordelia'll get no dowry.

We wonder if Cordelia can,
Without a dowry, get a man.
Without financial backing, she
Lacks interest for Burgundy.
The King of France though, is still keen
And asks her to become his Queen.

Of course, Cordelia grabs her chance.
They take the next boat back to France.

The Earl of Kent, the King's advisor,
Tries to persuade him to be wiser,
But Lear sees treachery in Kent's
Pleas in Cordelia's defence.
And for persisting, poor old Kent
Is sentenced to life-banishment.
Lear tells him, with his life he'll pay
If he's not gone by the tenth day.

       *   *   *

Though sovereignty he will concede,
The following, Lear says he'll need:
The title King which is his due,
One hundred knights, as retinue.
The girls, to show their gratitude,
Will house them and provide their food.
The King insists this deal be fair —
That Goneril and Regan share —
For one month at a time, each will
For Lear's group be responsible.

Within a fortnight, Goneril
Decides that she has had her fill
Of Lear and all his company
Of knights, to such extent that she
Instructs her servants to neglect
To treat the King with due respect.

Then on the scene comes this guy, Caius
[It's really Kent dressed in disguise.

He took a chance and never went
Abroad to live in banishment,
For, more than life or anything,
He only wants to serve his King].

He and the King's Fool hate to see
Lear being abused by family.
The fearless Fool goads Lear until
He goes to confront Goneril.
But she's just glad of the excuse
To give her father dog's abuse.
She claims his train is too extensive,
Ill-mannered, boorish and expensive.
The hundred, she demands he trim
To fifty knights, — old guys like him.

Goneril's husband is quite sad
To see the way she treats her Dad.

Tongue-lashed and emasculated,
Lear's utterly humiliated.
With Goneril he will not stay.
And so to Regan, he's away.
But Regan has received a letter
From Goneril, who's trying to get her
To support her efforts to
Diminish their Dad's retinue.

*   *   *

Gloucester is one of Lear's most loyal supporters.

The Earl of Gloucester's bastard son,
His father's confidence has won.
And Edmund, who's a devious rat,
With lies persuades his father that

Edgar, legally begotten,
Has turned out to be truly rotten.
He tells him Edgar hatched a plan
To murder Gloucester, their old man.
And Edmund says there was no way
That he would help his brother slay
Their Dad and following some angry words
The two of them then drew their swords.
But when he heard some people coming
The cowardly Edgar took off, running.

Gloucester swallows all these lies
And raging, sets out to apprise
All his supporters not to help
His totally disloyal whelp.

Now Edmund's sure that he will be
His father's heir, eventually.

* * *

Lear gets no sympathy at all
When he finds Regan and Cornwall
Who've gone to stay at Gloucester's place.
When he begins to make his case
He's told he should go back again
To Goneril's, from whence he came.

When Goneril arrives post-haste
The sisters take turns to lambaste
Their poor old Dad, determined to
Impress on him just who is who.
With not a shred of sympathy

They strip him of all dignity.
The numbers in his entourage,
The girls contend, are far too large.
They question why he has so many
Insisting there's no need for any.

Lear's self-esteem is badly battered;
His status and his pride are shattered.
And feeling totally forlorn
Walks off — into a violent storm.
The Fool and Kent, only these two,
Remain of all his retinue.

They walk out into wind and rain
And Lear's soul's screaming out in pain
Because the daughters that he sired
Against his Majesty've conspired.
Then on the heath, out in the storm,
While seeking shelter, dry and warm,
They meet, but do not recognise
Gloucester's Edgar in disguise.

Old Tom is Edgar
disguised as a madman.

Old Tom is the epitome
Of ranting, raving lunacy.
Lear thinks he's found someone who shares
And understands, his woeful cares.
For Tom to be in such a stew
He must have heartless daughters too.
Because of this and more such folly
It's obvious Lear's off his trolley.

*　　　*　　　*

[Meanwhile Caius, i.e. Kent,
A message to Cordelia sent,
Explaining all that's happened, and
Requesting that she lend a hand.]

* * *

The Earl of Gloucester's a sincere
And loyal subject of King Lear
And he's upset that Duke Cornwall
Forbids him help the King at all.
When he tells Edmund there's no way
That he will ever Lear betray
His bastard son agrees he's right.
So Gloucester tells him that that night
He got a letter all about
A planned rebellion to take out
The present leadership and then
Restore King Lear to power again.
Then Edmund his true nature shows
And sells his Dad out to his foes.

* * *

Gloucester meets with Kent and Co.
Tells them to Dover they should go.
Lear with Cordelia's re-united
And Kent and Co. are all delighted.

* * *

Gloucester, in his castle hall,
Is tried by Regan and Cornwall
And, heartlessly, this ruthless pair
Have him tethered to a chair.
They tell him Edmund's told them he
Is part of a conspiracy

To undermine them and advance
The cause of forces come from France.
Then Cornwall, 'cause of what he's done,
Plucks Gloucester's eyes out one by one.
Though for this deed he's made to pay —
A servant kills him that same day.

For being a treacherous double-crosser
Edmund's made the Earl of Gloucester.

The blind old man's thrown on the heath
And happens, quite by chance, to meet
Old Tom, and he confesses he
Is in this state of miscry
'Cause Edmund lied and he believed
And was so easily deceived
That he gave Edmund all his trust
And was to Edgar so unjust.
With so much guilt he's crucified
He's contemplating suicide.
That's when Old Tom reveals that he
Is Edgar in reality
And Edgar now is truly glad
To care for his poor, ailing Dad.
Their time together's short, alas, as
Soon thereafter Gloucester passes.

*   *   *

From France, an army has come over
And, with Cordelia, waits near Dover.
And there are Britons too who dream
Of overthrowing the new regime
And hope that Lear they can restore
Unto the British throne once more.

Lear's older daughters though, are sure
This rebel plot cannot endure
Without their father at its head
And want him caught, alive or dead.

Goneril and her husband row
'Cause Albany's upset at how
She and her sister 've turned so bad
They cheerfully abuse their Dad.

Goneril obviously feels free
To pursue Edmund lustily.
But Regan fancies Edmund too;
Between them trouble starts to brew.

But first to Dover they all go
And there they rout the rebel foe.
Lear and Cordelia are both caught
And back to Edmund they are brought.
And he gives orders that they be
Mistreated really shamefully
And thrown in dungeons where they'll lie
Until they're dealt with, by and by.
The Duke of Albany asks how
Come Edmund is the one that now
Makes these decisions that should be
Reserved, by right, to royalty.
His wife and Regan though, come forth
And both give Edmund their support.

Though Goneril to Albany's wed
It's Edmund she wants in her bed
And, fearing that he might prefer
Her sister Regan over her,

She's managed very sneakily,
To poison Regan, fatally.
But then she goes and gets a knife
And stabs herself; takes her own life.
[Shakespeare doesn't tell us why
She thinks that she herself must die.]

*   *   *

A herald comes with trumpet-sound
And calls on all to gather round
'Cause Edmund's challenged to a fight
By an armed and armoured knight.
And in the fight that does ensue
The knight [it's Edgar] runs him through
And Edmund's future plans are ruined
'Cause he's received a mortal wound.
Then Edmund, knowing he's facing death,
Confesses with his final breath
That, 'cause they feared that Albany
Was going to set the prisoners free,
He had resolved, with Goneril,
To tell the prison guard to kill
Cordelia but to take good care
To make it look like, in despair
And feeling that all hope had died,
She had committed suicide.

King Lear now finds that, tragic'ly,
He's outlived all his family,
And even his poor Fool's been killed.
With grief and sadness he is filled.
Distraught because of their demise,
He too gives up the ghost and dies.

The witches hail Macbeth as Lord [or
What the Scots call Thane] of Cawdor.
They also tell him something dafter:
That he'll be King quite soon thereafter.

MACBETH

From shortly after Shakespeare wrote it,
Thespians claim that they have noted
That bad luck dogs its cast and crew,
And so the superstition grew
That it is absolutely vital
Not to refer to it by title
In the theatre, so they say
They're putting on 'The Scottish Play'.

Who's Who:

DUNCAN, *King of Scotland,*
MACBETH, *Thane of Glamis, a General in the King's army.*
BANQUO, *Thane of Lochaber, a General in the King's Army,*
THREE WITCHES,
LADY MACBETH,
BODYGUARDS,
MACDUFF, *Thane of Fife.*
FLEANCE, *Banquo's son, ancestor of the Stuart Kings.*
MALCOLM, *one of King Duncan's sons.*

King Duncan's throne is safe again;
The rebel leader has been slain
By loyal Macbeth. The battle's o'er
And now, that Scotland's safe once more,
Macbeth and Banquo head for home.
Across a wind-swept heath they roam,

Duncan is King of Scotland.

Banquo and Macbeth are Generals in the King's army.

Whereon they are accosted by
Three witches — hags who prophesy
[With ne'er a hint of any evil]
Their future lives face great upheaval.

The witches hail Macbeth as Lord [or
What the Scots call Thane] of Cawdor.
They also tell him something dafter:
That he'll be King quite soon thereafter.
They speak to Banquo too, saying he
Will generate royal progeny.
The witches leave the awe-struck pair,
And disappear into thin air.

Two messengers come from the King,
And then — it is the strangest thing —
They greet Macbeth as Cawdor's Thane.
He asks these envoys to explain.
He asks if Cawdor's died, else how
Come he's to get his title now.
Seems Cawdor did the King betray
And, with his life, was made to pay.
Macbeth's brave deeds, the King has noted,
And reckons he should be promoted.
Part of the witches' tale's come true;
Macbeth now thinks the rest might, too.

*   *   *

When Macbeth's Mrs hears the story
She's rapt by dreams of royal glory.
To be the Queen is her ambition,
To gain which, she now plans sedition.
For, if Macbeth's to ascend the throne,
It's obvious that someone's going

To have to kill King Duncan first.
Macbeth's with indecision cursed,
So Lady M's forced to decide
To have a go at homicide.

      *   *   *

To honour further his new Thane,
The King announces he'll be staying
For a while at Inverness
Which is the Macbeths' home address.
The Macbeths' hospitality
Excels; the food and drink run free.
And, when the King bids all good night,
He and his bodyguards are tight.

Hours later, while the castle sleeps,
The Lady from her bedroom creeps,
And stealthily, with knife in hand,
Sets out to kill the King, as planned.
But, just as she's about to strike,
She sees how much the King looks like
Her Dad, and finds she can't proceed
To carry out the dreadful deed.

She nags and wheedles till Macbeth
Agrees he'll stab the King to death.

And all the while there's not a peep
From Duncan's guards, who're fast asleep.
But evil-minded Lady M
Has plans to screw the two of them.
Their hands and clothes and daggers she,
With Duncan's blood, smears liberally.

By these foul means, she hopes to frame
The guards, so they will get the blame.

Next morning, when the body's found,
There's pandemonium all around.
Ere they can speak in their defence
The host acts on the 'evidence'.
Their blood-stained weapons, hands and clothes
Combined, provide the 'proof' that shows
The guards are guilty, so Macbeth
Quickly puts them both to death.
The Thane of Fife and Duncan's sons
Suspect the guards were not the ones
'Cause they had not a thing to gain
By Duncan ending up being slain.
Macduff believes Macbeth has got

MacDuff is Thane of Fife.

A reason to have hatched the plot —
That his ambition might provide
The reason for this regicide.

And Duncan's sons both smell a rat;
The 'proof of guilt' is far too pat.
They fear that they too might be found
Dead if, for long, they hang around.
So they decide to run away
And live to fight another day.

Their going suits Macbeth just fine.
To Scotland's throne, he's next in line.
In Scone a hasty coronation
Makes him king of the Scottish nation.

*   *   *

But after he attains the crown
There's something that still gets him down.
The witches said Banquo, not he,
Will propagate a dynasty.
That surely constitutes a threat
To the line of Royal Macbeth,
So Banquo and his son must die
Ere they can breed and multiply.

Macbeth then finds two murderous villains
Who will oblige and do the killings
Of Banquo and his son, Fleance.
Though Banquo's slain, by happenstance
His son escapes and rides away
To start his dynasty some day.

* * *

At Macbeth's banquet, Banquo's ghost
Appears to argue with the host
Who, fearing that he's going insane,
Sets out to find that heath again;
Invokes the witches to appear
To help him deal with his great fear.
They tell him he should fear Macduff
But otherwise he's safe enough,
For no man born of woman will
Ever Macbeth's life-blood spill;
Nor will he suffer a defeat
'Less Birnam Wood should move to meet
The walls of Dunsinane which is
Another residence of his.

Birnam Wood is close to Dunsinane.

* * *

Still, Banquo's progeny he's shown —
Eight generations, on the throne.

*   *   *

From what the witches said, Macbeth
Believes that there is but one threat.
He sets out, on a sudden whim,
To get Macduff 'fore he gets him.
He kills the children and the wife,
But fails to kill the Thane of Fife,
Because Macduff's gone south to Malcolm
Where he receives a royal welcome.

Malcolm is King Duncan's son, and heir to the Scottish throne.

Now Malcolm, one of Duncan's sons,
With a great English army, comes
'Cause, if he wants the Scottish crown,
Macbeth must first be taken down.

*   *   *

Macbeth goes home, only to find
That Lady M has lost her mind.
'Cause Dunsinane's atop a hill
And readily defensible,
Macbeth's decided that's the place
The armies should come face to face.
This fortress he must now prepare
For battle 'gainst King Duncan's heir.
And then he's told his wife has died,
Most probably, by suicide.
Sad and morose, he gets moroser
When told that Birnam's Wood comes closer.
Malcolm's soldiers, camouflaged
With branches, shrubs and foliage,

Approach his walls, so Macbeth goes
To meet and battle with his foes.
Though he's been warned he should beware
The Thane of Fife, he doesn't care.

When on the battlefield they meet,
Believing that he can't be beat,
He taunts Macduff, the Thane of Fife,
Saying how he cannot lose his life
To any man of woman born.
Macduff's not fazed, just laughs in scorn
Saying he first saw light of day
Delivered the Caesarean way.
The witches' prophesy is clear,
And Macbeth knows his end is near.

Everybody loathes and hates him
And loves when Macduff terminates him.
And then Macduff cuts off his head
To prove to Malcolm that he's dead.

The victors then go off to Scone
Where Malcolm will ascend the throne.

The Duke, dressed as Friar Ludowick,
Goes to the gaol to have a quick
Word with the man who is condemned,
Tomorrow morn, to meet his end.

MEASURE FOR MEASURE

Who's Who:

THE DUKE, *ruler of Vienna.*

ANGELO, *Lord Deputy in the Duke's absence.*

CLAUDIO, *a young Gentleman.*

JULIET, *Claudio's girlfriend and lover.*

PROVOST, *an officer of the law, who arrests and confines wrong-doers.*

ESCALUS, *an elderly lord, Angelo's advisor.*

LUCIO, *a lecherous young dandy, an acquaintance of Claudio.*

ISABELLA, *Claudio's chaste sister who has entered a nunnery.*

FRIAR LUDOWICK, *the Duke in disguise.*

MARIANA, *had been Angelo's fiance and is still in love with him.*

The Duke's announced that he must spend   *The Duke of Vienna.*
Some time abroad where he'll attend
An international debate
With other dukes and heads of state.

Because for many years past he'd
To law enforcement paid no heed
The Duke is filled with deep unease

About the way the Viennese
Seem day by day to be deciding
To become less law-abiding.

The Duke tells Angelo that he
Must act as his Lord Deputy.
He has a reputation for
A strict adherence to the law.
A better man he couldn't get
'Cause Angelo's a martinet
And now there will be consequences
For any criminal offences
And fear will give the people cause
To be compliant with the laws.

The Duke, though, isn't going away;
With friars nearby he's going to stay
And keep an eye on how things go
In Vienna, under Angelo.

*   *   *

Claudio is a young   Signior Claudio has met
gentleman.   A lovely lass, named Juliet
And after some time they agree
That they will wed eventually.
But, fearing that her family might
Think that, for her, he isn't right,
They went ahead and jumped the gun
And went to bed and had some fun.
As a result of making hay
Now Juliet's in the family way.
An ancient law, that for some time
Has been ignored, says it's a crime

For any guy to impregnate
A lass outside the married state.
The provost makes a public show
When he arrests young Claudio.
It seems Lord Angelo has said
That, for this crime, he'll lose his head,
So other men will be afraid
To impregnate a single maid.

The provost is an officer of the law who arrests wrong-doers and carries out the sentence..

Escalus asks Angelo
To be less harsh with Claudio.
But Angelo's intransigent
And adamant he won't relent,
And orders that the matter be
Concluded expeditiously;
That Claudio's head be on the block
Tomorrow morn by nine o'clock.

Escalus is Angelo's advisor and assistant.

*   *   *

Claudio's sister, Isabella,
Has never even kissed a fella
And now she has decided she
Will take a vow of chastity.
Claudio decides to send
Lucio, a trusted friend,
To the convent of St Clare
[his sister is a novice there]
And see if she'll agree to go
And plead for him with Angelo.

Lucio is a notorious gossip who delights in denigrating people.

Isabella says that she'll
On Claudio's behalf appeal,
And then, with Lucio in tow,
Sets off to see Lord Angelo.

She asks that he condemn the deed
But let the man who sinned be freed.
But in response Lord Angelo says
That for the sin the sinner pays.
She sees the law is harsh but just;
[When Satan drives well then needs must!]
Lucio is not impressed
By the way she has addressed
Her brother's very serious plight
And says she must resume the fight.
She needs to be more vehement
And make a stronger argument.

She gets down on her bended knees;
Puts all her heart into her pleas;
From that inferior position
She humbly re-makes her petition:
The exercise of mercy can
Enhance the status of the man;
If she were he and he were she
Then she would show him clemency.
But Angelo says the Law is Judge
And, from its codes, he will not budge!
Then Isabella asks if he
Looks in his heart does he not see
Some vestige of the self-same flaw
In his adherence to this law;
That he's not pure as driven snow
Any more than Claudio.
Then Angelo concedes he ought
To give his judgement some more thought.
He tells her to come back next day
And they'll review the state of play.

Now Angelo's a bit perturbed
'Cause Isabella has disturbed
His peace of mind and self-control;
He finds that deep inside his soul
Her purity and innocence
Awakened his concupiscence.

So then it comes as no surprise
Next time they meet that Angelo tries
To get her to agree that she
Will give him her virginity.
And he says that he'll overturn
Her brother's sentence, in return.
Isabella's quite distraught;
Insists her virtue can't be bought;
Says she'll go public, let folk see
The depth of his depravity.
But he's not bothered 'cause he says
He's perfect in the public's gaze.
And 'cause her morals are too high
It's her fault Claudio will die.

*   *   *

The Duke, dressed as Friar Ludowick,
Goes to the gaol to have a quick
Word with the man who is condemned
Tomorrow morn to meet his end.
Like a good friar he does his best
To put the poor guy's mind at rest.
Isabella is about
To enter as the friar comes out.
The provost helps him to stay near,
But out of sight , so he might hear

Isabella and her brother
Say their farewells to each other.

Claudio's sister tells her tale,
How Angelo tried to prevail
On her to let him have his way
And thus for Claudio's freedom pay,
But she's a chaste girl and she thinks
That his vile proposition stinks.
Claudio, though, 's not sure it's bad
And that makes Isabella mad.

*   *   *

The friar meets Isabella an'
He tells her he has got a plan.
And Ludowick goes on to say
That Angelo had a fiancé.
Mariana was his girlfriend's name
But, much to Angelo's great shame,
He dumped her when he found out she
Had lost her dowry out at sea.
In spite of all, the friar is sure
She loves him still, and 'twill endure.

Isabella's told to go
Back to speak with Angelo
And there agree to do the deed
In order to have Claudio freed.
As neither wishes anyone
Might come to know what they'll have done,
Their tryst will be at dead of night;
They'll make no sound, they'll shed no light.
The plan, though, is that she won't do it
Instead she'll send a substitute.

Mariana, who is Angelo's ex
Says she'll be happy to have sex
Because the holy friar has said
That then they will have to get wed.

*   *   *

The friar goes to the gaol to see
The provost setting Claudio free.

Fearing that if he's let go
He'll seek revenge on Angelo,
The venal lord has sent a letter
Saying he would like it better
If Claudio should die at four,
And then he wants to see, what's more,
[As proof that he's not still alive]
His head upon a plate, at five.

The friar and provost want to spare
Claudio 'cause it isn't fair
That Angelo, who wrote the letter,
In terms of morals is no better
Than the man that he says must
Die for giving in to lust.
The provost knows he must comply
With orders or he too will die.
The friar, though, gets him off the hook;
He has a letter from the Duke
That the provost knows is real
Because it bears the Ducal seal,
And the letter clearly says
He's coming home in two more days.

The Duke's his friend and Ludowick
Says he'll appreciate their trick:
It seems another prisoner
Has died a little earlier.
At first glance, if one didn't know,
One might think 'twas Claudio.
They cut his head off and agree
'Twill fool the Duke's Lord Deputy.
And Claudio, for a few days,
They'll hide away from public gaze.

When Isabella comes to see
If Claudio has been set free
The friar says that he lost his head
In spite of what Lord Angelo said.

*　　　*　　　*

The Duke's back home and wants to know
How things have gone for Angelo.
He seems convinced his Deputy
Has managed efficaciously.
Then Isabella tells him that
His Deputy's a dirty rat,
A thief, a cheat, adulterer,
A lying sexual predator.
Angelo, of course, denies
This, saying that she's telling lies.
The Deputy's untruths prevail
And Isabella's sent to gaol.

Mariana speaks up to uncover
How Angelo became her lover;
That, in the dark, she took her place
When, much to Angelo's disgrace,

He abused Vienna's power
To be the one that would deflower
Isabella, who'd agreed
So that her brother would be freed.
Angelo admits it's true;
The Duke decides what they must do
Is get married straight away
And then come back without delay.

*　　　*　　　*

'Cause there are matters he can't mention
That need his personal attention
The Duke leaves Escalus to deal
With Signior Lucio's appeal:
Lucio has rashly claimed
That the Duke has been defamed
And his name dragged in the mire
By Ludowick, a so-called friar.
As Escalus to one side walks
And there with Isabella talks,
Friar Ludowick again appears
And Lucio's denouement nears.
They argue matters to and fro
And end up standing toe to toe.
Lucio, angered by what's said,
Pulls the friar's cowl from his head
And as the Duke's face is revealed
Lucio knows his fate is sealed.

*　　　*　　　*

The newly-weds now stand in fear
Of what they are about to hear.
The Duke says Angelo must be,
With Claudio, treated equally.

That means, 'cause Claudio is dead,
That Angelo must lose his head.
And Angelo agrees that he
Deserves to die for perfidy.
Mariana kneels down on the floor
To humbly, tearfully, implore
[As Angelo's ever-loving wife]
The Duke to save her husband's life.
And Isabella too, says she'd
Be well-content to see him freed.

And then to everyone's delight
It turns out Claudio's all right.
As Angelo's fate's supposed to be
The same as Claudio's, he's set free.

But Lucio, the Duke asserts,
Is going to get his just deserts.
For saying he knew the Duke to be
A lecher and a debauchee,
A craven coward and an ass
And sly and ignorant and crass,
The Duke says Lucio will be
Given the death penalty.
Then he recalls that Lucio
Had boasted, a short while ago,
That in a house of ill-repute
He'd had sex with a prostitute.
On learning that she'd borne his child
He'd said he'd wed her, then resiled.
The Duke then shifts the paradigm,
To make the punishment fit the crime,
Decides the sentence to commute
To marriage to the prostitute.

And when Vienna's people see
Their Duke wield his authority
With judgement stern and verdict fair,
Their lawless ways they will forswear.

The Duke then pardons everyone
For all the misdeeds they have done.

He says he wants to spend his life
With Isabella as his wife.
And she doesn't say him Nay
And, hand in hand, they walk away.

Because she's kept the veil in place
He asks if he might see her face,
But this Leonato disallows
Till after they've exchanged their vows.

MUCH ADO
ABOUT NOTHING

Who's Who:

DON PEDRO, *Prince of Arragon.*
LEONATO, *Governor of Messina, Hero's father.*
BENEDICK, *a young lord of Padua.*
BEATRICE, *Leonato's niece.*
CLAUDIO, A *young lord of Florence.*
HERO, *Leonato's daughter, falls in love with Claudio.*
DON JOHN, *Don Pedro's bastard brother.*
BORACHIO & CONRADE, *followers of Don John.*
MARGARET, *Hero's maid-in-waiting who is Borachio's girlfriend.*
FRIAR FRANCIS.
ANTONIO, *Leonato's brother and Beatrice's father.*

Don Pedro went to war and won.
Now, to Messina, he has come
Because, by way of celebration,
He's taking a few weeks vacation.
The lodgings he is looking for
Are with the city's Governor
Leonato, who is proud to boast
That he's to be the Prince's host.

Don Pedro is the Prince of Arragon.

Leonato is the Governor of Messina.

Don Pedro's entourage contains
Two handsome, brave and noble swains,
And Leonato thinks he can
Help his daughter get a man.
He also has a pretty niece...
Perhaps they'll get a man apiece.

*   *   *

Benedick is a young lord from Padua.
Beatrice is Leonato's niece.

A witty guy is Benedick
But Beatrice reckons he's too slick.
The two do not see eye to eye
And, when they meet, they make sparks fly,
'Cause neither one can stand to be
In the other's company.
With sneers and snide remarks each tries
To cut the other down to size.

Claudio is a young lord from Florence.

The second man, Count Claudio,
Finds that his heart is all aglow.
The daughter, he's attracted to,
But isn't sure quite what to do

Hero is Leonato's daughter.

And, fearing Hero might reject him
Should he declare his deep affection,
Decides that maybe 'twould be better
To ask for help in trying to get her.

The Prince agrees to help the lad;
He'll recommend him to her Dad.
And later on, [they're at the masque]
She thinks it's Claudio that asks
If he might come and walk her out.
That she'd love that, she leaves no doubt.

The Prince reports to Claudio
It's safe for him to have a go.
And once he knows she will approve
He very quickly makes his move.
Unbounded love for her he states,
A feeling she reciprocates,
And falling for each other's charms
They fall into each other's arms.
Because they know that they are fated
Never to be separated.
Claudio and Hero plan
To wed as soon as e'er they can.

Leonato says he needs at least
A few days to prepare the feast

The Prince says that the time will fly
If they'll agree to help him try
To bring about an armistice
'Tween Benedick and Beatrice.
And, if they're favoured from above,
These two might even fall in love.

*　　　*　　　*

When Benedick, alone, is near,
And knowing he can overhear,
Leonato tells the Prince his niece
From love-sickness gets no release.
'Tis Benedick for whom she longs;
To Benedick her heart belongs.
But Benedick must not be told
Because she knows what would unfold.
She knows that he'd humiliate her,
Embarrass, snub, shame and deflate her.

And 'cause she'll never be his wife
She'll live a sad and lonely life.

Benedick, filled with regret
That Beatrice is so upset,
Resolves with tenderness to treat her
From now on, whene'er he meets her.

*   *   *

Because it's worked with Benedick
The girls will use the self-same trick.

Hero and her maid-in-waiting
Some tasty gossip are debating.
Beatrice is told, by listening in
She might learn something interesting.
She hides so she can hear them talk
As they stroll on the garden walk.
She hears that Benedick's confessed
To Claudio, that he's distressed
'Cause Beatrice, whom he'll love forever,
Seems to hate him and will never
Love him back, but will instead,
Make snide remarks and wreck his head;
And when she can, humiliate him,
Embarrass and excoriate him.

If this is how her friends assess her
She's sure her future will depress her.
So Beatrice makes up her mind
That from now on she will be kind.

This mutual change of attitude
[Being pleasant now instead of rude]

They find that they appreciate,
And sweetness they reciprocate.
The more their spiteful traits they smother
The more, they find, they like each other.

*   *   *

The Prince's bastard brother, John,
Of ill-will, is the paragon.
He hates the Prince and Claudio
And so to any length will go
To ruin their happiness and joy —
The wedding plans he will destroy.

*Don John is Don Pedro's
nasty bastard brother.*

He pays Borachio, a friend,
The happy couple's joy to end.
[Hero, from home, will have been lured;
Her absence, therefore, is assured].

*Borachio is one of Don
John's followers.*

Borachio's dating Margaret
And has no doubt that he can get
His girlfriend to don Hero's clothes
And at her bedroom window pose,
And, late at night, sweet nothings speak
To him, while he's out in the street.

*Margaret is one of Hero's
maids-in-waiting.*

*   *   *

To Claudio and the Prince, John goes
And feigns concern for these their woes.
The guy is absolutely hateful —
He tells them Hero's being unfaithful,
Then takes the groom and Prince to see
Proof of her infidelity.
Distraught and heart-sore, Claudio vows,
Next day, to shame his would-be spouse.

Friar Francis is the
celebrant at the wedding.

Friar Francis starts the ceremony
And things are going swimmingly
Till Claudio, out of the blue,
Says Hero's wanton and untrue.

The Prince tells how, the previous night,
They'd been confronted by the sight
Of Hero flirting with a bloke
And, 'twasn't the first time they spoke.
Her reputation now in ruins,
Her blood runs cold and Hero swoons.

The Prince, his brother and the groom
Depart and leave an air of gloom.
Poor Hero lies there in disgrace,
Immobile, cold and pale of face.
Beatrice, kneeling by her side,
Is quite certain she has died.
Friar Francis, though, says she'll get well,
And he believes that time will tell
That she is faithful, and no way
Did she do what those others say.
But till they learn that they're mistaken
There are precautions to be taken.
That Hero's dead they must proclaim
And, on a headstone, carve her name.
Then Claudio will his words repent
That Hero, to her Maker sent.

*　　　*　　　*

Conrade is another of Don
John's followers.

Meanwhile, the cops out on the beat
O'erhear two drunks talk in the street.
Borachio's bragging to Conrade,
A thousand ducats he's been paid

For counterfeiting Hero's shame
And sullying her stainless name.
The Prince's brother, John, and he
Contrived this piece of villainy.

But now Don John cannot be found;
For justice, he's not hanging 'round.

Borachio, brought before the Prince,
Attests to Hero's innocence.
Then Claudio is racked with grief
That his mistaken, false belief
Caused Hero so much pain that she
Was broken-hearted, mortally.
Full of remorse, he says he'll do
Whatever her Dad asks him to.
Leonato says, 'cause Hero's dead,
The lad must wed his niece instead.

To Hero's tomb then Claudio goes
That chapter of his life to close.
He tells her he still loves her dearly
And promises to visit, yearly.

Next morning, all have come to see
The latest nuptial ceremony.
Antonio, 'father of the bride',
With his veiled 'daughter' by his side,
Walks with her to the chapel, so
That she can marry Claudio.
Because she's kept the veil in place
He asks if he might see her face,
But this, Leonato disallows
Till after they've exchanged their vows,

Antonio is Leonato's brother and Beatrice's father.

Which, when they've done, surprise, surprise!
Without her veil, before his eyes
Stands Hero who, to his delight,
Is live and well and smiling bright.

Before the ceremony closes,
To Beatrice, Benedick proposes
And she's delighted and says "yes".
Their union, too, the Friar will bless.

The General is angry and quite shocked
To find his young lieutenant's really crocked.
Such drunkenness and lack of discipline,
In one who is on guard, 's a grievous sin.

OTHELLO

Who's Who

DESDEMONA, *Brabantio's daughter and Othello's wife.*
OTHELLO, *a noble Moor in the service of the Venetian State.*
MICHAEL CASSIO, *Othello's Lieutenant.*
BRABANTIO, *a Senator and Desdemona's father.*
DUKE OF VENICE.
IAGO, *Othello's standard-bearer.*
EMILIA, *Iago's wife.*
BIANCA, *Cassio's mistress.*
LUDOVICO, *a relative of Brabantio.*
RODERIGO, *a Venetian Gentleman.*

Although pursued by handsome, titled gents
Sweet Desdemona seeks intelligence.
And when an army General comes to woo
Her, telling many tales of derring-do,
With him she is just totally besotted,
Believing, all she wants, Othello's got it.
His mind is razor-sharp; he is no dullard,
And even though she's white and he is coloured,—
Thus proving true the saying: 'Love is blind,'—
To marry him she fast makes up her mind.

Although her father is Othello's friend
They fear that, if he knew, he'd try to end

Desdemona is the daughter of Brabantio.

Othello is a noble Moor and is a General in the Venetian army.

Their plans to wed, so they decide to use

*Cassio is Othello's
Lieutenant.*

Young Cassio to carry billet-douxs.

*Brabantio, Desdemona's
father, is a Venetian
Senator.*

Brabantio considers black a flaw,

Not in a friend, but in his son-in-law,

And so he claims the Moor has won his daughter

By using sorcerous means he didn't ought to.

[In Venice, the death penalty's mandated

For sorcery and spells and deeds related.]

He'll use the law to cook Othello's goose

And gladly see him in the hangman's noose.

But when Othello's brought before the Duke

To answer to these charges, like a crook,

Word comes to say, 'round Rhodes, a naval force

Is gathering, preparing to set course

For Cyprus, where this warlike Turkish horde,

From Venice will wrench power, with fire

      and sword.

At such a time Othello would be missed

Because he's such a brilliant strategist.

The Duke shows wisdom then; he says

      he's gonna

Allow Othello's Mrs, Desdemona,

Give evidence of how she came to be

The black man's wife, and if her choice was free.

She tells the court she loves her father dearly,

But then goes on to state she has, quite clearly,

[Just as her mother too, in her time, had]

A preference for her husband o'er her Dad.

Brabantio accepts, though with poor grace,

His daughter and the Moor have won the case.

           *   *   *

Othello now must leave; he has to go
Immediately, to fight the Turkish foe.
And Desdemona says that where he leads
She'll follow and provide for all his needs.

* * *

Iago's heard an untrue rumour saying
That Emilia away from home is playing,
And he believes Othello's wrecked his life
By fornicating with his cheating wife.
As well as that, Iago's got the notion
That Cassio's been given his promotion.
Iago thinks he's been so badly slighted
The only way things ever can be righted
Is for those who've caused his suffering to pay
For disrespecting him in any way.
To get revenge, Iago knows he must
Get friendly with the Moor and gain his trust.
He reckons that Othello's power depends
Upon the trust and loyalty of friends
And the respect and love of his good wife,
And sets out to destroy Othello's life.

Iago is Othello's standard-bearer.

Emilia is Iago's wife.

* * *

As Othello reaches Cyprus to defend it,
Comes news that Turkey's threat of war has ended.
A mighty storm her fleet has badly battered;
Some ships were sunk, the rest were widely scattered.
It is Othello's wish, in celebration,
To inebriate the island's population.
But first, he orders Cassio to ensure
The guard does not succumb to drink's allure.

Iago then begins his planned sedition
By undermining Cassio's position.
As pseudo-friend, he sells the toper's lie,
"We'll have just one," but then goes on to ply
The younger man with alcohol until
He's sozzled, legless and incapable.
A collaborator's primed to start a fight,
Another's sent out to disturb the night
And ring the bell, which brings Othello down
To investigate what's happening in the town.

The General is angry and quite shocked
To find his young Lieutenant's really crocked.
Such drunkenness and lack of discipline,
In one who is on guard, 's a grievous sin.
Iago speaks in Cassio's 'defence'
With weasel words well-chosen to incense,
Resulting in young Cassio being demoted.
With self-satisfied success, Iago's bloated.

When sober, Cassio's filled with self-disgust
Because he's lost the Moor's respect and trust.
His pseudo-friend behaves as real friends do;
He listens, then advises Cassio to
Ask Desdemona, who is still his friend,
If, to her husband, she would recommend
That he might overlook, just this one time,
A very sorry soldier's drunken crime.
Iago says he's sure this wifely plea
Will get back Cassio's Lieutenantcy.
It's good advice, but he's a wicked man
Who's plotting to progress an evil plan.

*   *   *

And now that he has got Othello's ear
Iago, knowing that the Moor is near,
Feigns wonder and concern at their rapport,
Suggesting that, perhaps, there's something more
That causes Desdemona so to plead
On Cassio's behalf, when there's no need.
By hints and innuendos, such as this,
He undermines Othello's wedded bliss.
Now each time Desdemona makes a plea
On Cassio's behalf, it looks like she
And he, just possibly, might share
A sordid extra-marital affair.

And soon the Moor begins to doubt his spouse
Is quite committed to her marriage vows.
Perhaps, because she's married to Othello,
She feels the need to try a younger fellow.
And always, like an evil puppeteer,
Iago plays upon Othello's fear.
Pretending great reluctance and dismay
He claims 'tis only duty bids him say
If Desdemona could deceive her Dad,
As she, by wedding him, quite clearly had,
One might assume that she is naturally
Disposed to cheating and adultery,
But counsels that Othello make no move
Until there is real evidence to prove
That he, by Desdemona, is being cheated
Of favours to which Cassio's being treated.

*   *   *

Othello's Mum gave him, when she was dying,
A hanky with a strawberry design.
When he with Desdemona first began,
And she declared he was her only man,
To show his love for her was truly deep,
He'd given her that handkerchief to keep.
This symbol of the Moor's undying love
Now Desdemona values well above
All else, and when her husband is away
She showers kisses on it all the day.

Iago doesn't treat his wife too good,
And she believes that, if she only could
Steal Desdemona's hanky, he would be
So grateful that he'd treat her properly.
The handkerchief Emilia stoops to take
When Desdemona drops it by mistake.
Delighted with her prize, Iago sadly
Persists in treating poor Emilia badly.
This hanky fits the plan he has designed
He leaves it for young Cassio to find.

*   *   *

He cons Othello into the belief
That he has 'facts' to cause the Moor such grief
And anger, that he fears for life and limb
Should he impart this 'evidence' to him.
Iago tells, reluctantly it seems,
That Cassio speaks, sometimes, while he dreams,
And Desdemona's love, he's heard him tell
Of sharing, not too wisely but too well.

*   *   *

Bianca on young Cassio just dotes,

Bianca is Cassio's mistress.

While he, with her, is sowing his wild oats.
He asks her, being romantically soppy,
To take the hanky and to make a copy.
In love, at first she just does not presume
To question that he found it in his room.
On more mature reflection, later on,
She begins to think the tale's a classic con.
The story seems, to her, designed to cover
The fact that he has got another lover.
She returns to tell young Cassio she thinks
His yarn about the handkerchief just stinks.

Othello overhears and thinks that he
Has proof of his wife's infidelity.
Iago winds him up about his wife
Until he's mad enough to take her life.
And also says that he, himself, is willing
To find young Michael Cassio and kill 'im.

   *   *   *

From Venice, then, by Ludovico's hand

Ludovico is a relative
of Othello.

Come orders from the Duke which now command
Othello back to Venice, real post haste,
While in charge, in Cyprus, Cassio is placed.
The Moor decides all that can wait, for now
He's going home to have a blazing row
With Desdemona, whom he calls a whore
And browbeats with abusive rant and roar.
Though she has never strayed — that must be said —
She's tired of fighting, so goes off to bed.

   *   *   *

There is, though Desdemona doesn't know,
A guy who fancies her, named Rod'rigo.
Iago tells him there is not a chance
Of him and her beginning a romance
Unless, if Michael Cassio is killed,
Othello'll have to stay in Cyprus till
The Duke and Senators of Venice can,
To rule the island, find another man.

Roderigo is a young Venetian gentleman living in Cyprus.

Roderigo and Iago chance to meet
Young Michael Cassio, out in the street.
Roderigo draws his sword, but he's no good,
And Cassio responds, and he draws blood.
To even up the odds, with a coward's blow
Iago, from behind, stabs Cassio.
A crowd begins to gather 'round the fight.
Iago, fearing Roderigo might
Let slip 'twas he inspired this murderous plot,
Gives him the coup de grace, so he cannot.

Meanwhile the Moor decides that he is gonna
Go to her room and murder Desdemona.
And there a pillow places on her head
And keeps exerting pressure till she's dead.

He's done the deed but he's not satisfied —
His jealousy, with Desdemona, died.
He realises she was innocent
And with self-hate his heart and soul are rent.
And then, to add to all Othello's woe,
In come young Michael Cassio and Co.

Iago, as a prisoner, they've got
And promise that he'll suffer quite a lot —
For being such a horrid, nasty guy
They'll torture him before they'll let him die.

On Roderigo's body, not yet cold,
They'd found two letters, which quite clearly told
And proved, beyond the shadow of a doubt,
That 'twas Iago'd laid the whole plan out.

For murdering his wife, with guilt he's racked
So suicide's Othello's final act.

Marina's beauty far surpasses
That of all the other lasses.
The youths of Tarsus can't resist her
And they ignore her foster-sister.

PERICLES, PRINCE OF TYRE

Who's Who:

ANTIOCHUS, *King of Antioch.*
THE DAUGHTER OF ANTIOCHUS.
PERICLES, *Prince of Tyre.*
HELICANUS, *a lord of Tyre.*
CLEON, *Governor of Tarsus.*
DIONYZA, *Cleon's wife.*
THALIARD, *a lord of Antioch.*
SIMONIDES, *King of Pentapolis.*
THAISA, *Simonides's daughter.*
MARINA, *Pericles and Thaisa's daughter.*
LYCHORIDA, *Marina's nurse.*
CERIMON, *a lord of Ephesus.*
LEONINE, *Dionyza's servant.*
A PANDAR OR BROTHEL-KEEPER.
BOULT, *his Servant.*
LYSIMACHUS, *Governor of Mitylene.*

The King of Antioch's wife has died,
The woman on whom he relied
For warmth and comfort in his bed,
And his misfortune, sadly, led
To him doing stuff he didn't ought to
With his beautiful young daughter.

And she complies, at his behest,
To be his partner in incest.
This sin of theirs must not be known
If he's to keep her as his own,

*Antiochus is King
of Antioch.*

So Antiochus has decreed
For any suitor to succeed
And win his lovely daughter's hand
He first must solve a riddle and
The suitor first must realise
That if he fails, well then he dies.

Pericles, the Prince of Tyre,
To win this lassie does aspire.
He solves the riddle, but's in shock,
To learn the King of Antioch
And his daughter secretly
Are acting inappropriately.
Pericles has little doubt
The King won't want this secret out
And, fearing for his life, takes flight
As soon as it is dark that night.

He's sure that Antiochus will
Not feel his secret's safe until
Pericles has met his death
And can no longer pose a threat.
He'll be assassinated, or
Antioch might start a war
Which could see the decimation
Of Tyre's civilian population.

*Helicanus, a lord
of Tyre, is Pericles's
trusted advisor.*

Helicanus and he decide
That he should run away and hide.

*   *   *

The Prince to Tarsus will repair
Convinced he'll find safe haven there.
'Cause at this time, this luckless nation
Is suff'ring famine and starvation
Pericles fills ships with corn
To feed the hungry and forlorn.
Cleon and Dionyza say
They're glad to have him come and stay
In Tarsus as a refugee
And live with them, in safety.

Cleon is the Governor of Tarsus.

Dionyza is Cleon's wife.

He's only barely settled when
His peace of mind's upset again.
Helicanus has sent him mail
Saying Thaliard is on his tail,
So to avoid being tracked and found
And killed and buried in the ground,
He, once again, decides that he,
For safety sake, must go to sea.
But then, by gales his ship is tossed
And wrecked, and all but he are lost.

Thaliard, a lord of Antioch, has been sent by Antiochus to assassinate Pericles.

As the mighty tempest's roar
Abates, he's cast up on a shore
And finds the place where he now is
The locals call Pentapolis.
Some fishermen who're working there
Offer him their help and care.
They tell the half-drowned Pericles
That their good King, Simonides
For Princess Thaisa's birthday-do
Has organised for her to view
An entertaining tournament —
A great competitive event —

Simonides is King of Pentapolis.

Thaisa is Simonides's daughter.

Where many knights and princes will
Each display his jousting skill.
Pericles says he would love
To play a part in the above.
Just then a fisherman shows what
In their fishing net's been caught
Now that the seas have got much calmer:
'Tis Pericles's suit of armour.

Next day, in rusty armour dressed
He enters for the jousting test
And after he's declared the winner
The King treats everyone to dinner.
As he's the competition's ace,
At table, he gets pride of place
Where he's the subject of a toast
Raised by the daughter of the host.
To find out who this stranger is
The King subjects him to a quiz.
He says he's Prince of Tyre but he
Was lately shipwrecked while at sea.
Quite soon it's obvious that he's a
Hit with beautiful Thaisa.
She tells her Dad of her desire
To marry the young Prince of Tyre.
Dad speaks with Pericles and he
Agrees he'll wed her, happily.

*   *   *

In Tyre, the hearts of the lords burn
Impatiently, for the return
Of Pericles, their noble Prince
Who, fearing Antioch, long since

Had left the city so that he
Might save it from calamity.
Now Antiochus and his daughter
No longer pose a threat of slaughter
Because the gods had had enough
Of that vile pair's incestuous stuff
And sent a ball of fire that fried
Their chariot in which both died.
The lords are now petitioning
Helicanus to be their king
But he politely turns them down
Saying Pericles still owns the crown
And they should spend their energies
Searching for King Pericles.
If in twelve months he's not been found
Helicanus will accept the crown.

*   *   *

For many months the lords have tried;
Sought information far and wide;
They travelled near, and also wrote
To places that were more remote.
But by the time that Pericles
Gets one of these communiques
Much time's elapsed and it appears
That now the twelve-month deadline nears,
So he and Thaisa, immediately
Set sail for Tyre, across the sea.
But there's another deadline too
Their baby's birth is almost due.

A short time after they set sail
They run into a howling gale

And, as the mighty tempest blows
Thaisa into labour goes.

*Lychorida, after Thaisa's
'death' becomes the
baby's nurse.*

Lychorida, Thaisa's nurse,
Though downcast, thinks things could be worse,
'Cause, though the Mum did not survive,
Her baby girl is still alive.

Two sailors come to Pericles
Because their superstition says
Thaisa's body can't be stored
And therefore must go overboard.
So in a well-sealed wooden chest
Thaisa's body's laid to rest
With odourant spices and a note,
And then the casket's set afloat.

The trip to Tyre's still very long
And as the baby isn't strong
Pericles decides to make

*Marina is Pericles's and
Thaisa's daughter, so
called because she was
born at sea.*

For Tarsus for Marina's sake.
There Cleon and Dionyza will
The role of foster-parents fill
While he takes off across the sea
To beat his deadline so that he
The oath of office can intone
And take his place upon Tyre's throne.

*   *   *

Thaisa's wooden casket's reached
Ephesus and there it's beached.
Beachcombers find it whereupon

*Cerimon, a lord of
Ephesus, is a highly-skilled
physician.*

They take the box to Cerimon,
A learned man who has terrific
Knowledge of things scientific.

When opened up, first thing they see
Is Thaisa laid out lovingly,
And there's a note that clearly says
That she's the wife of Pericles;
'Cause she's his Queen, he hopes that she's
Interred with proper obsequies.

But Cerimon cannot detect
The signs of death that he'd expect.
The erudite physician's sure,
If he can raise her temperature
And use his scientific skills,
His potions, medicines and pills,
[He's heard of this being done before]
The lady's health he can restore.

When she recovers Thaisa vows,
Being dead to Pericles, her spouse,
If she can't be her husband's wife
She'll live a vestal virgin's life
And spend her time in service of
Diana, the goddess of love.

*   *   *

Marina's beauty far surpasses
That of all the other lasses.
The youths of Tarsus can't resist her
And they ignore her foster sister,
So, in a fit of jealous rage,
Dionyza's driven to engage
A guy to kill Marina so
That Philoten can get a beau.
Leonine can proceed no further
Than trying to commit the murder

Philoten is the daughter of Cleon and Dionyza.

Leonine, Dionyza's servant, is tasked with murdering Marina.

131

Marina bravely fights him and
Is 'rescued' by a lawless band
Of pirates who come on the scene
And take her off to Mitylene.

Leonine decides to tell
Dionyza, everything went well;
That having killed Marina, he
Then chucked her body in the sea.

Cleon and Dionyza know
They'll need a story apropos
Marina not being with them when
Her Dad comes back for her again.
They'll tell him she got really sick
And that her death was very quick.
So now, to throw him off the scent,
They'll build a massive monument
To the lovely girl they mourn
As though she were their very own.

*   *   *

At Mitylene, the pirate ship
Ties up and ends Marina's trip.
But things get worse for her when she
Is sold into sex-slavery
To serve men as a prostitute
In a house of ill repute.
But all the customers who come
With lewd intent find they succumb
To chaste Marina's argument
And leave determined to repent,
Swearing they will nevermore
Darken any brothel's door.

The Governor of Mitylene,
Lysinachus, comes on the scene.
Her words persuade him that he can
Be a proper gentleman
And she's so virtuous that he
Decides to take up chastity.
She is so good that he enjoins
Her to accept a few gold coins.

Much to the pandar's deep dismay
She's turning wealthy clients away
So he tells Boult take her to bed
And rid her of her maidenhead.
But she bribes Boult to tell his boss
That there's a way to cut his loss:
Wealthy families would pay
To have their daughters shown the way
To sew and weave and sing and dance
Preparing to be debutantes;
She'll teach their daughters so they'll be
The best in high society.
His business won't be damaged and her
Wages will go to the Pandar.

A pandar is a brothel-keeper.

Boult is the pandar's servant.

        *   *   *

Having dealt with his catharsis
Pericles returns to Tarsus
So that he can re-acquire
His daughter, the Princess of Tyre.
Such happiness, though, he's denied;
He's told that she got sick and died;
He can't believe that all this pain
Has come into his life again

And Pericles is so distressed
That he becomes so self-obsessed
He sits and broods and in this state
Refuses to communicate.

Now Fate decides to intervene
And blows his ship to Mitylene.
Lysichamus goes out to greet her
And, when aboard, he asks to meet her
Owner, but is told that he
Has suffered personal tragedy
To mourn which, he is resolute;
He sits alone, broods and stays mute.

Lysichamus knows of a maid
Who's got the power to persuade
A man to turn away from sin
As, recently, she'd done with him.
If he can get her to address
This man's terrible distress,
He's pretty sure her intercession
Will talk him out of his depression.
She'll help relieve his mental pain
And he'll begin to talk again.
And so Marina's brought on board
And asked if she will have a word
With the old man who sits alone
And will not speak with anyone.

Pericles, she will regale
By telling him her own life-tale;
She tells him how she got her name
And how the stock from whence she came,

Just like his own, is very good
'Cause, in her veins, runs royal blood.
Her family history reflects
His own so closely he suspects,
An' her answers to his questions tell
Him she's his daughter, 'live and well.

Now that he knows her ancestry,
Lysichamus requests that he
Might be allowed to court her and
In marriage win Marina's hand.

Pericles, while sleeping, dreams
Diana, the love-goddess seems
To call on him with this advice:
If he will offer sacrifice
In her Ephesian Temple, then
He'll be the happiest of men.

*　　　　*　　　　*

They go to Ephesus to do
What Diana told him to
And there, before her altar, he
Finds Thaisa, 'cause there she
Is serving as the high-priestess
To the fertility goddess.

Marina, then, and her birth-mother
Lovingly embrace each other,
And everybody is delighted
That their family's reunited.

The fact that he will have to part
From Juliet just breaks his heart.
But ere he goes he will delight
In Juliet's company for one night.

ROMEO AND JULIET

Who's Who:

ROMEO, *son of Montague, falls in love with Lord Capulet's daughter, Juliet.*

BENVOLIO, *Lord Montague's nephew; Romeo's cousin and close friend.*

MERCUTIO, *a relative of the Prince and Romeo's companion.*

TYBALT, *Lady Capulet's hot-headed nephew.*

LORD *Capulet.*

NURSE *to Juliet.*

JULIET, *Capulet's daughter who secretly marries Romeo Montague.*

FRIAR LAURENCE, *a Franciscan.*

PRINCE OF VERONA.

PARIS, *a young Nobleman a relative of the Prince.*

In Verona town, in Italy,
Two Houses, both nobility,
Named Montague and Capulet,
Have fought like cats, whene'er they've met.
The reason for their enmity
Is lost in dim antiquity.

Now, Romeo Montague, 'twould seem,
Fell for a lass named Rosaline.
His friend, Benvolio, does profess
She'd win a prize for ugliness,

*Benvolio is Romeo's cousin
and close friend.*

Though, just to prove that love is blind,
No fault in her can Romeo find.
But though he fancies her a lot,
Responsive, Rosaline is not.

Benvolio vows to extricate
His friend from such an ugly fate.

And then the Capulets extend
An invitation to attend
A dinner party they are throwin'
For friends and neighbours, in their home,
To stimulate some fun they ask
That every guest should wear a mask.

Of course, if you're a Montague
You're not invited to this do.
But Romeo, Benvolio,

Mercutio, a relative of the And their friend, Mercutio,
Prince, is another close Very heavily disguised,
friend of Romeo.
So that they won't be recognised,
Decide that they are going to crash
The Capulet's exclusive bash.

Romeo is very keen;
He's hoping to meet Rosaline.

Because this party will be brimmin'
With lots of beautiful young women,
Benvolio feels that Rosaline should
Be well outshone in pulchritude.
He's hoping that his friend will find
A Beauty that will change his mind

And induce the termination
Of Romeo's infatuation.

Benvolio's plan comes to fruition
When Romeo spies an apparition
Entering the Banquet Hall.
He thinks this Beauty outshines all
The other girls he's ever met
In all the life that he's lived yet.

Great admiration he expresses;
But Tybalt overhears and guesses
'Tis Romeo, a Montague
And seeks a sword to run him through.
Old Capulet, to avoid a scene,
Will not let Tybalt vent his spleen.
With rage the hot-head is still boiling;
For a fight with Romeo he's spoiling.

Tybalt is Lady Capulet's nephew.

Romeo doesn't have a clue
About what Tybalt tried to do.
He meets the girl; his chat-up line
Is a success and works just fine
And from the beautiful young Miss
He manages to steal a kiss.
But then before they get to know
Each other's names, she has to go.
He asks her nurse, 'Who is her mother?'
The nurse says that she is none other
Than the Lady Capulet,
And her daughter's name is Juliet.
The nurse it is who tells her too
That he is Romeo Montague.

*   *   *

The party's o'er and all the guests
Are going home to get some rest,
But Romeo has lost his heart
And is reluctant to depart.
The lovesick youth decides to linger
Underneath his new love's window,
Ecstatic, knowing that he's near
The one, whom now, he holds most dear.
His heart jumps quite excitedly,
When she walks on her balcony.
And then, his heart jumps once again
To hear her voice caress his name.
And Oh! what joy, when up above
Juliet proclaims her love,
Although she doesn't know that he
Is listening 'neath her balcony.
Then he tells her he loves her too.
And she decides what they should do
As for each other then, this pair
Undying mutual love declare.
And then before she goes to bed
She tells him they must soon be wed.

*   *   *

By now a new day's dawn is breaking,
And Romeo's heart, with love, is aching,
As he makes his way to see
Laurence is a Franciscan   Friar Laurence in his monastery.
Friar that Romeo trusts.   The Friar agrees to wed these two
Believing that good will ensue
And that the marriage of these spouses
Will end the feud between their Houses,
Though all agree it's far too soon
To tell their families what they're doin'.

Following their marriage rite
The couple separate, till night.

*   *   *

As Romeo, heart full of joy's
Going home, he hears some noise.
His friend, Mercutio, has met
The fiery Tybalt Capulet,
And Tybalt is still feeling sore
About events the night before.
They're trading insults, left and right;
And Tybalt's spoiling for a fight.
When he calls Romeo a villain,
Mercutio is more than willin'
To fight, but he is injured badly,
And his wounds prove fatal, sadly.
But Tybalt still wants Romeo's blood,
And Romeo believes he should
Avenge his cousin's death, and so
They face each other, toe to toe.
The outcome's fatal, once again
But this time Tybalt 'tis who's slain.

For Tybalt's death, the Prince is gonna
Banish Romeo from Verona.

Romeo who's with Friar Laurence,
Is filled with absolute abhorrence.
The fact that he will have to part
From Juliet just breaks his heart.
But ere he goes he will delight
In Juliet's company for one night.
That night is full of sweetest sorrow
For Romeo must leave tomorrow.

Alas, too soon, the break of day
Bids Romeo be on his way.

*   *   *

Her father always likes to vet
The guys who fancy Juliet.
And now a rich young gentleman
Has asked him for his daughter's hand.
Her Dad is sure this guy he's found
Suits Juliet down to the ground.
The Count of Paris, he can tell,
Will treat his daughter very well
And that is why Lord Capulet
Says he may marry Juliet.

Of course, her father doesn't know
That she has married Romeo.

*   *   *

She takes her problem, in distress,
For good Friar Laurence to address.
The Friar declares its resolution
Demands a desperate solution.
He has a potion, in a phial,
Which, if she drinks, after a while,
All signs of life 'twill over-ride,
And everyone will think she's died.
The potion's power will not default
Before she's buried in the vault.

Friar Laurence says all will go well.
He'll send a messenger to tell
Their desperate plan to Romeo,
In Mantua, to let him know
He must return to be there when
His bride 'comes back to life' again.
Together then, they will embrace
And go and live some other place.

*   *   *

The night before she is to wed
She drinks the potion; goes to bed.
Next morning, Paris has no bride;
It seems that Juliet has died.
Verona's people all believe
That she has died and come to grieve,
And weep to see her body blessed,
And taken to be laid to rest.

*   *   *

It's ever so, when there's disaster —
Bad news always travels faster.
The Friar's envoy's overtaken,
And Romeo's whole world is shaken.
The only news to reach his ears
Is of her death, which, when he hears
He pledges to go to her tomb
And kill himself in that same room.
Then he sets off without delay,
And buys some poison on the way.

*   *   *

With pick and crow-bar, an assault
He makes upon his sweetheart's vault.

The Count of Paris is upset
About the loss of Juliet.
Because he's suffering from grief
Sleep doesn't come to give relief.
Afraid that if he sleeps he'll dream
He walks down to her mausoleum
Where he's confronted by the sight
[quite indistinct because it's night]
Of some guy trying to burglarise
The crypt where Juliet's body lies.
But when he tries to apprehend
The vandal, Paris meets his end
By Romeo's hand, 'cause it is he
The Count confronts combatively.

The lad's intent on going inside
For one last look at his dead bride.
When Romeo opens up the tomb
And sees laid out in that cold room
The body of his darling wife,
He takes the poison and his life.

Then Juliet gives a little cough —
And, as the wonder-drug wears off
She sees her husband on the floor,
And knowing he'll arise no more
She takes a knife and one last breath,
And then, she stabs herself to death.

When Laurence, later, tells the tale
It makes their fathers' faces pale,
Because, at last, they come to see
That 'twas their stupid enmity —
The hatred, feuding and the strife —
Caused each to lose a dear child's life.

They swear, in future, to be friends.
That's how this play of Shakespeare's ends.

That, if Antonio can't repay,
He will let Shylock cut away
A pound of flesh from off whichever
Part of his body gives him pleasure.

THE
MERCHANT OF
VENICE

Who's Who:

ANTONIO, *a wealthy Merchant of Venice.*
BASSANIO, *his destitute friend.*
SHYLOCK, *a rich Jew, a money-lender.*
PORTIA, *a rich Heiress.*
DUKE OF VENICE.

The merchant of this tale, you know,
Is rich and called Antonio.
He imports silks and spices which,
O'er many years, have made him rich.
With all this wealth, so we are told,
He's bought more produce to be sold
As soon as e'er his ships reach shore.
This to his wealth will add some more.

Bassanio, the merchant's friend,
Has not a penny he can spend.
[The dosh he got when his Dad died,
He'd rashly squandered far and wide.]

In Belmont, there's a girl he's met
Who, at this time, is trying to get
A man with whom to share her life,
Whom he would like to be his wife.
He needs a loan to have a chance
To travel thither for romance.
The loan, he says, he will repay
As soon as ever he can lay

Portia is a rich heiress.
His hands on Portia's fortune which,
Once they are wed, will make him rich.

Alas! Alack! Ah, woe is he!
The merchant's money's all at sea.
But his good friend, Antonio,

Shylock is a Jewish money-lender.
Decides to Shylock he will go
And borrow money for his mate
Although Bassanio's profligate.

*   *   *

Shylock feels Antonio is
Taking business that is his.
He hates the merchant 'cause he lends
Money interest-free to friends
And slanders Jews and causes hurt
And treats them all like they were dirt.

They start negotiating and
Antonio's asking for three grand
Which Shylock will advance if he'll
Sign his name to this strange deal:
That, if Antonio can't repay,
He will let Shylock cut away
A pound of flesh from off whichever
Part of his body gives him pleasure.

You'd wonder if Antonio's sane;
With all to lose and naught to gain,
He funds Bassanio to acquire
The object of his heart's desire.

*   *   *

Portia's father, R.I.P.,
Three caskets had locked with a key.
On each he had inscribed a few
Words, as a sort of cryptic clue.
In only one, though, did he place
A picture of his daughter's face.
The man who opens this box will
All of his hopes and dreams fulfil,
For Portia's Dad, before he died,
Who she should wed had specified:
The wise and loving man he knew
'Twould take to figure out his clue.

Each suitor, though, must first agree,
Before he makes his choice, that he
Will swear an oath that, should he choose
One of the others, he will lose
His right to ever take a wife
And must stay single all his life!

Noble men, from far and wide,
Have come to Belmont and have tried
Their luck deciphering the clues.
Each hoped to be the one to choose
The casket — silver, gold or lead —
Containing, so her Dad had said,
Portia's portrait, meaning he
Could take her, matrimonially.

Happily all efforts failed
Until Bassanio's prevailed.
And Portia's very pleased 'tis he
Has won her in this lottery.
To seal the deal she doesn't linger;
She slips a ring onto his finger.
He promises that there 'twill stay
Until forever and a day.

Just then a messenger arrives
With news to shatter their young lives.
The substance of this tragic tale:
A storm, right off the Beaufort scale,
Caught all Antonio's ships at sea
Resulting in calamity.
His wealth and fortune, at a stroke,
Have gone, and now Antonio's broke.

Repayment is now overdue
Of what he borrowed from the Jew.
And Shylock thinks that's really neat
'Cause he can claim his pound of meat.

Bassanio and Portia try,
Their friend Antonio's debt to buy.
But Shylock, who's consumed by hate,
Refuses to co-operate,
And from his contract he won't budge.
The case goes to the Duke to judge.
Bassanio rushes off to court
To lend Antonio support.

*   *   *

A learned counsel Portia knows,
And from him borrows lawyer's clothes.
She picks his brains, and quickly learns
To argue well, in legal terms.
But in those days, so long gone by,
'Twas only men could qualify
To practise in a court of law —
A rule that sticks in Portia's craw.
She isn't just a pretty face;
She means to fight Antonio's case.

The court officials do not twig
'Tis she who, 'neath a lawyer's wig,
Confounds the Duke and everyone.
They are surprised a 'man' so young,
[That 'tis a woman they can't tell]
Should know the law so very well.

Then, greatly to the Jew's delight,
The lawyer declares he has the right
To cut flesh from Antonio,
But pleads that he should mercy show
And take three times the debt instead
[And that's an awful lot of bread].
Shylock merely hones the knife
He'll use to take Antonio's life.
But then his glee is turned to pain.
He hears that fresh-faced lawyer sayin'
The contract has a fatal flaw,
For, while it says he may, by law,
Remove a pound of flesh, he should
Not spill a single drop of blood!

Then Shylock, sounding very brash,
Says that he'll settle for the cash!
Not only is the cash refused,
But now, because he has abused
The legal system, he is told
To pay a fine of half his gold.
The Duke says too, the rest must go
To compensate Antonio.
But if he'll give up being a Jew
To be a Christian, good and true,
And make a will that recognises
Another good man he despises —
The Christian son-in-law he's spurned —
Antonio's share will be returned.
That's how Antonio, the saint,
Shows he's got class while Shylock ain't!

*   *   *

Bassanio then tries to pay
The lawyer who has won the day.
And though he offers anything
The lawyer only wants the ring —
The one that Portia made him swear
He would forever, always, wear.
Reluctantly he parts with it
Not relishing one little bit,
Explaining, as he'll have to now,
Why he, so quickly, broke that vow.

With heavy heart he meets his bride;
The ringless finger he can't hide.
When he confesses what he's done
His wife decides to have some fun.
She tells him she can't understand
How he could give away that band.

He says, when he attempted to
Pay the learned counsel who
Had saved Antonio from the knife
That Shylock honed to take his life,
The lawyer said the only thing
'He' would accept was Portia's ring.
He first refused, then thought 'twas rude
To show so little gratitude.

Portia feigns being in a huff
And claims that she is mad enough
That, should she ever chance to meet
That lawyer, she will freely treat
Him to comfort and delights
And let him share her bed at night.
Bassanio says that he repents;
Assures her that, if she relents,
He'll ne'er again — to this he'll swear —
Break any promise made to her.
Antonio says he'll guarantee
Bassanio's sincerity.
Portia reckons it's now time
To end her little pantomime.
When she discloses everything
And gives him back the purloined ring
Bassanio is really pleased
To find that he was just being teased.
And the guys are well impressed
To learn that it was Portia dressed
In lawyer's robes that cleverly
Ensured Antonio walked free.

The tale thus ends in fun and laughter
And all live happy ever after!

From upstairs, Mrs Page comes down
With 'Mrs Prat' in 'her' large gown.

THE MERRY WIVES OF WINDSOR

Who's Who:

SIR JOHN FALSTAFF, *a work-shy knight with no moral compass.*

SHALLOW, *a Country Justice who wants Anne Page to marry his cousin.*

ANNE PAGE, *in love with Fenton.*

SLENDER, *Shallow's tongue-tied, shy cousin.*

SIR HUGH EVANS, *a Welsh Parson.*

MISTRESS QUICKLY, *Dr Caius's servant.*

PETER SIMPLE, *Slender's servant.*

DR CAIUS, *a French Physician.*

MRS FORD,
MRS PAGE, } *the Merry Wives of Windsor*

PISTOL & NYM, *followers of Falstaff.*

FORD, *a gentleman of means who suspects his wife is unfaithful.*

BROOK, *Ford in disguise.*

PAGE, *a gentleman of means, Anne Page's father.*

FENTON, *a young gentleman in love with Anne Page.*

HOST *of the Garter Inn.*

John Falstaff is a rotund knight
Whose girth is greater than his height.
He beat up Justice Shallow's men
And broke into his lodge and then
Went out and killed one of his deer,
And says that he has got no fear
Of being arrested 'cause ever after
Shallow'd be the butt of laughter.

Falstaff is a knight with very questionable morals.

Shallow is a Country Justice, a gentleman of status in Windsor.

*   *   *

There's a young woman in these parts
Who's stirring many young men's hearts;
Anne Page is one good-looking honey
And she is coming into money.
She's cultured, self-assured and kind,
Has character and strength of mind.
Shallow's got a cousin and
He'd like for him to win her hand,
But Slender's very shy and he
Gets tongue-tied very easily,
And 'cause he's shy he isn't good
At making himself understood.

Anne Page has a number of suitors.

Slender is Justice Shallow's cousin and one of Anne Page's suitors.

Pastor Evans, Shallow's friend,
Says he can some assistance lend;
He knows a woman who knows Anne;
He'll write and ask her if she can
Put in a good word and thus render
A helping leg-up to young Slender.
He writes to Mrs Quickly and
Asks Peter Simple, Slender's man
To take the note immediately
And give it to the addressee,

Sir Hugh Evans is a Welsh parson and friend of the Ford and Page families.

Mrs Quickly is a friend of Anne Page.

Simple is Slender's servant.

Who promises she'll recommend
Young Slender to Anne Page, her friend.

Mrs Quickly mends and sews
And cooks and cleans and washes clothes
For Dr Caius, a single man
Who hopes to win Anne Page's hand.

There's also a young gent named Fenton
Tells Mrs Quickly he's intent on
Doing everything he can
To be the one to marry Anne.

Fenton is the one with whom Anne Page is in love.

      *   *   *

Falstaff's nearly stoney-broke
But he is not the kind of bloke
To look for work to raise some dough
If there's an easier way to go.
'Cause of his straightened circumstances
He needs some help with his finances.
With the ladies he's proactive
Believing they find him attractive,
So Mrs Page he's going to try
[He's sure she's given him the eye],
And Mrs Ford must like men bigger
The way she's eyeing up his figure,
And each of them is in sole charge
Of sums of money, very large.
He's sure with sexual panache
He'll separate them from some cash.
He writes to each of the above
Declaring his desire and love,
And asks his two mates, Nym and Pistol,
Each to deliver an epistle,

Mrs Page is one of the merry wives.

Mrs Ford is the second merry wife.

Nym & Pistol are followers of Falstaff.

But they refuse — they've had enough
Of Falstaff and his dodgy stuff.
And they tell Messrs Page and Ford

Page & Ford are two rich gentlemen, the husbands of the merry wives.

Of Falstaff's vile intentions toward
Their wives whom he plans to beguile
And have in bed in a wee while.

Mrs Page is greatly peeved
'Cause of the letter she's received
From Falstaff wherein saucily
He propositions her saying he
And she like fun and any night
He'll help her fancy to take flight.
And Mrs Ford says that she too
Received the self-same billet-doux;
And she is also quite upset,
And both decide they want to get
Revenge on Falstaff for the way
He's brazenly assumed that they
Are so immoral and so sly
They'd leave their husbands high and dry.
[' Course neither one would break the vows
She took when marrying her spouse.]
They plan that they'll humiliate
The horrid, nasty reprobate:
They'll let him think they are disposed
To meet with him as he's proposed.

From Mrs Quickly Falstaff hears
He's made his mark with these two dears;
That Mrs Ford says she's no doubt
From ten her husband will be out
And for an hour she will be free
To entertain him amorously.

And Mrs Page regrets to say
Her husband seldom goes away
But she is waiting in suspense
For his next expedition hence.

*   *   *

Mr Ford's a jealous wuss;
He fears his wife's adulterous.
As Mr Brook he masquerades

Mr Brook is Ford disguised to deceive Falstaff.

And speaks with Falstaff and persuades
The dirty knight that he will pay
To have the woman led astray.
Brook explains he's been pursuing
Mrs Ford in hopes of wooing
Her, but she's said "no", 'cause she
'S a model of fidelity.
If Falstaff proves that that's a lie
She'll not be able to deny
That Brook can have her in his arms
And in her bed enjoy her charms.
Falstaff says they have a deal;
He's heard from Mrs Ford and he'll
Be meeting her at ten [about]
'Cause then her husband will be out.

Ford plans to catch her in the act
When she's with Falstaff in the sack!

As the time approaches ten
Mrs Ford and her best friend
Have made the final preparation
For Falstaff's first humiliation.

When into Ford's house he is shown
Mrs Ford is all alone
And she is very obviously
Receptive to his flattery.
But his expressions of devotion
Are interrupted by commotion,
As Mrs Page, in consternation,
Comes with distressing information
That Mr Ford and half the town
[Good friends of his] are coming round.
His wife, he knows with certainty,
Is acting inappropriately
And, with some fellow's all aglow
In flagrante delicto.
If they can't get the knight away
There surely will be hell to pay.
The women push the knight inside
A laundry basket where he'll hide
While servants lift it and proceed
To take it down to Dachet-mead
And leave it in the tender care
Of the laundress working there.

Ford finds no shred of evidence
When he looks through his residence.

*   *   *

The knight meets Brook and talks about
The strange way that events turned out;
How in the river he was thrown
And sank like the proverbial stone,
Though, as the water wasn't deep,
He managed to the bank to creep.

The knight says he's determined to
Go back to Mrs Ford and do
Whatever it is must be done
For him and her to have their fun.
As she's arranged another date
The service will resume at eight.

Falstaff's barely in the door
When Mrs Page arrives once more
To warn that Ford comes home again
Accompanied by many men.
And he's insisting he is right:
His Mrs entertains the knight.
Lest Falstaff, in a panic, legs it
He's placed armed guards at every exit.

Mrs Ford has got a maid
Whose big fat aunt at one time stayed
And when she left, forgot to pack
A dress for which she's not come back
'Cause Ford dislikes her with a passion
And threatened to give her a thrashin'.
He's said that he won't entertain
That woman in his house again.

As he comes in with Mr Page
Ford is clearly in a rage
And when he spies the laundry basket
He very nearly blows a gasket;
He flings the contents in the air
But finds no trace of Falstaff there.
From upstairs Mrs Page comes down
With 'Mrs Prat' in her large gown
[That woman that he cannot stand
To such extent that he has banned

This is Falstaff wearing Mrs Prat's voluminous dress.

Her from his house]; and with a roar
He thumps and kicks 'her' out the door.
The search ensues trying to discover
Mrs Ford's be-knighted lover,
But there is neither hide nor hair
Of any cuckold-maker there.

*   *   *

The merry wives have had their fun
And tell their husbands what they've done,
And Ford admits he now has learned
He never should have been concerned,
'Cause his wife's the epitome
Of marital fidelity.
Then, all together, they agree
The randy knight deserves to be
Made to suffer such disgrace
That he will totally lose face.

The women write a billet-doux
And then ask Mrs Quickly to
Take it to the pompous knight
And tell him, in the dead of night
They'll meet him where they'll all make free
In Windsor Park beneath a tree.
They say, though, that it would be wise
For him to dress up in disguise:
'Cause rumour says it's hereabout
That Herne-the-hunter's ghost comes out.
If Falstaff wears a big buck's head
He'll fill stray passers-by with dread.

Locals believe that the ghost of Herne, a one-time gamekeeper, roams the Park at night.

Evans says he'll organise
A gang of kids dressed in disguise
And teach them how they are supposed
To torment Herne-the-hunter's ghost
'Cause they're all going for a lark
In moonlight down in Windsor Park.

*   *   *

Fenton's in the Garter Inn
Conversing with the Host therein.

The Host, or Landlord, of the Garter Inn.

He says the Pages don't agree
On whom their daughter's spouse should be.
Page thinks Slender would be grand;
His wife thinks Caius should win her hand.
And each of them, so it would seem,
Has come up with the self-same scheme:
While Anne is like a fairy dancing
And with the other elves is prancing
'Round Herne-the-hunter in the dark
She'll slip away out of the park
With her suitor, who they swear
Will know her by the dress she'll wear.
Her father's told her to wear white
So Slender'll know her in the night.
Her mother's told her to wear green
So that by Caius she'll be seen.
But Anne can't think of anything duller
So she'll dress in a different colour;
Leave both these fellows in the lurch
While she and Fenton head for church.

Fenton says Anne Page and he
Will need to marry hurriedly
And asks the Host if he will try
To have the vicar on stand-by
In church to, later on tonight,
Administer the marriage rite.

*   *   *

Then to the park [they said they would]
Both women come; Wow! Things look good
And Falstaff's luck improves apace
As he and Mrs Ford embrace.
But then they hear noise coming near
And both the women disappear.
Falstaff's totally confounded
When suddenly he is surrounded:
Hobgoblins, fairies, apparitions
With songs and chants and repetitions
Hold tapers to his fingers sayin',
"If he be chaste, he'll feel no pain."
They pinch and poke him, make him sweat
And rant and scare him half to death.
Then, at a signal, they all flee
And he's back in reality.

And then the Pages and the Fords
Come back to have a few more words.
With glee they mock the knight and chide
Him for his arrogance and pride
Till he admits he has been crass
And acting like a silly ass.
He promises to make amends,
And all of them end up being friends.

And then the Pages realise
That Anne's rejected both their guys.
She's disobeyed them and instead,
'Cause she loves Fenton, they've been wed.

Her husband, though 'tis not yet noon,
Remarks, "How brightly shines the moon".
When Katharine says that everyone
Must surely see that that's the sun.

THE
TAMING OF
THE SHREW

Who's Who:

INDUCTION:

A LORD.

CHRISTOPHER SLY, *a Tinker.*

A PAGE

SERVANTS

THE PLAY:

LUCENTIO, *a university student in love with Bianca.*

BAPTISTA, *a rich gentleman of Padua.*

BIANCA, *Baptista's younger daughter.*

KATHARINE, *the Shrew, Baptista's elder daughter.*

GREMIO & HORTENSIO, *rivals for Bianca, seeking Baptista's approval.*

TRANIO, *Lucentio's servant.*

CAMBIO, *Lucentio disguised as a tutor.*

PETRUCHIO, *a Gentleman of Verona who wishes to marry Katharine.*

GRUMIO, *Petruchio's servant.*

LICIO, *Hortensio disguised as a music teacher.*

A WIDOW *who marries Hortensio.*

A TAILOR.

VINCENTIO, *an old gentleman of Pisa, Lucentio's father.*

INDUCTION:

The lord just happens to ride by
And in the gutter, sees Chris Sly,
A man who is by trade a tinker
And by choice a heavy drinker
Who visited the Inn and chose
To drink till he was comatose.
The lord tells servants to transport
Sly to his castle for some sport;
To bathe and dress him so that he
Will look like he's nobility.
And when he regains consciousness
The lord tells them they're to address
The tinker with great reverence
And treat him with great deference
And by their every deed and word
Try to persuade him he's their lord
Who has for years past been insane
But, thankfully, 's now well again;
That, in the throes of lunacy,
'His Lordship' thought himself to be
A commoner with lowly roots
Who followed common folk's pursuits;
And family and friends are pleased
His mind no longer is diseased.
In drag, a page is masqueraded
And Sly is finally persuaded
This lovely 'Lady of the house'
Is his ever-loving spouse;
That he's a lord and 'she's' his wife
Both born into this noble life.
'She' says the doc says he'd advise
[Though 'she' would wish it otherwise]

From sex and stuff they should refrain
Until his mind is strong again,
And that 'twill do his mind some good
To keep him in light-hearted mood.
An acting troupe asks if they may
Present a very funny play;
'His Lordship' and his 'wife' agree
They'll sit and watch this comedy.

THE PLAY:

Lucentio, a Pisa lad,
Has come to be an undergrad
At the university
Of Padua, in Italy.
He's only reached the city when
He overhears a group of men
And women earnestly debate;
It seems that two men wish to date
The younger daughter of the third.
Baptista thinks 'twould be absurd;
He says Bianca has to wait
Until her elder sister, Kate,
Has got a fellow and that she
Is settled matrimonially.
Meanwhile Bianca needs a tutor
Rather than a lusty suitor.
Hortensio and Gremio
[Each hopes to be Bianca's beau]
Know that the chances aren't great
Of finding Katharine a mate,
['Cause who'd want to be married to
A carping, sharp-tongued, scolding shrew?].

*Lucentio is a young
university student from
Pisa.*

*Baptista is a rich
gentleman of Padua.*

*Bianca is Baptista's
younger daughter.*

*Katharine is Baptista's
elder daughter.*

*Hortensio & Gremio are
middle-aged suitors to
Bianca.*

They say they'll work together till
Bianca's free to choose who will
Be the lucky guy that she
Will choose to wed eventually.

Lucentio's thoughts have taken flight
He loves Bianca at first sight;
So straightaway he does propose

Tranio is Lucentio's servant.

That Tranio and he swap clothes.
As Cambio he will, he's sure,

Cambio is Lucentio disguised as a teacher.

The job of teaching her procure.
So he goes to Bianca's home;
Starts teaching her 'bout Greece and Rome
And, as her tutor, hopes that he
Can court her surreptitiously.
And Tranio, his servant, will
Pretend to be Lucentio till
Bianca is his wife, and then
They'll change back to themselves again.

      *   *   *

Petruchio is a young gentleman from Verona.

A Verona man, Petruchio
Is visiting Hortensio.
The reason he's come to this town
Is that he wants to settle down.
He asks Hortensio, his friend,
If there's a lass he'd recommend;
There's only one proviso which is
She must be well-endowed with riches.
Hortensio thinks that Katharine will
Almost surely fit the bill.
She's pretty and her Daddy's rich
But there's one disadvantage which
Is known to cause men aggravation
And that's her shrewish reputation.
Surprisingly, Petruchio

Is only interested in dough.

Grumio, his servant, thinks
He'll get the better of the minx
And, if she's shrewish, she will find
Petruchio'll pay her back in kind.

*   *   *

Tranio [dressed as his boss,
Lucentio] then comes across
Hortensio and Gremio
And to be fair he lets them know
That he, 'Lucentio', means to be
Bianca's suitor, number three.

*   *   *

Kate's jealous 'cause Bianca's got
A lot of beaux and she has not.
And this Bianca seems to flout
So Katharine gives her sis a clout.

*   *   *

Hortensio wants to gain access
To sweet Bianca, so he'll dress
As a musician of repute
And teach Baptista's girls the lute.
He's totally unrecognised
When, as Licio, he's disguised.
Baptista tells him to begin
To teach his eldest, Katharine,
But that bad-tempered malcontent
Just whacks him with his instrument.
He thinks perhaps that he should thank her,
When told instead to teach Bianca.

*   *   *

Bianca's tutors place some clues
In the lessons that they use.
They're trying to gain the inside track
Behind her Dad, Baptista's, back.
By using subterfuge and spin
Each hopes Bianca's heart to win.
She's more impressed by Cambio
Than by the older Licio.
Sure that his rival's won the race,
Hortensio gives up the chase;
And then, without delay, he goes
To court a widow that he knows.
She loves him, ' least that's what she's said,
And shortly after that they're wed.

*   *   *

Baptista says Petruchio may
Meet Katharine and make his play,
To speak with her and see if he
Thinks they could live in harmony.
Her every effort to insult
Him has the opposite result;
He takes her words and makes them seem
To say something she doesn't mean
Till her cantankerous word-play
Allows him say something risqué.
Again she shows her violent streak
And slaps Petruchio on the cheek.
Another similar attack
He says will mean he'll hit her back
Then, blithely goes on to express
How much he loves her gentleness,
Her sweetness, charm and her allure
Which all combine to make him sure

That they are meant to be together
Now, an' from this day on, forever.

Baptista, at this point, returns
And from Petruchio he learns
That Katharine and he agree
Next Sunday they will married be.
Kate says, in one last great outburst
She'll see him hanged on Sunday, first.
He says they bargained 'tween the two
In public, she'll still act the shrew;
Alone, she smothers him with kisses
Insisting she will be his Mrs.
When faced with this quite blatant lie
Kate's lost for words; makes no reply.
Dad, happy that she's got a man,
The wedding-feast goes off to plan.
And Petrucio says he goes
To Venice to buy wedding clothes.

On Sunday, Katharine's forced to wait
Because Petruchio is late
For their wedding ceremony.
She's even more upset when he
Arrives in garb he says will do
Although it's very far from new.
And when their wedding vows they've said
He acts like he's a thoroughbred
Bad-mannered, crass and nasty lout
And starts to throw his weight about.
He knocks the vicar to the floor
And drinks some wine and calls for more
And then on top of all of this
He loudly gives his bride a kiss.

And then insists that they are gonna,
Straightaway, leave for Verona.
But Kate objects saying there's no way
She's going anywhere today;
Invites the guests into the hall
To join the feast and have a ball.
Petruchio reacts like he
'S concerned for Katharine's safety;
Tells Grumio to draw his sword
And save his mistress from this horde;
Claims, as his wife, she does belong
To him and so must come along.

*   *   *

He'll tame this shrew the way one might
Train a falcon or a kite;
He'll keep her hungry and awake,
And thus her feisty spirit break.
He claims her food's contaminated;
Would make her nauseous if she ate it;
With constant fuss and chat denies
Her any chance to shut her eyes.
All this, Petruchio declares
He's doing for her because he cares.

This 'taming' will continue till
She is submissive to his will.

A tailor brings a cap and gown
That he has diligently sewn.
Petruchio immediately
Finds fault with Kate's new millinery.
He says the cap is much too small;
His wife says that's not so at all

And when she says she loves the dress
Her husband claims it is a mess,
And he insists that Katharine
Must travel in the clothes she's in
As they return to see her Da
Back in her home-town, Padua.

He says it's seven now so they
Should reach her Dad's around midday.
But she points out it's after two;
Thinks supper-time's the best they'll do.
He tells her, as he is the boss,
She can't be arguing the toss.
The time he says it is, is right
And she must learn not to deny 't.

Next morning as they're travelling
The sun shines bright and small birds sing
Her husband, though 'tis not yet noon,
Remarks, "How brightly shines the moon".
When Katharine says that everyone
Must surely see that that's the sun.
Petruchio says he's getting sick at
Constantly being contradicted
And says they'll turn their horses roun'
And head back to Verona town
And won't go to her Dad's until
She learns to be agreeable.
So Kate agrees she'll sing his tune
And says, "Of course it is the moon".
And, from now on, she says, if he
Says black is white, she will agree.

They've travelled on a mile or two
When an old man comes into view.
Petruchio tells her to embrace
This woman with the lovely face.
Without a word she does comply
And straightaway she hugs the guy;
Then asks him pardon what she's done
Saying she was dazzled by the sun.
Petruchio is quite impressed
That Kate has passed another test.
Old Vincentio's the Dad
Of Lucentio, the undergrad
And he is on his way to see
His son at university
In Padua, so it makes sense
To join them on their journey hence.

*　　　*　　　*

Bianca and Lucentio
[Her erstwhile tutor, Cambio]
Have found a priest who secretly
Performed their wedding ceremony.
Though neither of the spouses sought
Their Dad's permission, as they ought,
Baptista and Vincentio now
Say they are happy to allow
The marriage stand, and they will bless
Their offsprings' shot at happiness.

The newly-weds invite a few
To join them for a wedding do.
Three weddings they must celebrate:
Their own, and though a little late,
The widow's to Hortensio
An' Katharine's to Petruchio.

When everyone's stuffed to the craw,
And ladylike the wives withdraw,
Each husband boasts his wife will do
Whatever he requests her to.
So they propose a little test
To see which wife proves to be best.
They'll each send for his wife and see
Which one responds most speedily.
And each guy bets a massive sum
That his will be the first to come.
Lucentio's the first to send
To ask Bianca to attend,
But she refuses, saying she
Is much too busy, currently.
And when Hortensio requests
The widow come, she says he jests,
But if he thinks they must confer
Then he is free to come to her.
Then Grumio's sent to Katharine and
Relays Petruchio's command
To come to him immediately
And she responds obediently.
She tells the wives that each one needs
To follow where her husband leads
An' submit to his authority
'Cause he's head of the family.
She's learned a wife must never cross
Her husband, 'cause he is the boss.

They find a table that's replete
With all the food that they might eat.
Alas, before they can partake,
A flying Harpy makes them quake.

THE TEMPEST

Who's Who:

PROSPERO, *the rightful Duke of Milan.*

ANTONIO, *his brother, who usurped Prospero's title and domains.*

ALONSO, *King of Naples who, at Antonio's behest, had dispossessed and banished Prospero.*

MIRANDA, *Prospero's daughter.*

GONZALO, *an honest Counsellor who remained loyal to Prospero.*

CALIBAN, *a savage, deformed sub-human slave, the offspring of Sycorax, a wicked witch.*

ARIEL, *an airy Spirit with magic powers.*

FERDINAND, *King Alonso's son who falls in love with Miranda.*

SEBASTIAN, *King Alonso's brother.*

TRINCULO, *a Jester.*

STEPHANO, *a drunken Butler.*

A ship's tossed on the raging seas;
Aboard, the noble families
Of Naples and Milan don't know
They're soon to meet with Prospero
Who'd ruled Milan for quite a while
Before being banished to this isle.
For all the time that he was Duke
He'd had his head stuck in a book
Perusing many arcane tracts
In search of occult skills and facts.

Prospero is the exiled Duke of Milan

His younger brother was the one
He had employed, Milan to run.

*Antonio is Prospero's
younger brother.*

Antonio though, began to lust
For all the power and broke the trust
That Prospero had, in him, placed,
And to the King of Naples raced
And swore he'd be the King's true man
If he were made Duke of Milan.

With Naples' power, Antonio's guile
Saw Prospero and his only child,
Miranda, who was only three,
Exiled, from whence they could not flee.

*Gonzalo is an honest
old Counsellor, loyal to
Prospero.*

Gonzalo, Prospero's loyal friend,
Contrived, in secrecy, to send
His books to him so he would find
The means to exercise his mind,
For there was not a single trace
Of other humans, in this place.

*Caliban is an ugly,
sub-human slave.*

*Sycorax, Caliban's
mother, had been a
cruel witch.*

There was a thing called Caliban
A monstrous brute, not quite a man,
Spawned by Sycorax, a witch
Who used dark spells and powers which
The spirits of the isle found tragic
With no defence against her magic.
The only talent Caliban had
Was he was good at being bad.
Prospero worked him very hard
In return for bed and board.

As years went by his brainy daughter
Learned everything that Prospero taught her.
Now, beautiful and erudite,
Though living like a troglodyte,
He thinks that she deserves a chance
To have a shot at real romance.

*   *   *

Many, many years before,
When first they'd set foot on this shore
He'd found a howling, captive Sprite
Who, in a tree, had been locked tight
By Sycorax, that horrid dam
Who'd given birth to Caliban.
She'd died, so Ariel seemed condemned
To captivity without an end,
Till learned Prospero found the key
To set the captive spirit free.
Then Ariel, in light-hearted mood,
Declared, with deepest gratitude,
His magic he'd henceforward use
However Prospero should choose.

Ariel is a fairy-like Sprite with magic powers.

*   *   *

Recently, Alonso's been
Informed his daughter's to be Queen
Of Tunis, and this means that she's
Going to get married overseas.
He and the friends he has invited
Are all excited and delighted
And getting ready for this trip
Aboard a sturdy sailing ship.

By arcane means old Prospero
Their travel plans had come to know.
He called on Ariel's powers to force
The King of Naples' ship off course.
That's how this Tempest came to be
That lashes their ship violently.
Now Ariel makes those nobles think
Their creaking craft's about to sink.
Scared witless by the storm's great roar
They abandon ship and swim for shore.
They all make land-fall safe and sound
In small groups scattered all around.
But none of those that have survived
Knows that the others are alive.

*   *   *

Prince Ferdinand is heir to the throne of Naples.

Prince Ferdinand, Alonso's son,
Who's come to shore all on his own,
The unseen Ariel's voice hears tell
That Naples' King drowned in the swell.
His grief's forgotten when he sees
This Beauty in among the trees:

Miranda is Prospero's daughter.

Miranda, whom he thinks divine,
Her beauty is just so sublime.

And her heart, too, swells with delight;
For her, it is love at first sight.

Believing that his Dad is dead,
'Cause that's what Ariel had said,
The first young man she's ever seen
Then asks her to become his Queen.

But Prospero thinks it would be best
To put their young love to the test.
The lad, he says, is making vile
And treacherous plans to steal his isle.
So he takes out his magic wand
And casts a spell on Ferdinand
Who finds that now he wants to do
Whatever Prospero tells him to.

He works him like a lumberjack —
The toil near breaks the Prince's back —
Miranda cannot bear to see
Her new love used so cruelly.
She tells him he should rest awhile;
She'll shift the logs to the woodpile.
But chivalrous Prince Ferdinand
Just will not let her lend a hand.
And Prospero is quite impressed
By how the two have passed his test.
He gives them both his heartfelt blessing
But warns against pre-nuptial messing.

*   *   *

Elsewhere, the King of Naples sleeps
While traitors round about him creep.
Antonio, who'd usurped Milan,
Is winding up Sebastian
To cut the King of Naples down
And take his older brother's crown.
While Seb the dirty deed will do
Antonio'll run Gonzalo through.
Ariel, who is hovering near,
Whispers in Gonzalo's ear,

Sebastian is King Alonso's brother.

Who, startled, then wakes up in time
To cause them to abort the crime.

Alonso, then, his group leads on
To try to find his missing son.
The searchers search until footsore,
Their spirits low and sinking lower
From hunger and the lack of rest.
But then they think that they are blest;
They find a table that's replete
With all the food that they might eat.
Alas, before they can partake,

A Harpy is a mythical
monster with a woman's
face and body and the
wings and talons of a
vulture.

A flying Harpy makes them quake.
With lightning flash and thunder roll
Its wings, the banquet food enfold.
And all that lovely food has vanished
And still the King & Co are famished.
They try to draw their swords to kill
The Harpy, which is Ariel
In a monster-like disguise.
He casts a spell that leaves these guys
Too weak to raise their swords to fight
And tells them that their present plight
Has come about 'cause of the way
They had conspired back in the day,
And plotted with Antonio   .
To oust and banish Prospero.
For this betrayal they're told the cost
To Alonso, is his son's been lost.
Then in a flash, the Harpy's gone
An' Alonso and his group move on
Not realising that they now are
Under Prospero's magic power.

*   *   *

Caliban, out gathering fuel
Meets Trinculo, Royal Naples' Fool
And Stephano, the Butler who's
Found a stash of good strong booze.
Caliban, not used to drink,
Rebellious thoughts, begins to think.
[When in an alcoholic stupor
A tiny brain can think it's super.]
He claims that many years ago
The isle was his, but Prospero
Usurped his power and stole his land.
To get his own back, he has planned
That Stephano the isle can keep
If he'll kill Prospero in his sleep.
And then when Prospero is dead
He'll make Miranda share his bed.

Ariel hears them hatch this scheme,
And he decides to intervene,
And being a very clever fairy
Makes magic music, light and airy,
That puts the plotters in a trance
And makes their legs perform a dance.
The monster, butler and the fool
All dance into a stinking pool.
When they emerge they're sopping wet
And smelly too, and need to get
A dry and decent change of clothes,
And Caliban says that he knows
Where Prospero keeps a lot of spare
Attire that they can steal and wear.
But as they're trying on the gear
Ariel and his boss appear

Trincolo is the King of Naples' Jester.

Stephano is the King of Naples' Butler. He is a drunkard.

And Prospero decides that they
For all their evil deeds must pay.
Fierce hounds are conjured up to chase
The hapless trio 'round the place.

*   *   *

The King and his few followers still
Can't exercise their own free will.
They're brought before a kind of court
Where Prospero is holding forth.
There Prospero lifts the magic spell
So that their consciences can tell
The difference 'tween wrong and right
And on their deeds he shines a light.

Gonzalo's given thanks and praise.
The rest of them he then upbraids
For being treacherous and plotting
[And being absolutely rotten]
Enabling an unworthy man
Replace the true Duke of Milan.
The King's filled with remorse and so
Returns Milan to Prospero
Who dons his hat, straps on his sword.
Now, with his Dukely mien restored
He holds no grudge for what they've done
And therefore pardons everyone.

*   *   *

Alonso, though, is still upset
'Cause Ferdinand's not turned up yet,
So Prospero tells him all is well
And lets him look inside his cell.

And there he sees Miranda and
His only son, Prince Ferdinand
Are playing chess and obviously
Just love each other's company.
The Prince then tells his Dad they plan
To marry as soon as they can.

* * *

'Twas magic that had made them think
Their storm-tossed ship was going to sink.
Her officers now come to tell
The ship rides safely on the swell
And on her they will all be carried
To see Alonso's daughter married.

The Butler, Fool and Caliban
Must make his cell nice, spick and span
Then, Prospero says, they'll be forgiven
And can resume their 'normal' living.

Of magic, Prospero's had enough;
He takes his wand and books and stuff
And buries them beneath the ground
So deep they never will be found.

She says she's not at all impressed
By how her ardour's been expressed
And tells him he can keep his letter.
He says that he'll re-write it better.

THE TWO GENTLEMEN OF VERONA

Who's Who:

VALENTINE, *one of the Two Gentlemen of Verona, in love with Silvia.*
PROTEUS, *Valentine's friend from boyhood, the second of the Two Gentlemen.*
JULIA, *in love with Proteus.*
LUCETTA, *Julia's maid-in-waiting.*
ANTONIO, *Proteus's father.*
SILVIA, *in love with Valentine.*
SPEED, *Valentine's servant.*
DUKE OF MILAN, *Silvia's father.*
THURIO, *Valentine's rival for Silvia's hand who has her father's approval.*
SEBASTIAN, *Julia disguised as a boy.*
EGLAMOUR, *Silvia's useless and cowardly 'protector' in her escape.*
OUTLAWS *with Valentine.*

'Tis in Verona, Italy
That two young friends, till now carefree,
The closest pals from boyhood days,
Have reached the parting of their ways.

Valentine is one of the Two Gentlemen.

In search of honour, Valentine,
With Milan's Duke, will serve his time,

Proteus is the other of the Two Gentlemen.

While Proteus thinks 'tis sheer bliss
To love an independent Miss

Julia is a beautiful young lady of Verona.

Named Julia, who's playing hard to get,
So he's not made much progress yet.

Proteus has written her a letter

Lucetta is Julia's maid-in-waiting.

That, when delivered by Lucetta,
Her waiting-woman, Julia feigns
Indifference and pure disdain
And will not read to see what's in it,
And tells the maid to go and bin it.

Regretting her too hasty act
She calls her maid-in-waiting back
Because she wants to read the note
So she can see what Proteus wrote.
But, to the maid, she won't admit
She's interested one little bit.
No way she'll let Lucetta know
That she'd like Proteus for her beau.
She shreds the letter and what's more
She throws the pieces to the floor,
And tells Lucetta leave them there
And go, the dinner to prepare.

She gathers up the shredded letter
And tries to put it back together.
Some shreds she can unite and thus
She reads, 'love-wounded Proteus'.
To write back, she makes up her mind,
To 'poor forlorn Proteus' in kind.

Proteus thinks things can't get better
'Cause she's responded to his letter.
It says the love with which he burns
Her heart, with interest, returns.
That's when his father comes along
And asks him who the letter's from.
And in a panic he starts lying
And says that it's from Valentine
Who writes that life is really good
In Milan, and Proteus should
This new, exciting lifestyle share
And pack his bags and join him there.

Hoist with his own petard is he;
His father says he does agree.
Antonio doesn't think it's right

Antonio is Proteus's father.

That his son's idle day and night
While others of his age and station
Are travelling for education,
Or gone to war or on the tide
To seek adventure, far and wide.

So to Milan, without delay
Poor Proteus must make his way.
But first, there's one thing he must do;
To Julia he must bid adieu.
Rings they exchange, as symbols of
Their mutual, undying love.

*   *   *

'Way in Milan, the love bug's bitten
Valentine, who's truly smitten
By love of Silvia, to his mind

Silvia is the Duke of Milan's daughter.

The prettiest and most refined

Young lady he's been trying to woo
With many, many billets doux.

Seems 'twas a wasted exercise
Because his notes got no replies.
And then his pride takes quite a blow;
She asks him to write to her beau
To say her heartbeat throbs apace
When she imagines his embrace.
But, when one's suffering rejection,
It's hard to find words of affection
For this other guy who seems
To 've won the object of his dreams.
She says she's not at all impressed
By how her ardour's been expressed
And tells him he can keep his letter;
He says that he'll re-write it better.
She bids him read it when it's done
And, if he's happy with this one;
Its contents she won't need to view
And he can keep this letter too.

So he's to keep what he has written
To the guy with whom she's smitten
And Valentine is so confused
'Cause all his hard work won't be used.
Why keep her love so well expressed
From him to whom it is addressed?

Speed is Valentine's servant.

Speed solves the problem: obviously
The writer is the addressee,
Which means, he says, that all this time
The one she loves is Valentine.
Now knowing he's got the inside track,
To courting Silvia, he goes back.

*   *   *

The Duke thinks Thurio's the man
He'd like to win his daughter's hand,
But Silvia can't stand the bloke
An' with Valentine, means to elope.
And that's when Proteus arrives
And starts to mess up all their lives.

Thurio is Valentine's rival for Silvia's love.

Valentine tells his best friend
How he and Silvia intend
To steal away so they can be
United matrimonially.

Proteus's heart with envy's rotten,
His love for Julia is forgotten.
From when he first sees Silvia's face
He's in venality's embrace
And with desire begins to slaver
And schemes how he himself might have 'er.

Proteus hopes, if he can neuter
Valentine as Silvia's suitor,
That maybe he might stand a chance
To interest her in a romance.
And so he tells the Duke that she
And Valentine are going to flee
And secretly get married and
That for that night their flight is planned;
That when it's dark his daughter hopes
To use a ladder made from ropes
To climb down from the tower where he
Locks her each night, and takes the key.

The Duke considers this a crime
And banishes young Valentine.

Dishonoured and disgraced, he's gonna
Be unwelcome in Verona.

*   *   *

He has but half the journey made
When by a gang he is waylaid.
When they demand he give them money
He tells them that he hasn't any
And that he's on the road because
He killed a guy and broke some laws
And soon as e'er he had been banished
All prospects of good fortune vanished.
The outlaws tell him, some of them
At one time had been gentlemen
Until some misdemeanour meant
They, too, were faced with banishment.
Young Valentine's impressed them and
They now want him to lead their band.

*   *   *

Meanwhile Julia's all alone
And doesn't like being on her own.
She misses Proteus and so's
Getting dressed-up in men's clothes
To travel safely to Milan
Where she intends to join her man.

But when she gets there she's quite shaken
To find her lover serenading
Silvia who, though, has no time
For anyone but Valentine.
She's adamant that she won't go
With Proteus or Thurio.

Although he has betrayed her trust
Julia still loves Proteus.
So while she's still dressed as a boy
She gets a job in his employ
And now known as Sebastian
She is quite hopeful that she can
Keep an eye on what he's doing
And undermine his fickle wooing.

*　　　*　　　*

Silvia keeps on saying "no",
She will not marry Thurio.
The Duke intends to press her till
Eventually she'll say she will.
She realises it's now time
To leave and find her Valentine.

She mustn't travel all alone
When through the countryside she's going
That's why she turns to Eglamour
And asks him to accompany her.

She asks Eglamour to help her escape and to be her protector on what might be a dangerous journey

They've not been travelling very long
When everything starts to go wrong.
They're halfway through a forest when
They are attacked by highwaymen.
Silvia's seized; they say they need her
To go with them to meet their leader.
[Her male protector, Eglamour,
Runs off and then is seen no more].

*　　　*　　　*

While Valentine is reminiscing
'Bout Silvia whom he is missing,
He hears some ructions start nearby
And thinks he'll go and find out why.

He finds the woman of his dreams
Who very recently it seems
Has been recovered from some men
Who had waylaid and seized her when
Proteus, his friend from boyhood, and
A serving 'lad', Sebastian,
Recognising her great need,
This lady in distress had freed.
It seems that they'd been on her tail
Since she first set out on this trail.

He hears Proteus proclaim that she
Should show her thanks romantic'ly.
When she upbraids him for dishonour
He says he'll force himself upon her.
So Valentine steps forth saying he
Is hurt by such base treachery
And that his friend's unbridled lust
Has totally destroyed his trust.

Then Proteus comes to his senses
And shows remorse for his offences.
As soon as ever he repents
The noble Valentine relents
And makes a gesture he thinks grand
But we just cannot understand.

To prove their friendship's on again
He offers Proteus free rein
In his pursuit of Silvia.
This really upsets Julia
Who, much to everyone's surprise,
Admits she's dressed up in disguise
Because her heart is still in thrall
To Proteus, in spite of all.
He now regrets he strayed and clearly
States it's Julia he loves dearly.

*　　　*　　　*

The outlaws come and they've in tow
Sweet Silvia's Dad and Thurio
Who says she must become his wife.
But Valentine tells him his life
Is forfeit if he makes a move
On Silvia who's his true love.
When Thurio is not prepared
To fight for her because he's scared
The Duke says he'll be happy for
Val to be his son-in-law.

To celebrate he says that he'll,
The outlaws' banishments, repeal.
When last we see them they're all heading
Home to have a double wedding.

And then, soon as he's finished there,
He's chased and savaged by a bear.

THE WINTER'S TALE

Who's Who:

LEONTES, *King of Sicilia.*

POLIXENES, *King of Bohemia.*

HERMIONE, *Leontes's wife.*

CAMILLO, *a lord of Sicilia who supports Hermione.*

PAULINA, *Antigones's wife and Hermione's loyal friend.*

PERDITA, *Leontes and Hermione's daughter.*

ANTIGONES, *a lord of Sicilia tasked by Leontes with disposing of the infant Perdita.*

MAMILLIUS, *King Leontes's son and heir.*

A SHEPHERD, *who finds the infant Perdita and rears her as his own.*

FLORIZEL, *Prince of Bohemia, Polixenes's son, in love with Perdita.*

Leontes rules Sicilia;
Polixenes, Bohemia.
From youth, their friendship's meant so much
That, through the years, they've kept in touch,
And now Polixenes has come
To visit Leontes at home.

He's spent nine months in Sicily
And, sadly, feels it's time that he

Returned home from vacationing
To work at being Bohemia's king.
Leontes asks him to consider
Postponing his returning thither
Suggesting that his friend could tweak
His plans and stay another week
But finds there's nothing he can say
To make his guest prolong his stay.
Polixenes is adamant;
Time and again insists he can't.

And yet, first time she makes the plea
He gives in to Hermione.
So now Leontes starts to think
There is some surreptitious link
Between his best friend and his Queen
And he suspects it is obscene.
The green-eyed monster in his head
Is telling him they've shared a bed
And that the child she's carrying
Was fathered by Bohemia's King.

Hermione is Leontes's wife and Queen of Sicilia.

Leontes speaks such bitter words
T' Camillo who's one of his lords,
Saying that Hermione has strayed
And by Polixenes was laid.
Leontes is extremely stressed
'Cause there's a cuckoo in his nest.
He thinks perhaps his dynasty
'S endangered by this pregnancy,
E'en though Mamillius, his son,
He has no doubt, 's his very own.

Mamillius is the son of Leontes and Hermione and heir to the Sicilian throne.

For sullying Leontes' wife
Polixenes must lose his life.
Camillo's asked to organise
This bad Bohemian's demise.
Camillo asks that, in return,
The King will not Hermione spurn.

When, in the end, push comes to shove
Camillo finds he is a dove
And not a hawk who might, with ease,
Assassinate Polixenes.
Instead, he asks to parley an'
Reveals Leontes' nasty plan.
Together they decide that they
Must make a speedy getaway.

Leontes thinks their sudden flight
Provides more evidence he's right.
He publicly harangues his Queen
Accusing her of being so free 'n'
Easy with her charms that she's
Been bedded by Polixenes.
These efforts to disgrace her fail,
And when he sends her off to gaol
The lords and ladies of the court
All give Hermione their support.
The ladies say that they intend
To be there with her and attend
To all her obs and gynae needs
As into childbirth she proceeds.

Leontes sent to Delphos, lords
To hear the Oracle's wise words.

He's sure they will confirm what he
Is saying about Hermione.

*   *   *

Some time's elapsed; it's come to pass
Hermione's had a little lass.

Paulina assumes the role Paulina thinks that if he sees
of Hermione's protector. His new-born child then Leontes
She is married to Will know, instinctively, that he
Antigones. 'S the source of her paternity.
Leontes, though, is not for turning;
With unrelenting rage he's burning;

Antigones is a lord of He tells Antigones to take
Sicilia. Possession of the child and make
His way to some far barren spot
And there abandon the wee tot.

*   *   *

In court Leontes sits as judge;
Sets out his wife's name to besmudge.
Hermione's called and is indicted.
Among the charges that are cited:
High treason, in so much as she
Is guilty of adultery;
Conspiring to assassinate
Her husband who's the head of state;
And giving aid and succour so
Polixenes and Camillo,
Who partnered her in these offences,
Escaped the lawful consequences.

'Though all these charges are untrue
There's nothing that the Queen can do.

Leontes is a biased judge
Who bears a quite unfounded grudge.
Her only hope is that he will
Consult Apollo's Oracle.
As luck would have it that is when
The messengers return again.
The scroll the Delphic priest had sealed
Is now, in court, to all revealed.
It says Hermione is chaste;
Polixenes, who left in haste,
And Camillo bear no blame.
Leontes, though, should feel great shame
For being the sort of tyrant who
His infant daughter did eschew.
No heir of his will e'er be crowned
If she who's lost cannot be found.

These truths Leontes first denies
Implying the Oracle tells lies.
But, as his spleen, he's venting thus
Comes word his son, Mamillius,
Was so disturbed, being forced to see
His Mum ill-treated cruelly,
His will to live he'd sadly lost
And now has given up the ghost.

Hermione can take no more;
She faints and falls down to the floor.
Paulina takes her off to get her
Nursing care to make her better.

The King accepts his jealous pride
Is why his son and heir has died.
If he'd believed the Oracle
Mamillius would be living still.

Full of remorse, he now intends,
For his foul deeds, to make amends.
Paulina then returns to say
Hermione too, has passed away.

*   *   *

Antigones, in a strange dream,
Received a visit from the Queen.
She told him he would doubtless find
A lonely place to leave behind

Perdita is the daughter of Leontes and Hermione.

The infant child she names Perdita,
In the kingdom of Bohemia.

Bohemia is a land-locked country. Shakespeare takes artistic licence saying it is 'a desert country near the sea'.

He finds the perfect piece of ground
Whereon he lays Perdita down.
In case she's found before she dies
He leaves a bag full of supplies.
And then, soon as he's finished there

Shakespeare's most famous stage direction: Exit, pursued by a bear.

He's chased and savaged by a bear.

A shepherd, searching for lost sheep,
Finds the infant fast asleep.
Her clothing is high quality
Like that of the nobility.
The stash of wealth left by her side
For her up-bringing, will provide.

*   *   *

By sixteen years, time has moved on
An' Polixenes's youthful son,
Like many lads of teenage years,
For hours on end, just disappears.
His Dad is worried sick, not knowing

Florizel is Polixenes's son and heir.

Where Prince Florizel is going.

He and Camillo think it wise
That they should dress up in disguise
And follow him when he goes out
T' see what the secrecy's about.
They tail him to a shepherd's house
That looks to be quite prosperous.
It seems that once, away back when,
The shepherd had been poor, but then
Good fortune smiled on him and he
Worked hard and gained prosperity.

Sheep-shearing season's ended and
Great preparations are in hand
To celebrate a fruitful year
With song and dance and food and beer.
Dressed as a shepherd so that he
Maintains his anonymity
The Prince is wooing Perdita an' she
Dressed in her pretty finery,
As hostess of this celebration
Presents each guest with a carnation.
While mingling, doing the hostess thing,
She meets Camillo and the King
Whom nobody can recognise
'Cause both of them are in disguise.

When music starts young Florizel
Begins to dance with his ma'm'selle.
Polixenes then asks her Dad
Who is the confident young lad
That holds her in his warm embrace
And matches her steps pace for pace.
The shepherd says the lad claims he
Is from a noble family;

He loves Perdita, so he's stated,
And his love's reciprocated.
But then, when the young couple both,
Each to the other, pledge their troth
The Shepherd's happy they're engaged
Polixenes, though, is enraged,
Drops his disguise, and says that he's
Insisting these proceedings cease.
The Prince is being a fool, he says,
And, straightaway, must mend his ways.
For being a covetous gold-digger,
Perdita's face, he will disfigure.
And from a gallows, hanging high,
He sentences her 'Dad' to die.

The Prince thinks that their only hope
Of happiness is to elope.
Camillo says that, should they flee,
The place to go is Sicily
And there tell Leontes that he's
An envoy from Polixenes.

Because Camillo knows each King,
He says he'll sort out everything.

*   *   *

Down through the years, Paulina's built
On Leontes's sense of guilt
By keeping him reminded he
Must bear responsibility
For the double loss of life —
First, of his son, then of his wife.
'Cause of this guilt he's forced to carry
Leontes says he won't remarry

Unless Paulina, who will vet
Prospective candidates, can get
A woman who could possibly
Replace his dead Hermione.

Prince Florizel has come and plies
Leontes with a pack of lies:
He's on a mission of goodwill,
Sent by his Dad who's very ill.
And, on his way through Libya,
He'd met this Princess, Perdita.

Alas, his story's undermined
And he's left in a proper bind;
When Leontes gets a Royal request,
The errant couple, to arrest.

To the Bohemian King, it seems,
Camillo's gone and spilled the beans.
And, in pursuit of Florizel,
They've reached Sicilia as well.
Then, as they're walking down the street,
Perdita's 'Dad' they chance to meet.
Camillo and Polixenes
Agree to hear the Shepherd's pleas.
He tells them that Perdita is
Not really a true child of his;
That sixteen years ago he found
Her left out on some barren ground
And close to her, he'd found a stash
Of gold and jewels and hard cash,
And that he'd also found a note
Pinned to the baby's little coat.
He says he took her to his home

And raised her as his very own.
Then, from a bag, in his defence,
He takes out all the evidence
That proves, which makes them all so glad,
That Leontes is Perdita's Dad.
Having found this long-lost child,
Everybody's reconciled.
There's lots of joy and happiness
Perdita is a real Princess,
And both their families are delighted
To see her and her Prince united.

When told how she was sorely tried,
How, of a broken heart, she'd died,
Perdita weeps for her dead Mum.
Paulina, then, asks all to come
Around to hers, where they can see
A statue of Hermione.
It's so lifelike that everyone
'S impressed by what the sculptor's done.
This statue is so true to life
Leontes wants to kiss his wife.
Paulina takes the 'statue's' hand
And helps her step down from the stand.
And everybody's happy she's
Alive and back with Leontes.

And when she's dressed up like a boy
The Duke agrees that he'll employ
This 'eunuch' named Cesario
[The name by which Viola'll go].

TWELFTH NIGHT; OR WHAT YOU WILL

Who's Who:

VIOLA, *stranded in Illyria falls in love with the Duke.*

A SEA CAPTAIN, *who rescued Viola when their ship sank.*

SEBASTIAN, *Viola's twin brother.*

ORSINO, *Duke of Illyria, besotted with the Countess Olivia.*

CESARIO, *Viola disguised as a boy.*

OLIVIA, *a rich Countess who falls in love with Cesario.*

MALVOLIO, *Olivia's steward.*

SIR ANDREW AGUECHEEK, *fancies himself in love with Olivia.*

SIR TOBY BELCH, *Olivia's uncle encourages Aguecheek.*

ANTONIO, *a Sea Captain, Sebastian's friend.*

LAW OFFICERS.

A PRIEST.

The life-boat's made it to the shore
And so Viola's safe once more.
Her dear twin-brother's probably
Been, very sadly, lost at sea.
The captain says there's still some hope —
He saw Sebastian grab a rope
And saw him bind his body fast
To an enormous floating mast.

Viola has been shipwrecked off the coast of Illyria.

Sebastian and Viola are fraternal twins with identical facial features.

The captain tells her that they are
'N a place known as Illyria

*Duke Orsino is in love
with the Countess Olivia.*

That's ruled by Duke Orsino who,
At this time is going through
A spell of hardship in his life:
The girl he wants to be his wife
Is in deep mourning for the sad
Loss of her brother and her Dad.

Olivia is a rich Countess.

For seven years, Olivia's sworn
Her brother and her Dad she'll mourn;
Intends for all this time that she'll,
Behind a veil, her face conceal.
No happiness will she allow
To tempt her break this sacred vow.

In this strange land Viola must
Find a way to earn a crust.
She buys men's gear and gets her hands
On clothes just like Sebastian's.
And when she's dressed up like a boy
The Duke agrees that he'll employ

*Cesario is Viola, disguised
as a eunuch, enabling her
to get a job as the Duke's
trusted messenger.*

This 'eunuch' named Cesario
[The name by which Viola'll go].
From the start the Duke finds he
Enjoys the young 'man's' company;
The 'lad's' trustworthy, that is why
The Duke decides he can rely
On 'him' to visit his true love,
Olivia, to tell her of
His passionate desire to stir
Reciprocal desire in her.

Cesario is obstinate;
Refuses to turn from her gate.
'Cause of her curiosity
Olivia allows that 'he'
May be admitted to her house;
She'll see if 'he' has got the nous
To match 'his' rash determination
T' engage with her in conversation.
At first there's banter to and fro
And then the young Cesario
Tells her that she's the object of
Orsino's unremitting love;
With love for her the Duke is fraught
Though this is something she's not sought.
She knows Orsino's virtuous
And valiant and generous,
But though his love for her persists
Her love for him does not exist.
That's why she says there's not a chance
That they will ever share romance.
Olivia, though, is most impressed
By how the Duke's case is expressed
By this eloquent young 'guy'
Who's very easy on the eye.
And it begins to look as though
She's fallen for Cesario.

The Countess sends Malvolio
To follow young Cesario
To give 'him' back the golden band
She says had fallen from 'his' hand.
Cesario wonders if by chance 'he's'
The one the Countess really fancies.

Malvolio is Olivia's steward.

It's possible because, remember,
She doesn't know the 'lad's' true gender.

Viola's amorous frustration
Provides a further complication,
For she's in love with Orsino,
But he thinks she's Cesario.

*   *   *

Sebastian didn't drown at sea
But had, by chance, quite luckily
Been washed to shore and rescued by
Antonio is an old enemy of   Antonio, a caring guy
the Duke.   Who'd helped his battered body mend
And sees him now as his best friend.

Antonio's mate, Sebastian,
Is heading for Illyria an'
He'll ask the Duke for help and then
He'll get his life on track again.
But years ago Antonio
Had fought against Duke Orsino
So now Illyria's a place
Where he just shouldn't show his face.
But then, he thinks he'll chance his arm
And hope that he won't come to harm.

On reaching town they separate;
Sebastian wants to contemplate
The sights and places tourists go,
And while he does, Antonio
Will find some lodgings so that they
Will have a place to eat and stay.

Antonio gives his wallet to
Sebastian so he can do
What tourists do when they come here
And buy himself a souvenir.

      *   *   *

The Duke sends his young envoy back
To carry on his love-attack;
To tell Olivia, in his soul
There's passion that will not run cold,
And that Orsino, the romancer,
Will not accept "no" for an answer.
But though with passion his soul burns
All pleas on his behalf she spurns.
And she is very forward and
She takes Cesario by the hand
And openly declares that she
Loves only 'him' and ardently.
But 'he' tells her no woman will
Ever give 'his' heart a thrill.
Olivia hopes that she can find
A way to make 'him' change 'his' mind
And tells 'him' she might entertain
'His' pleas, if 'he' comes back again.

Sir Andrew Aguecheek's seen them in
Her garden quietly natterin'
And thinks her body language shows
She wants to be Cesario's.
Her uncle Toby says she knew
That that's how Aguecheek would construe
The goings-on that he had seen
And, being enraged, would intervene.

Sir Andrew Aguecheek fancies himself a suitor of Olivia.

Sir Toby Belch is Olivia's alcoholic uncle. He is a prankster who spurs on Aguecheek's foolishness.

It was a signal, very clearly,
To show Aguecheek she loved him dearly.
But having failed to read the sign
There's no way he's still first in line.
The only way to put things right
'S to challenge the Duke's 'youth' to fight
And when she learns he fought with valour
Defending her much-valued honour,
Deep gratitude Olivia'll show
By taking Aguecheek as her beau.

*　　　*　　　*

Cesario's back and hoping 'he'
Can get the Countess to agree
To crown 'his' efforts with success
And tell the Duke her answer's "yes".
But she insists, once and for all,
'Tis to 'himself' her heart's in thrall.

Then who should young Cesario meet
As 'he' sets foot upon the street
But Aguecheek, with his sword in hand
Demanding the 'lad' take a stand
And draw 'his' weapon and prepare
To fight a duel then and there.

Before the duel can begin
Antonio comes barging in
With rapier drawn, prepared to face
Aguecheek, and take Sebastian's place.
['Cause they're the image of each other
He thinks Viola is her brother.]
But sadly for Antonio,
He has been recognised and so

Two officers arrest him and
He's going to be held on remand.
He asks 'Sebastian' to give back
His wallet full of cash, 'cause lack
Of cash resources will entail
A harder time for him in gaol.
Cesario though, can't give what,
In honesty, 'he' hasn't got.
Antonio, still penniless,
Is taken off in some distress.

Sir Toby tells Aguecheek to chase
Cesario; get in 'his' face
And trounce 'him' for the way that 'he'd'
Refused to help 'his' friend in need.

Aguecheek then meets Sebastian
And, thinking that he's found his man,
He gives Sebastian a smack
But gets a half a dozen back.
As Toby tries to intervene
Olivia comes on the scene.
She sees her uncle draw his sword;
Him and 'Cesario' en garde.
She tells the swordsmen to desist;
Turns to 'Cesario' to insist
That he return back home with her.
Sebastian does not demur.

Olivia's infatuation
Has brought her to this situation:
She turns tradition on its head
And she proposes they be wed.

Sebastian agrees they may;
She finds a priest and straightaway
[To strike the iron while it's hot]
They go to church and tie the knot.

Sebastian's fallen on his feet
This rich, good-looking, very sweet
Young woman's asked to be his wife
And now he is set up for life.

*   *   *

The Duke, fed up with being put down;
Decides to walk across the town
And asks Cesario if 'he'
Will tag along for company.
He's going to tell Olivia of
The depth of his undying love
And hopes for pity's sake that she'll
Succumb to his heartfelt appeal.

Close to her house, out on the street
They happen there by chance to meet
Two lawmen with Antonio,
His enemy from long ago.
The Duke says that he is surprised
Antonio was so ill-advised
And so bereft of acumen
He'd walked into the lion's den.

Trying to explain, Antonio
Pointing to Cesario,
Tells how he saved him from the sea
And, for three months, had carefully
Nursed and made him well again;
Tells how they'd grown so close that when

His friend said he was coming here
He felt that he should volunteer
To come with him so that he might
Be sure the lad would be alright.
He'd drawn his weapon to defend
The guy he thought was his best friend.
'Twas at that point that he got caught
And their close friendship came to naught;
The lad ran off and what was worse
Refused to give him back his purse.

Olivia then approaches an'
She thinks she sees Sebastian.
When she speaks to Cesario
It's obvious to Orsino
That she has fallen for the 'lad'.
Now the Duke, with anger's mad
So much so that he threatens he
Will kill the 'lad' for treachery.
Countess Olivia claims that they
Were married earlier today.
Much to Olivia's surprise
Cesario, of course, denies
That 'he' has married anyone
And claims 'he's' still a singleton.

The priest, in no uncertain terms,
Their newly-married state confirms.

And then, there is some more confusion
As they must deal with an intrusion;
Sir Toby and Aguecheek display
The bleeding wounds they claim that they

Received from young 'Cesario'.
Olivia orders them to go
And see the surgical physician
In case their wounds require some stitchin'.

Just then, to everyone's surprise
Her spouse comes to apologise
T' Olivia for the hammerin'
He's given to one of her kin.

When Antonio sees the man,
He calls out to Sebastian
And they are, both of them, delighted
To be in friendship re-united.

Everybody's thunderstruck
By how Seb and Cesario look
So much alike that 'tween the two
It's hard to tell which one is who.
Sebastian, initially,
Is quite confused, but happily
Cesario then tells the tale
Of 'his' deception; lifts the veil,
Revealing they've familial ties
'Cause 'he's' Viola in disguise.

The Countess, hearing what's been said,
Is wondering which one she wed.
To one of them she lost her heart
But she can't tell the two apart
'Cause by her eyes she is deceived.
Olivia is so relieved
The twin she married is the man;
She's happy with Sebastian.

The fact Olivia rejected
His proposal has affected
Duke Orsino not at all,
'Cause now he's sure he can recall
His handsome serving-'lad' express
Words of love and tenderness.
'Cause 'twas a 'eunuch' spoke thus, he
Thought that 'twas naught but flattery.
Now, realising he was wrong,
The 'lad' being female all along,
And summing up the situation —
His erstwhile trust and admiration
And feelings he admits were tender
Now that he knows Viola's gender —
He proposes straight away
And she accepts and makes his day.

Denis O'Leary is a retired second-level teacher
living in Dublin. He spent most of his career
in St Declan's College, Cabra, and retired as
Deputy Principal in 2007.

He wrote these poetic twists on Shakespeare's
plays for his own amusement. Friends and
colleagues who read and enjoyed them,
have persuaded him to share them with a
wider readership.

Printed in Great Britain
by Amazon

54037311R00127

In England, back in Tudor days,
Shakespeare wrote a lot of plays
With characters and themes that are,
Today, still widely popular.
This book contains plot-summaries
Of twenty of the best of these.
Some are comic, some are tragic,
Some are interspersed with magic.
Some tell of treachery, feuds and wars
And sex and sexual predators;
And good guys being cruelly treated
And usurpers being unseated.
Some tell romantic stories of
Young couples in pursuit of love;
And, when they see an urgent need,
Women stepping in to lead.

Denis O'Leary is a retired second-level teacher
living in Dublin. He spent most of his career in
St Declan's College, Cabra, and retired as Deputy
Principal in 2007.

He wrote these poetic twists on Shakespeare's plays
for his own amusement. Friends and colleagues
who read and enjoyed them, have persuaded him to
share them with a wider readership.

ISBN 9798581978856

90000

9 798581 978856

Bordeaux brûle

Mat Kastellov